Practice in PHYSICS

SECOND EDITION

AKRILL • BENNET • MILLAR

Hodder & Stoughton

A MEMBER OF THE HODDER HEADLINE GROUP

Acknowledgements

We are grateful to the following companies, institutions and individuals who have given permission to reproduce photographs in this book. Every effort has been made to trace and acknowledge ownership of copyright. The publishers will be glad to make suitable arrangements with any copyright holders whom it has not been possible to contact.

© Allsport/G Mortimore 13.25; Imperial War Museum 17.53; Kodansha Ltd 20.4; *Physics is fun: Book 3* JT Jardine (Heineman Educational Books Ltd) 2.11; *PSSC Physics 1st Edition* (© D. C. Heath & Co 1960) 1.5, 1.41, 21.5; *Waves*, D. C. Chaundy (Longman) 27.4

Cover photo by kind permission of Dr Jeremy Burgess/ Science Photo Library.

The publishers and authors would also like to thank Red Herring Design and Illustration and the Parkway Group for preparing the illustrations.

Orders: please contact Bookpoint Ltd, 39 Milton Park, Abingdon, Oxon OX14 4TD. Telephone: (44) 01235 400414, Fax: (44) 01235 400454. Lines are open from 9.00 - 6.00, Monday to Saturday, with a 24 hour message answering service. Email address: orders@bookpoint.co.uk

British Library Cataloguing in Publication Data
Akrill, T. B.
Practice in Physics. – 2Rev.ed
I. Title
530
ISBN 0 340 54243 8
(ISBN 0 7131 0338 8 1st edition)

First published 1994
Impression number 15 14 13 12 11 10 9 8 7 6
Year 2004 2003 2002 2001 2000 1999 1998

Typeset by Litho Link Ltd, Welshpool, Powys.
Printed in Great Britain for Hodder & Stoughton Educational, a division of Hodder Headline Plc, 338 Euston Road, London NW1 3BH by Scotprint Ltd, Musselburgh, Scotland.

Contents

About this book . . .

This is a book of questions to help you understand Physics at A or AS Level. None of the questions are from previous examination papers; questions in examination papers are meant to test you at the *end* of your course. What you need *during* the course is to do questions which will help you to check whether you have understood what you are being taught. That is why we have called this book ***Practice in Physics***.

The first edition of this book was originally published in 1979 and it has been in print ever since. We have revised it to take account of the new syllabuses for Advanced Level courses from September 1994. Some of the questions test whether you have understood the principles, and a few (very few) should make you think quite hard. At the end of the book there are answers to all the questions (except for one or two where to give the answer would take away any need to think). You will not need to do all the questions! But we hope you enjoy doing most of them because part of the pleasure of doing Physics is to discover that you can get the right answers and that you understand the ideas.

The questions are arranged in sections which correspond to the text book ***Physics*** which we have also revised. So if you are doing questions in, for example, Section 10.3 you will find that Section 10.3 in that textbook can help you.

Tim Akrill
George Bennet
Chris Millar

1 Describing motion

Data $g = 9.81\,\text{m s}^{-2}$

1.1 Measuring speed

1.1 The diagram shows the oil spots left on a road by a motorbike with a leaky sump as the bike travels from A to G. Describe the journey, assuming that the drips come at regular time intervals.

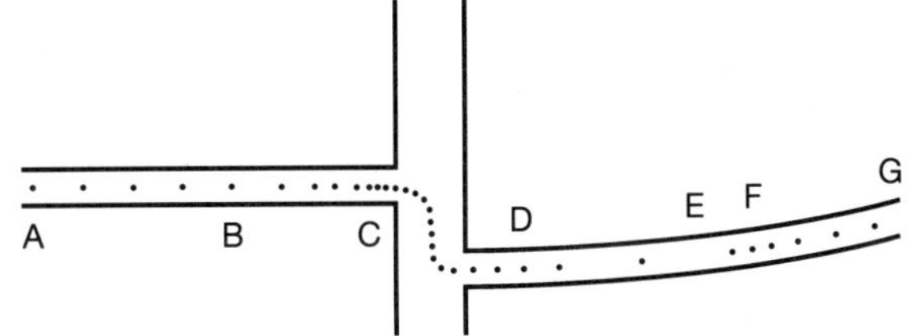

1.2 A 100-metre track is marked out with an uncertainty in its length of ±0.50 m, and a stop-watch used for timing a runner on the track has an uncertainty of ±0.20 s. If the stop-watch records a time of 12.5 s for a particular runner, what is the runner's average speed? Which of the measurements introduces the greatest uncertainty into the result, and what is this uncertainty?

1.3 A starting pistol is fired in front of a microphone and the sound is arranged to start a scaler-timer which counts in milliseconds. When the sound reaches another microphone 12.0 m away the scaler-timer is stopped. If the speed of sound in air is $340\,\text{m s}^{-1}$

(a) calculate the time which would be recorded by the scaler-timer

(b) calculate the % error in this result.

1.4 The diagram shows the movement of a smoke particle in a Brownian motion experiment.

(a) Use a ruler to find (i) the total distance moved by the smoke particle in going from A to B, and (ii) the displacement AB.

(b) If it took 0.20 s to travel from A to B calculate (iii) the average speed, and (iv) the average velocity of the smoke particle.

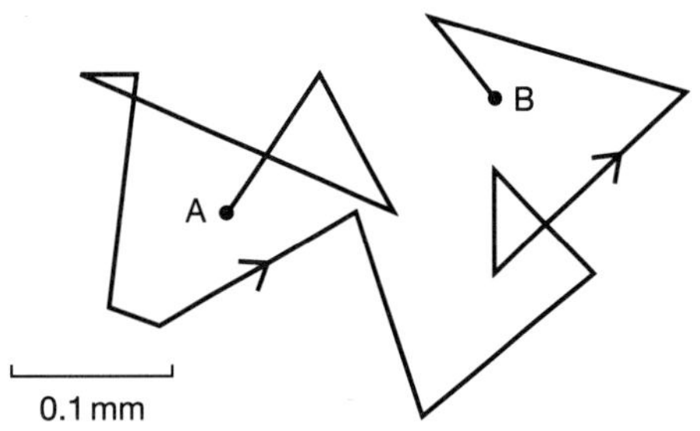

1.5 Measure the distances between the centres of the images of the ball in the photograph. The diameter of the ball shown was 50 mm. Use this to calculate the distances moved by the ball between successive exposures. If the exposures were made at intervals of 1/25 s, find the average speed of the ball for each of the distances you have calculated, and plot a speed-time graph.

1.6 The figure shows a piece of paper tape on which a ticker-timer has been making 50 dots each second; the tape was twice the size of the tape shown in the figure. Measure the lengths of successive five-space lengths of tape, starting from the left-hand edge of the tape, and calculate the average speed for each of these five-space lengths. Hence plot a graph of speed against time.

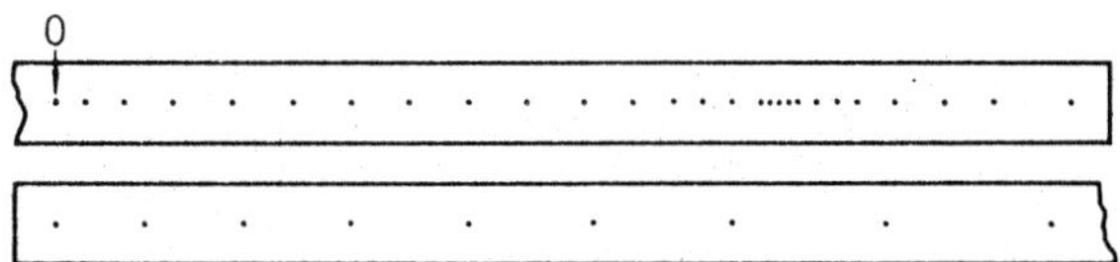

1.7 How would you use school laboratory apparatus to measure the speed of

(a) a snail

(b) a model train

(c) an air rifle pellet?

1.2 Velocity, a vector quantity

1.8 What is the change of velocity when

(a) $+6.0\,\text{m s}^{-1}$ becomes $+15\,\text{m s}^{-1}$

(b) $+6.0\,\text{m s}^{-1}$ becomes $-15\,\text{m s}^{-1}$

(c) $+6.0\,\text{m s}^{-1}$ becomes $-6.0\,\text{m s}^{-1}$

(d) $5.0\,\text{m s}^{-1}$ east becomes $15\,\text{m s}^{-1}$ west?

1.9 A skier is moving at $11.0\,\text{m s}^{-1}$ down a 16° slope. What is the skier's

(a) vertical velocity

(b) horizontal velocity?

1.10 Estimate

(a) your average velocity

(b) your average speed

when you travel to school or college from your home.

1.11 Approaching Terminal 3 at Heathrow Airport passengers P and R use the walkway but passenger Q chooses to walk alongside it. Neither Q nor R has any heavy luggage, and they both walk briskly at $1.2\,\text{m s}^{-1}$. P stands still. The walkway moves at $0.80\,\text{m s}^{-1}$, and is 40 m long.

(a) Calculate how long P, Q and R take to reach the other end of the walkway.

(b) Suppose that a boy on the walkway moved diagonally across it at an angle of 20° to the direction of the walkway, and at a speed of $0.80\,\text{m s}^{-1}$. What is his actual velocity (i) parallel to the walkway (ii) across the walkway?

(c) Calculate the boy's resultant velocity.

1.12 The diagram shows the forces acting on a child and sledge moving down an icy slope. Calculate the resolved part of each force

(a) vertically

(b) parallel to the slope.

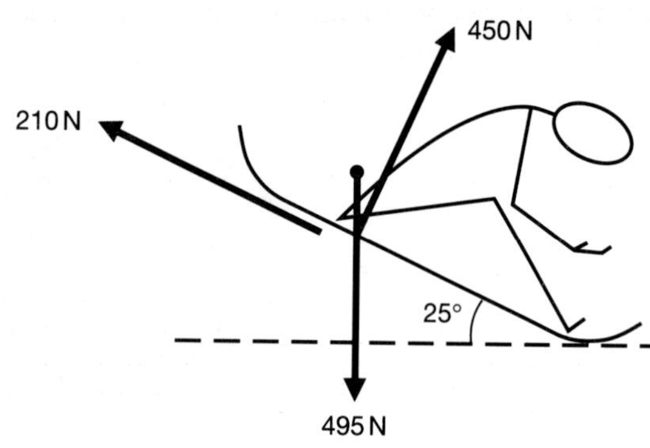

1.13 The figure shows a particle moving in a circle ABCDA of radius 8.0 m at a constant speed. It completes one revolution in 5.0 s. What is

(a) its average *speed* for one revolution

(b) its average *speed* from A to B

(c) its average *velocity* for one complete revolution

(d) its average *velocity* from A to C

(e) its average *velocity* from A to B

(f) its change of velocity from A to C

(g) its change of velocity from A to B?

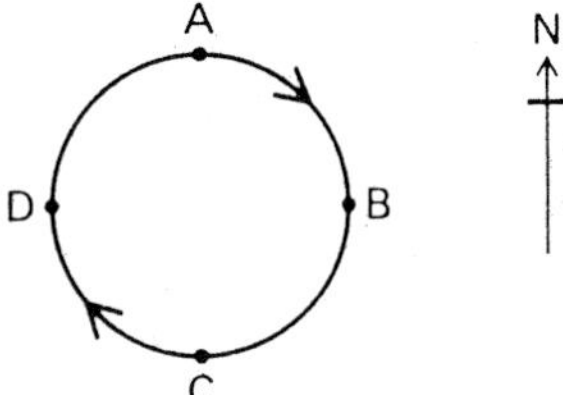

1.14 Use a scale diagram

(a) to add a displacement of 5.6 m north to a displacement of 3.5 m NW

(b) to add a velocity of $3.2\,\text{m s}^{-1}$ SW to a velocity of $1.8\,\text{m s}^{-1}$ N 20° W.

[Note: it helps to draw scale diagrams on graph paper.]

1.15 What is the total displacement of

(a) a person who walks 5.0 m north and then 2.0 m south

(b) a car which drives 100 m north and then 50 m east

(c) a boy who runs once round a 400 m running track

(d) a girl who runs halfway round a circular 400 m running track, starting at its most southerly point?

1.16 A swimmer dives in and is timed at various points in a 50 m race.
The record is as shown in the table:

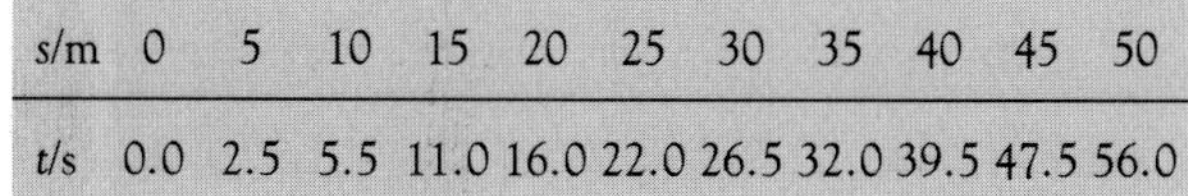

s/m	0	5	10	15	20	25	30	35	40	45	50
t/s	0.0	2.5	5.5	11.0	16.0	22.0	26.5	32.0	39.5	47.5	56.0

(a) Plot a graph of *s* (up) against *t* (along) and draw a *smooth* line through the points.

(b) Work out the average speed over the first 10 m, the middle 10 m and the last 10 m. Can you suggest why the average speeds are different?

(c) Draw a tangent to the curve at $t = 40$ s and work out the swimmer's speed at that time.

1.17 The figure shows a body's initial velocity v_1 and final velocity v_2. Calculate its change of velocity.

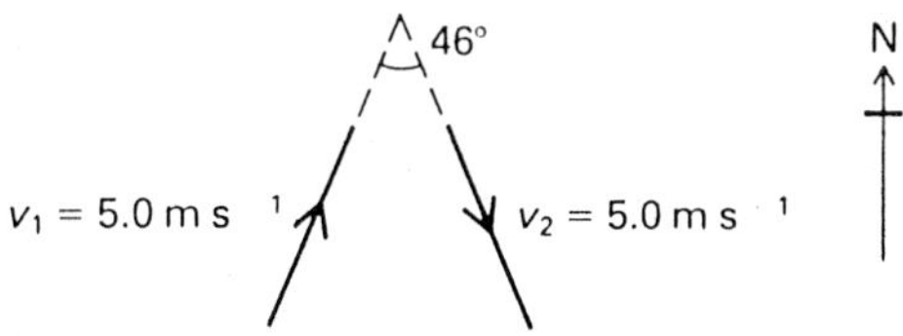

1.3 Acceleration

1.18 A man, John L. Stapp, travelling in a rocket powered sledge accelerated from 0 to 284 m s^{-1} (about 630 m.p.h) in 5.0 s and then came to a stop in only 1.5 s. Calculate his acceleration while

(a) he is speeding up

(b) he is slowing down.

1.19 A person who is properly held by a seat belt has a good chance of surviving a car collision if the deceleration does not exceed 30*g*. Assuming a uniform deceleration at this rate, calculate the distance by which the front end of the car must be designed to collapse if a crash occurs at 27 m s^{-1} ($\approx$ 70 m.p.h.).

1.20 A high speed train can slow down smoothly from a speed of 120 m.p.h. to rest within a distance of 1.0 mile. Convert this data into SI units and estimate its average acceleration when this occurs (1 mile $\approx$ 1.6 km).

1.21 The figure shows (actual-size) a piece of ticker tape with three successive dots on it; the ticker-timer was making 50 dots per second. Measure the distances between the dots and deduce the acceleration (assumed to be constant) of the body to which the tape was attached.

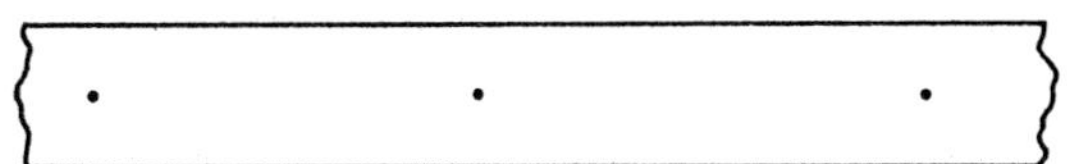

1.22 One type of aeroplane has a maximum acceleration on the ground of 3.4 m s^{-2}. What is the minimum length of runway needed if it is to reach its take-off speed of 110 m s^{-1} and how long a time will this take?

1.23 In order to bring a car to rest a motorist needs time not only for the brakes to stop the car, but also for his own initial mental and physical reactions to the danger to cause him to brake.
Make a table of thinking distances, braking distances and stopping distances for a motorist with a reaction time of 0.50 s driving at initial speeds of 72 km h^{-1} and 108 km h^{-1}, and for decelerations of 8.0 m s^{-2} (dry road) and 4.0 m s^{-2} (wet road).

1.24 The best throwers in the world, baseball pitchers, can release a ball at 40 m s^{-1}. In so doing they accelerate the ball through a distance of 3.5 m. Calculate the average acceleration of the ball.

1.25 An air track glider is placed on a linear track which is slightly tilted. It is given a velocity of 1.5 m s^{-1} *up* the track. If its acceleration is 0.50 m s^{-2} *down* the track, find the time at which it is 1.0 m below its starting point.

1.26 A particle moves in a straight line. Its motion can be described as follows:

$t = 0, v = 0$
$0 < t < 10\,s, a = 4.0\,m\,s^{-2}$
$10\,s < t < 20\,s, a = -4.0\,m\,s^{-2}$.
Sketch the velocity-time graph and use it to find the change of displacement of the particle between $t = 0$ and $t = 20$ s.

1.27 A road test report gives the following data for a standing start acceleration test for a car.

t/s	0	5	10	15	20	25	30	35	40
v/ms^{-1}	0	14	24	30	34	37	39	40	40

(a) Draw a velocity-time graph for the car (using graph paper), and hence find the displacement of the car when it has reached a speed of (i) 25 m s^{-1} (ii) 35 m s^{-1}.

(b) Use the velocity-time graph to find (iii) the acceleration of the car when its speed is 30 m s^{-1} and (iv) the maximum acceleration of the car.

1.28 The graph shows the result of studying a sprint start using a ticker-tape timing technique.

(a) What was the maximum velocity reached? Convert your answer to m.p.h., given that 1 m s^{-1} is equal to 2.24 m.p.h. How long did it take this sprinter to reach this maximum velocity?

(b) Calculate the acceleration of the sprinter (i) as she leaves her blocks (ii) after 2.0 s.

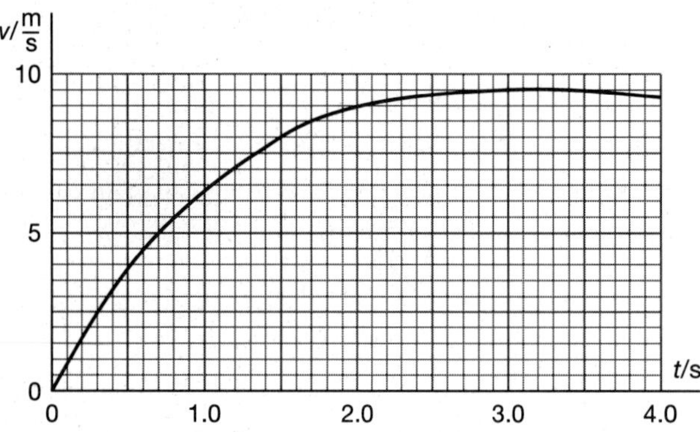

1.29 Suppose you are travelling on a bicycle with brakes which, at best, can produce an acceleration of $-2.5\,m\,s^{-2}$.

(a) Draw velocity-time graphs showing how you and the bicycle will slow down, with the brakes full on, from initial speeds of 15 m s^{-1}, 10 ms^{-1} and 5 ms^{-1}.
[Hint: use the same set of axes for all the v–t graphs and draw the 15 m s^{-1} graph-line first.]

(b) Calculate the distances you travel in coming to rest in each case.

1.30 A man throws a ball straight up into the air and catches it again. Take the upward direction to be positive and sketch the velocity-time graph for the ball, assuming that air resistance is small enough to be neglected. How could you use your graph to find the height reached by the ball?

1.31 Draw a velocity-time graph for a sky diver who is released from rest and who falls through the air from a great height. Explain the shape of the graph.

1.32 Draw velocity-time graphs for the following situations. In ***(a)*** and ***(c)*** take the downward direction to be positive, and ignore air resistance. In ***(b)*** and ***(c)*** assume that some of the kinetic energy is converted into internal energy at each bounce.

(a) A tennis ball falling to the ground.

(b) A snooker ball striking a cushion at right angles, and bouncing backwards and forwards between opposite cushions.

(c) A tennis ball falling to the ground and bouncing several times.

(d) A trampolinist from the top of one bounce to the top of the next bounce.

1.33 Draw displacement-time, velocity-time and acceleration-time graphs for the following situations. Use the same time axes for all three graphs for each situation. [Hint: you will probably find it is easiest to begin with the velocity-time graph.]

(a) An electrically-powered milk float moving from one house to another on a straight road.

(b) A ball, attached by an elastic cord to a fixed point on the ground, and hit horizontally away from that point.

1.4 Free fall

1.34 *(a)* How long does a ball take to fall a distance of
(i) 1.0 m (ii) 2.0 m?

(b) Why is the answer to (ii) not twice the answer to (i)?

1.35 A steel ball is held by an electromagnet. When the current in the electromagnet is switched off the ball falls. As it leaves the electromagnet an electric circuit is broken and a scaler-timer starts. The ball falls a distance of 456 mm and strikes a trip-switch which stops the scaler-timer. The time recorded is 301 ms.

(a) What value does this experiment give for the free-fall acceleration *g*?

(b) What sources of error are there likely to be in such an experiment?

1.36 A bullet is fired horizontally at a speed of 200 m s^{-1} at a target which is 100 m away.

(a) How far has the bullet fallen when it hits the target?

(b) What angle does its velocity then make with the horizontal?

(c) Explain whether air resistance would cause the bullet to fall a greater or lesser amount than the distance you give.

1.37 A kangaroos was seen to jump to a vertical height of 2.8 m. For how long was it in the air?

1.38 *(a)* Slow-motion photography shows that a jumping flea pushes against the ground for about 0.001 s during which time it accelerates upwards to a maximum speed of 0.8 m s^{-1}. Calculate its upward acceleration during this 'take-off'.

(b) It then moves upward with an acceleration (assumed constant) of −12 m s^{-2} (more than *g* because of air resistance). Calculate (i) how long it takes from leaving the ground to get to the top of its jump, where its velocity is zero (ii) how high it jumps.

1.39 A body is projected from ground level with a speed of 25 m s^{-1} at an angle of 30° above the horizontal. Neglect air resistance, and calculate

(a) the vertical resolved part of its velocity

(b) the time taken to reach its highest point

(c) the greatest height reached

(d) the horizontal range of the body.

1.40 Describe how you would determine the free fall acceleration by a laboratory experiment and make an estimate of the uncertainties in the measurements you make. [You may assume all your measuring instruments are accurately calibrated.]

1.41 *(a)* Measure the *horizontal distances* of the second, fourth, sixth, etc., images of the ball from the left-hand edge of the photograph below. Comment on your results.

(b) The white lines in the photograph represent vertical distances of 152 mm. Measure their separation on the photograph and hence calculate how much larger the actual distances are than the distances in the photograph. Hence find (in metres) the vertical distances *s* of the centres of the balls when the second, fourth, sixth, etc., flashes occurred. For vertical motion starting from rest $s = \frac{1}{2} gt^2$, so that $\sqrt{s} \propto t$. Draw a graph of $\sqrt{s}$ (on the *y*-axis) against time *t* (on the *x*-axis) to verify this. [Keep your graph for question *1.42*.]

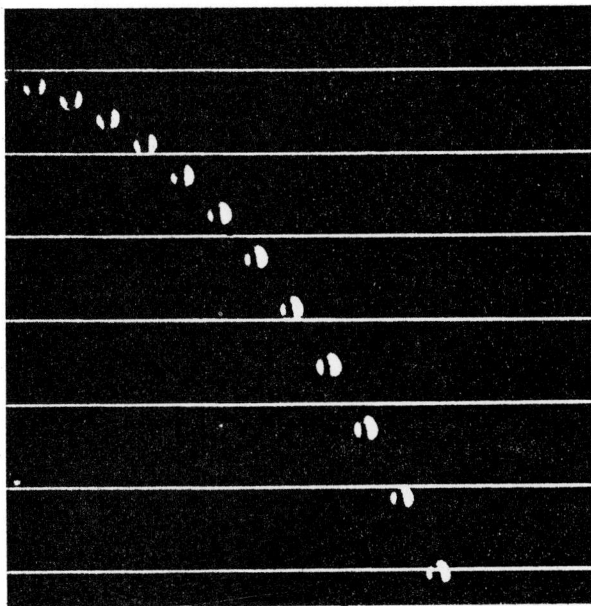

1.42 The slope of the graph represents $\sqrt{(\frac{1}{2}g)}$. If the intervals between flashes were $\frac{1}{20}$ s, measure this slope. Hence find a value for g.

1.43 Parachutists are trained to hit the ground at $6\,\mathrm{m\,s^{-1}}$. How high a platform is needed for them to jump off in order to give them practice at hitting the ground at this speed?

1.44 The cliff divers of Acapulco, Mexico, take off from a rocky cliff face 26.5 m above the surface of the water. In the course of their flight, of which all but the last 1.5 m of their horizontal motion is above rock, they travel 8.0 m forward.

(a) For how long are they in the air?
(b) For how long are they over the water during their flight?
(c) What is their vertical velocity on entry?
(d) At what angle is their path as they enter the water?
(e) Make a sketch of the cliffs and water, and draw on the flight path of a diver.

2 Momentum and force

Data $g = 9.81\,\mathrm{m\,s^{-2}} = 9.81\,\mathrm{N\,kg^{-1}}$

2.1 Mass and momentum

2.1 What is the momentum of
(a) a boy of mass 50 kg running round a running track at a constant speed of $3.0\,\mathrm{m\,s^{-1}}$ at the moment when he is (i) facing north, (ii) facing south
(b) a car of mass 800 kg moving east at a speed of $25\,\mathrm{m\,s^{-1}}$
(c) an oil tanker of mass 250 000 tonnes which is moving west at a speed of $20\,\mathrm{m\,s^{-1}}$?

2.2 *(a)* Two air track gliders are at rest with a spring compressed between them: a thread tied to each stops them moving apart. When the thread is cut, one glider moves away with a speed of $0.32\,\mathrm{m\,s^{-1}}$, and the other moves in the opposite direction with a speed of $0.45\,\mathrm{m\,s^{-1}}$. If the first glider has a mass of 0.40 kg, what is the mass of the other?
(b) Could this experiment have been performed (i) on the Moon, (ii) deep in outer space?
Would the result have been the same in each case?

2.3 A loaded supermarket trolley was rolled towards a stationary stack of five empty trolleys. After colliding and sticking to them it was noticed that the speed of the six trolleys was half the initial speed of the loaded trolley. If an unloaded trolley has a mass of 8.0 kg what can you deduce from this observation? Explain your reasoning.

2.4 *(a)* A woman of mass 60 kg steps, at a speed of $2\,\mathrm{m\,s^{-1}}$, off a canoe, of mass 40 kg, onto a river bank. What happens to the canoe?
(b) A rugby player of mass 70 kg, running south at $6.0\,\mathrm{m\,s^{-1}}$, tackles another player whose mass is 85 kg and who is running directly towards him at a speed of $4.0\,\mathrm{m\,s^{-1}}$. If in the tackle they cling together, what will be their common velocity immediately after the tackle?

2.5 Two trolleys are at rest and are exploded by the release of a spring-loaded piston or plunger at the front of one of them. Each trolley has a mass of 1.0 kg but one carries a block of unknown mass m. The result of the action is shown in the diagram on the next page. What is m?

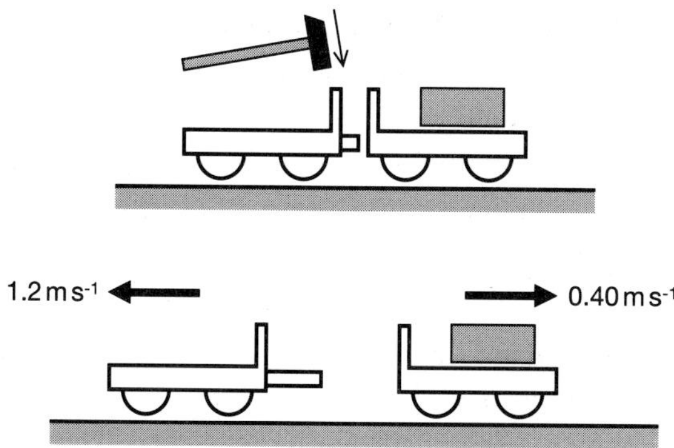

2.6 ***(a)*** Body A of mass 3.0 kg has a velocity of $+4.0\,\mathrm{m\,s^{-1}}$ and collides head-on with body B, which has a mass of 2.0 kg and a velocity of $-2.0\,\mathrm{m\,s^{-1}}$. After the collision the velocity of B is found to be $+3.0\,\mathrm{m\,s^{-1}}$. Find the velocity of A.

(b) Sketch a graph to show how the momentum of the two bodies varies with time before and after the collision.

2.7 When a bullet hits a 'baddie' in the chest in a television Western, he sometimes slumps forward. As a physics student you know he ought to jerk backwards. Explain why.

2.8 This is a question taken from an examination paper set in 1882.
'A bottle weighing 8 ounces is on top of a wall. A boy throws a lump of wet clay weighing 1 ounce, so as to strike the bottle with a velocity of 12 feet per second. The clay sticks to the bottle and the two move off the wall together. With what velocity?'

2.9 An α–particle is emitted from a polonium nucleus with a speed of $1.800 \times 10^7\,\mathrm{m\,s^{-1}}$. If the relative masses of the α-particle and the remaining part of the nucleus are 4.002 and 212.0, find the recoil speed of the nucleus.

2.10 Two boys stand a few metres apart on a trolley which can move freely on a horizontal surface without any resisting force. One throws a large heavy ball to the other, who catches it. Describe what happens to

(a) the speed of the trolley

(b) the position of the trolley

during each phase of this process.

2.11 The photograph shows the result of an air-track collision between the two gliders. The upper trace shows the positions of the straws (fixed to the gliders) before the collision, and the lower track shows the positions of the straws after the collision. Make measurements on the photograph to find the speeds (in arbitrary units, e.g. mm per flash) of the gliders before and after the collision (on this occasion there is no need to know the scale of the photograph, since we are concerned only with the relative sizes of the speeds).

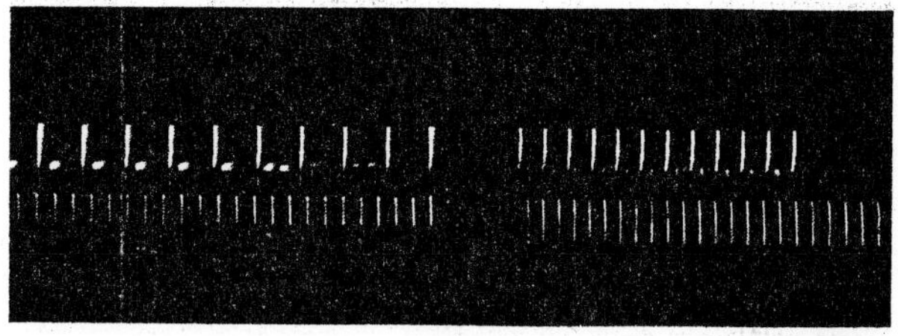

The mass of the left-hand glider is 0.20 kg, and that of the right-hand glider is 0.30 kg. Bearing in mind the limited precision with which you were able to measure the distances, do you think this experiment supports the fact that momentum is conserved in this collision?

2.12 A bullet of mass 10 g is fired into a block of wood of mass 200 g and becomes embedded in it. If the speed of the bullet was $500\,\mathrm{m\,s^{-1}}$, what is the speed of the block immediately after the impact?

2.13 Discuss how momentum is conserved when

(a) a train accelerates from rest

(b) a lump of plasticine falls to the ground and stays there

(c) a ball falls to the ground and bounces up again.

2.2 Forces

2.14 The figures show **(a)** a man holding a suitcase, **(b)** a man sitting on a chair and leaning his elbows on a table and **(c)** a man leaning against a wall.

Draw a free-body force diagram for each man. Mark the forces on the men, label the forces, and describe them in a phrase like 'W is the pull of the Earth on the man'.

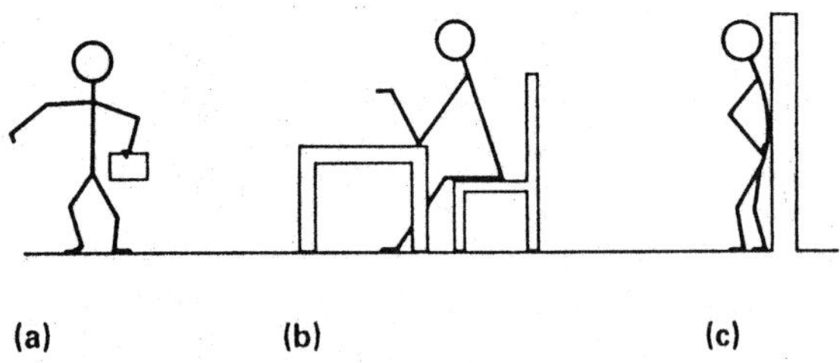

2.15 Draw a separate free-body force diagram for each of the italicised bodies in the following situations:

(a) a *girl* sitting on a *box* which rests on the ground.

(b) a *stone* sliding over a rough horizontal floor.

(c) a *man* standing in a rowing *boat* which is floating on a lake.

Write a phrase of the form 'the push/pull of A on B' to describe each force.

2.16 A racing car is shown in the figure together with a free-body force diagram describing the forces acting on it.

(a) Copy the diagram and list the forces using phrases which end with 'on the car'.

(b) How big are the forces P and Q?

(c) What would happen to the size of (i) W and (ii) F if the car was moving more slowly, e.g. at 70 m.p.h.?

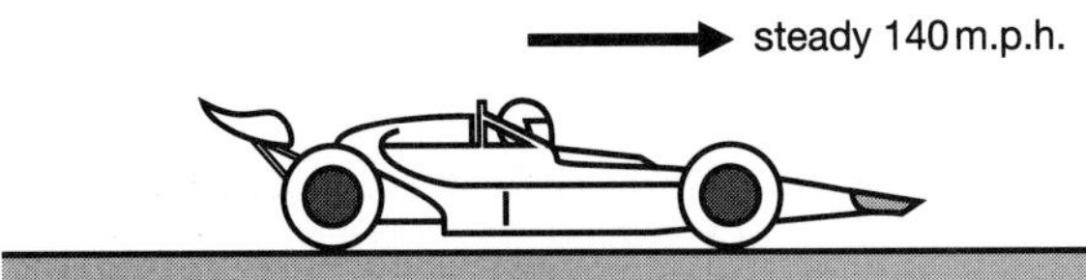

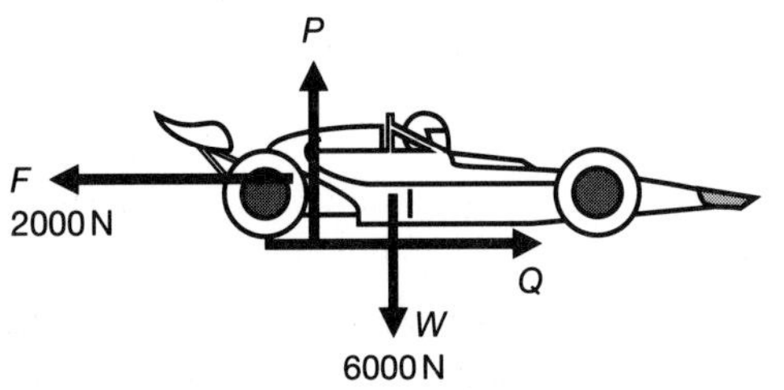

2.17 A patient with her leg in plaster is sometimes stretched using a system of weights and pulleys such as those shown in the figure below. The medical name for such treatment is traction.

(a) Draw a free-body force diagram for pulley B ignoring its own weight, i.e. draw a sketch of pulley B and add arrows to show the forces acting on it.

(b) If the rope is at 45° to the horizontal both below and above pulley B calculate the total pull on the pulley B. What is the total pull of the traction system on the patient's leg?

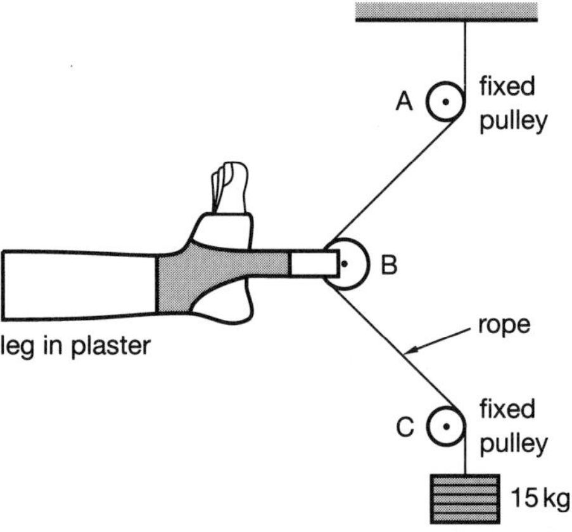

2.18 A force P is 20 N in a direction N 60° E. What is the resolved part of P in the following directions:

(a) north

(b) east

(c) N 30° E?

2.19 A man pushes a lawnmower with a force of 80 N directed along the handle which makes an angle of 40° to the vertical.

(a) Sketch the situation and draw a free-body force diagram for (i) the lawnmower and (ii) the man.

(b) What is the size of the resolved part of the push of the man on the lawnmower (i) in the horizontal direction and (ii) in the vertical direction?

2.20 Describe three situations (as different as possible) where a body is moving with constant velocity. For each situation

(a) draw a free-body force diagram for the body, giving each force a symbol
(b) write a phrase to describe each force, for example, 'X is the push of the air on the parachute'
(c) say what you can about the sizes of the forces you have marked.

2.21 A block of wood of weight 6.0 N slides at constant speed down a slope which makes an angle of 20° to the horizontal.
(a) Is it in equilibrium?
(b) By resolving the forces perpendicular to and parallel with the slope calculate the size of the perpendicular contact force and the frictional force.

2.22 In designing a supermarket, there is often a need for connecting ramps between different parts of the shop. If it is decided to limit the push required by shoppers to push a 24 kg trolley to less than 25 N, what is the maximum angle at which ramps can be built? State any assumptions which you make.

2.23 A car of mass 1250 kg runs down a slight gradient at a constant speed. If the frictional push of the ground on the car is 320 N, calculate the angle of the slope.

2.24 A framed picture of weight 50 N is to be hung on a wall, using a piece of string. The ends of the string are tied to two points, 0.60 m apart on the same horizontal level, on the back of the picture. Draw a free-body force diagram for the picture, and find the tension in the string if
(a) the string is 1.0 m long
(b) the string is 0.66 m long.

2.25 One man uses a rope to pull a tractor horizontally: he pulls due north with a force of 450 N. Another man pulls horizontally with a force of 370 N in a direction N 50° E. Use a scale diagram to find the sum of these two forces.

2.26 A pendulum bob of weight W is attached to a thread of length l and hung from a rigid support. Another thread is attached to the bob: this thread is pulled sideways with a horizontal force P so that the bob moves sideways. The thread then makes an angle θ with the vertical, and the *horizontal* displacement of the bob is d. Show that
(a) $\tan \theta = P/W$
(b) $\sin \theta = d/l$.
(c) Hence show that the pull P is approximately proportional to d, if d is small compared with l.

2.3 Moments and equilibrium

2.27 A pram and baby weighing 140 N has dimensions as shown on the diagram.
(a) In order to lift the front wheels up a step moving forward the pusher exerts a downward force F on the handlebar. Calculate the minimum value of F.
(b) What is the corresponding minimum upward force P the pusher needs to exert to lift the back wheels of the pram up a step moving backwards?

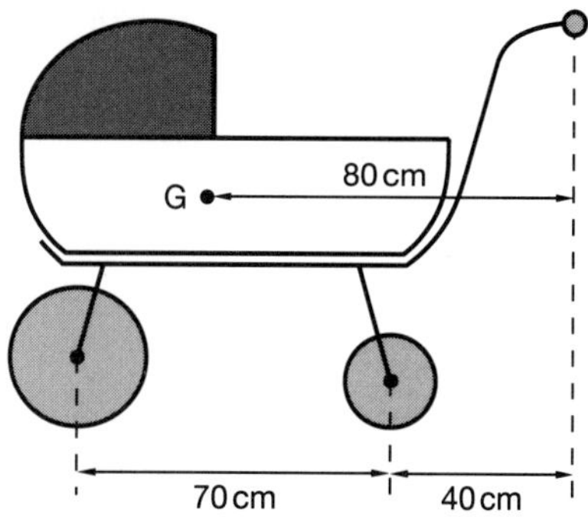

2.28 Two men are walking and carrying a ladder of length 12 m and weight 200 N: it may be considered to be uniform. The first man is 2.0 m from the end of the ladder; the back man holds it at the end. Draw a free-body force diagram for the ladder and calculate the force which each man exerts on the ladder.

2.29 In order to find the mass m of a heavy clampstand it is supported in equilibrium as shown in the diagram below. G is its centre of gravity.
(a) Draw a free-body force diagram for the clampstand and calculate m if, when x is 42.0 cm, the reading

on the spring balance is 4.6 N. Take a to be 6.5 cm.

(b) Plot a graph showing the relationship between F, the reading on the balance, and x for different positions of the balance.

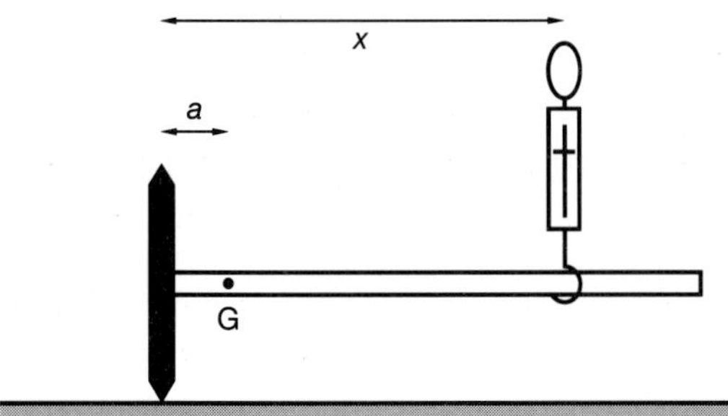

2.30 Describe how you would use the apparatus shown in the diagram below to locate the position, relative to his feet, of the centre of gravity of a human being with his arms at his sides. Estimate the likely errors in the measurements you would take and hence the uncertainty which could be achieved in the experiment?

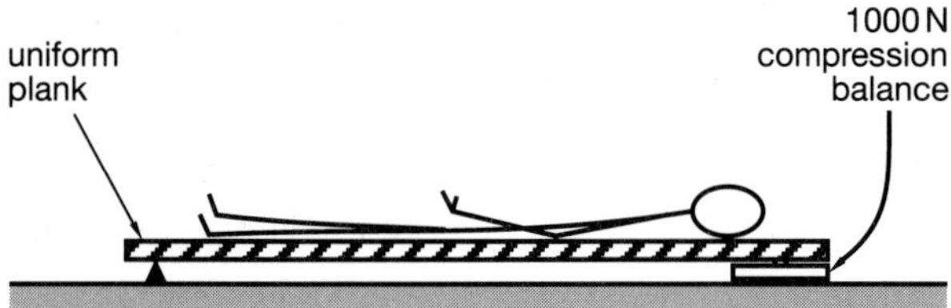

2.31 A uniform horizontal beam of weight 200 N and length 2.5 m is freely hinged at one end to a wall. A rope is attached to the free end and the other end of the rope is tied to the wall, at a point 1.0 m vertically above the beam.

(a) Draw a free-body force diagram for the beam.

(b) Calculate the tension in the rope.

(c) Calculate the horizontal and vertical resolved parts X and Y of the push of the wall on the beam.

(d) Show on your diagram the direction of the resultant X and Y.

2.32 A non-uniform tree trunk PQ of weight 20 kN and length 10 m lies on the ground. A cable attached at Q makes an angle of 40° with the horizontal and pulls with a force of 12.5 kN. The trunk may be considered to be horizontal, with Q lifted just clear of the ground, and touching the ground only at P. Draw a free-body force diagram for the trunk, and find

(a) the position of its centre of gravity

(b) the horizontal and vertical resolved parts X and Y of the push of the ground on the tree trunk

(c) the resultant of X and Y.

2.33 A uniform ladder of weight 150 N and length 4.00 m leans with its upper end against a frictionless vertical wall. Its lower end rests on the ground, 1.00 m from the foot of the wall. Draw a free-body force diagram for the ladder, showing the direction of the push P of the ground on the ladder. Calculate

(a) the angle which P makes with the vertical

(b) the size of P

(c) the push of the wall on the ladder.

2.34 The upward pull of the biceps to hold the forearm horizontal is 250 N (see the diagram below).

(a) If the weight of the forearm is 25 N, what is the downward push of the upper arm at the elbow?

(b) Calculate the pull of the biceps on the forearm if a mass of 5.0 kg is held in the hand at a distance of 350 mm from the elbow.

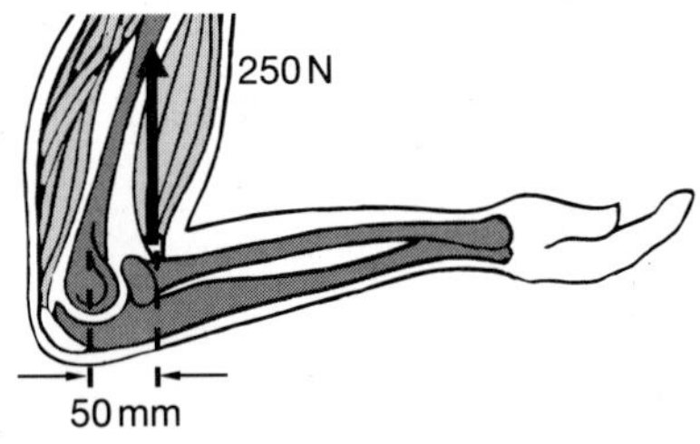

2.35 A table lamp has a circular base of diameter 100 mm and is weighted so that when it stands on a table its centre of gravity is 60 mm above the surface of the table. Through what angle can the lamp be tilted before it falls over? [Hint: draw a diagram of the lamp at the point when it is just about to fall over.]

2.4 Newton's second law

2.36 Superman slams head-on into a train speeding along at $30\,\mathrm{m\,s^{-1}}$, bringing it to rest in an amazing 0.01 s and saving Lois Lane, who was tied to the tracks.

(a) What is the acceleration of the train?

(b) If the train's mass is 200 tonnes (200 000 kg), what is the push which Superman exerts on the train?

2.37 A sprinter accelerates because there is an unbalanced force acting on him, the horizontal push of the starting blocks. The graph shows how this force varies with time as he accelerates forward.

(a) Why do you think there was a horizontal forward force of 100 N from the blocks before he started to accelerate?

(b) If the sprinter had a mass of 80 kg calculate his average acceleration during the sprint start.

(c) Assuming that this start lasted for 0.30 s, with what velocity did he leave his blocks?

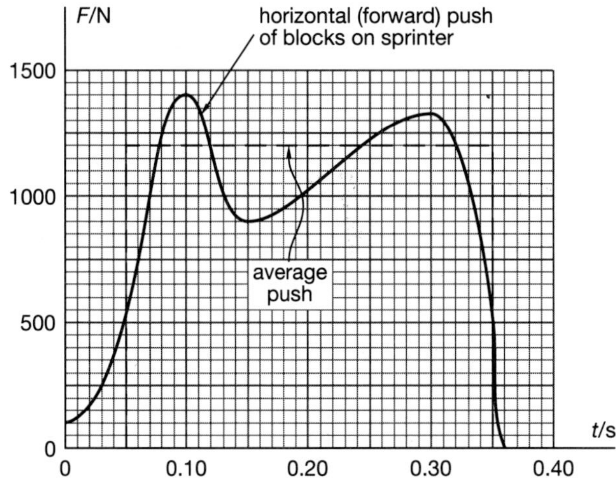

2.38 A lift of mass 1200 kg is being pulled vertically upwards at a steady speed of *(a)* $1.0\,\mathrm{m\,s^{-1}}$, *(b)* $2.0\,\mathrm{m\,s^{-1}}$. What is the tension in the cable in each case.

2.39 The two pieces of ticker-tape shown in the figure were attached to the same body on two different occasions. What is the ratio of the forces which were exerted on the body on those occasions?

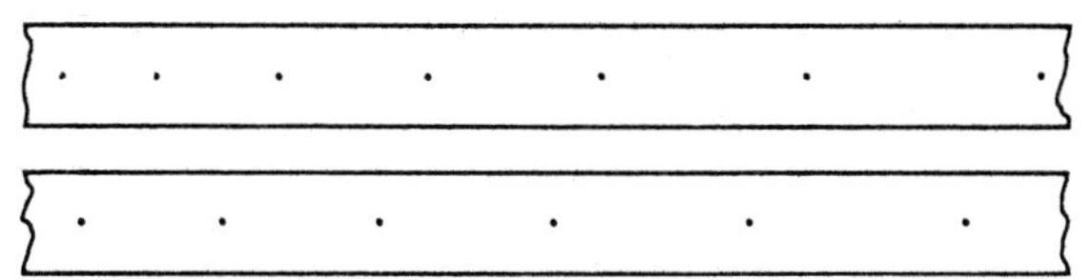

2.40 In one 10-minute interval during the *Apollo* 11 flight to the Moon the spacecraft's speed decreased from $5374\,\mathrm{m\,s^{-1}}$ to $5102\,\mathrm{m\,s^{-1}}$ (with the rocket motors not in use). If the mass of the spacecraft was 4.4×10^4 kg, find the average force on the spacecraft during this time.

2.41 *(a)* Two women push a car of mass 800 kg to get it started. If each pushes with a force of 300 N, and the resistance forces are equivalent to an opposing force of 160 N, what is the acceleration of the car?

(b) A tractor pulls a log of mass 2000 kg. When the tractor is pulling with a force of 1300 N the acceleration of the log is $0.050\,\mathrm{m\,s^{-2}}$; what resistance force does the ground exert on the log?

2.42 A superheavy weightlifter of mass 130 kg can produce a maximum upward pull on a barbell of 4400 N. Calculate

(a) the maximum acceleration of a 240 kg barbell

(b) the distance this barbell will move from rest in 0.40 s under this maximum force.

2.43 Explain how, in the laboratory, you would demonstrate that the acceleration of a body is inversely proportional to its mass for a given resultant force. State how you would process and present any measurements you take so as to achieve the aim of the demonstration.

2.44 A block of mass 2.0 kg rests on a rough horizontal table. The surface is such that the maximum frictional force which the table can exert on the block is 0.30 times the perpendicular contact force. The block is pulled horizontally with a force of 15 N.

(a) What is the acceleration of the block?

(b) What would be the acceleration of the block if its mass were doubled?

2.45 Refer to the previous question. Calculate the

acceleration of the 2.0 kg block if the pull of 15 N made an angle of 20° with the horizontal.
Explain in words why this answer is greater than the answer to the previous question.

2.46 The table gives the results of a standing-start acceleration test for a car of mass 1100 kg.

t/s	0	2	4	6	8	10	12
v/m s^{-1}	0	9	15	19.5	23	26	29

(a) Draw a graph of its speed v against time t.
(b) Estimate the resultant force acting on the car when its speed was (i) 15 m s^{-1} (ii) 25 m s^{-1}.

2.47 The figure shows free-body force diagrams for
(a) a child accelerating down a playground slide and
(b) a man pushing a packing case across a rough horizontal floor. Describe each of the marked forces by a phrase like 'W is the pull of the Earth on the child'. Estimate possible sizes of the forces.

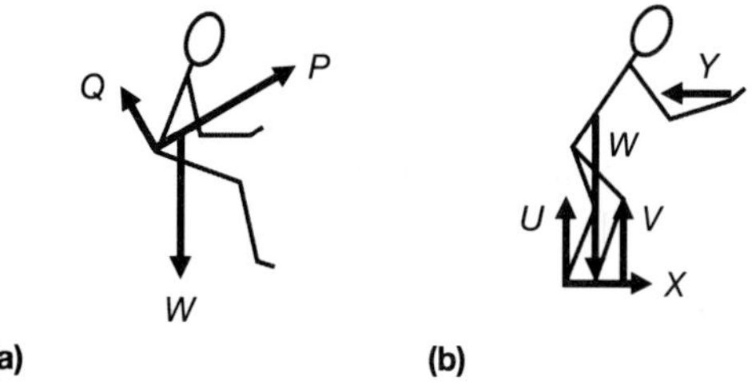

2.48 A pendulum bob hangs by a thread from the roof of a railway carriage. Describe and explain, using free-body force diagrams for the pendulum bob, what happens to the bob when the train is
(a) accelerating forwards
(b) moving at a constant velocity
(c) slowing down to rest.
For ***(a)*** make any possible calculation if the acceleration is 0.80 m s^{-2}.

2.49 The figure shows a block on a horizontal frictionless table. A thread attached to it runs horizontally to a pulley at the edge of the table, passes over the pulley, and supports a load of mass 1.0 kg. The size of the acceleration of both the block and the load is 2.0 m s^{-2}.
(a) Draw free-body force diagrams for (i) the block, (ii) the load, labelling as T the pull of the thread on each of the bodies.
(b) Use the free-body force diagram for the load to find the size of T.
(c) Now use the free-body force diagram for the block to find the mass of the block.

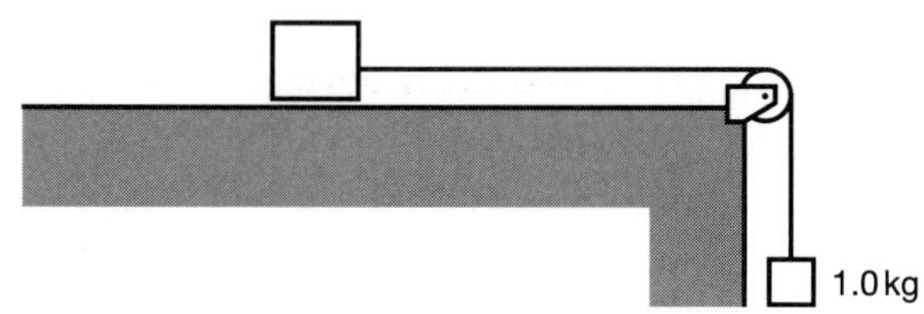

2.50 In the figure below the dashed line shows the weight of a parachutist as she falls: her weight is constant. The solid line shows the size of the air resistance force on her (and her parachute, when open) as she falls. She opens her parachute at time t_1 after falling freely.
Explain the shape of this graph, and draw a graph to show the variation of her acceleration with time.

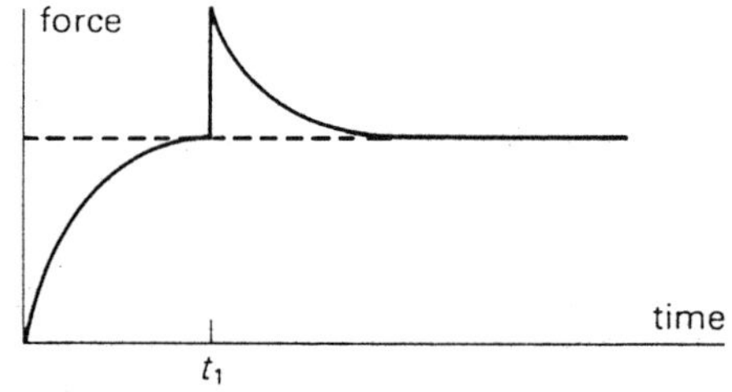

2.51 Three boxes in contact are being pushed along a system of rollers. The two outer boxes each have a mass of 140 kg and the middle box has a mass of 80 kg. The single pushing force is 220 N.
By drawing appropriate free-body force diagrams calculate
(a) the acceleration of the boxes

(b) the push of each of the outer boxes on the middle box.

2.52 What is the impulse of the forces in the following situations:

(a) a man pulling a garden roller eastwards with a horizontal force of 300 N for 10 s

(b) a rock of weight 20 N moving vertically downwards for 5.0 s

(c) a rock of weight 20 N moving vertically upwards for 5.0 s?

2.53 A tennis ball of mass 58 g is moving horizontally, at right angles to the net, with a speed of $20\,\mathrm{m\,s^{-1}}$. A player hits is straight back so that it leaves his racket with a speed of $25\,\mathrm{m\,s^{-1}}$. What is

(a) the change of momentum of the ball

(b) the impulse of the force which the racket exerts on the ball?

2.54 A girl catches a cricket ball of mass 160 g which is moving at a speed of $20\,\mathrm{m\,s^{-1}}$.

(a) Find the force which she must exert to stop it in (i) 0.10 s (ii) 0.50 s.

(b) Describe how she can vary the time in this way, and explain the advantage of lengthening the time in which the ball is stopped.

(c) Describe two other situations (as different as possible from this one) in which care is taken to lengthen the time during which an object is brought to rest.

2.55 The figure shows how the push of a tennis racket on a tennis ball of mass 58 g varies with time.

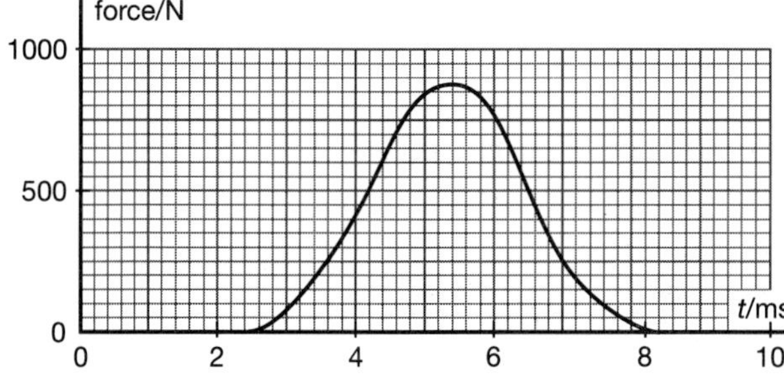

(a) Estimate the change of momentum of the ball, and, if it was initially at rest, its speed now.

(b) What is the maximum acceleration of the ball?

2.56 *(a)* Calculate the average force exerted by a golf club on a golf ball of mass 46 g, if the ball leaves the club at a speed of $80\,\mathrm{m\,s^{-1}}$ and the contact between club and ball lasts for 0.50 ms. State an object which would have a weight approximately equal to this force.

(b) Sketch a graph to show how the force on the golf ball might vary with time.

2.57 A railway wagon of mass 10 tonnes is seen to be moving at a speed of $2.0\,\mathrm{m\,s^{-1}}$ to the right. After 3.0 s it collides with another wagon of mass 30 tonnes moving at a speed of $1.0\,\mathrm{m\,s^{-1}}$ to the left. After the collision, which takes 1.0 s, the second wagon is moving at $0.20\,\mathrm{m\,s^{-1}}$ to the left.

(a) What is the velocity of the first wagon after the collision?

(b) Draw a graph of momentum against time for each wagon, using the same axes, for the period $t = 0$ to $t = 7.0$ s. Assume that in the collision the momentum of each wagon varies uniformly with time. (1 tonne = 1000 kg.)

(c) What is the significance of the slopes of these graphs? Calculate the slopes for the period $t = 3.0$ s to $t = 4.0$ s.

2.58 Why is a rubber-headed hammer not as good for driving a nail into a block of wood as a hammer with a head made of metal, even if both hammers have the same mass? In your answer you should consider the ideas of *momentum, rate of change of momentum* and *force.*

2.5 Animal and vehicle propulsion

2.59 The figure overleaf shows ***(a)*** a man pulling a suitcase across a table and ***(b)*** and ***(c)*** free-body force diagrams for the suitcase and the man respectively.

Describe each of the forces in a phrase like 'A is the pull of the Earth on the suitcase'.
Do any of the forces have the same size *because of* Newton's *third* law?

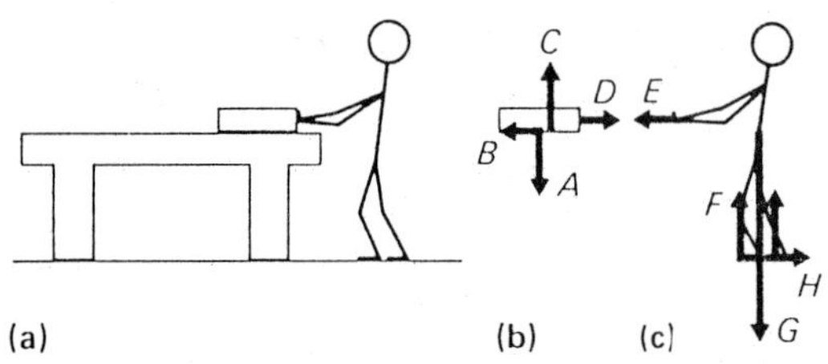

2.60 A man stands still on the surface of the Earth. Draw free-body force diagrams for ***(a)*** the man ***(b)*** the Earth, marking and labelling the forces acting on these bodies.
State which pairs of force are equal because of Newton's first law, and which pairs are equal because of Newton's third law.

2.61 A park swing for small children has a bucket seat supported by chains. Copy the free-body force diagram of the seat shown below and write a phrase underneath it for each of the forces acting on the seat. (*P* is *not* the weight of the child.) Draw another free-body force diagram for the child and name the forces acting on her. Which of the forces you have named form a Newton's third law pair?

2.62 An articulated lorry consists of a tractor unit of mass 4.0 tonnes and a trailer of mass 26 tonnes. Ignoring all resistive forces, calculate, when the lorry has an acceleration of $0.20\,\mathrm{m\,s^{-2}}$,

(a) the forward push of the road on the driving wheels of the tractor

(b) the forward pull of the tractor on the trailer.

2.63 Draw separate free-body force diagrams for the tractor and trailer in the previous question. Which pairs of forces are equal because of Newton's third law?

2.64 A man of mass 65 kg stands on a weighing machine in a lift which has a downward acceleration of $3.0\,\mathrm{m\,s^{-2}}$.
What is the reading (in N) on the weighing machine? Make it clear at what stage you need to use Newton's third law.
Explain why the answer does not depend on the direction in which the lift is moving.

2.65 A sprinter of mass 60 kg reaches her top speed of $12\,\mathrm{m\,s^{-1}}$ in the first 15 m of her run.

(a) Calculate her acceleration during this process.

(b) Hence calculate the horizontal force (assumed to be constant) which the ground has been exerting on her.

(c) What size horizontal force has she been exterting on the ground? Explain.

2.66 A packing case of mass 50 kg rests on a rough horizontal floor. The surface is such that the maximum frictional force which the floor can exert on the case in 0.40 times the perpendicular contact force. Describe what happens when someone pushes horizontally on the packing case

(a) with a force of 98 N

(b) with a force of 196 N

(c) with a force of 294 N.

2.6 Jets and rockets

2.67 The figure shows how the momentum of a body varies with time. Estimate the force acting on the body

(a) at $t = 1.0$ s
(b) at $t = 2.0$ s.

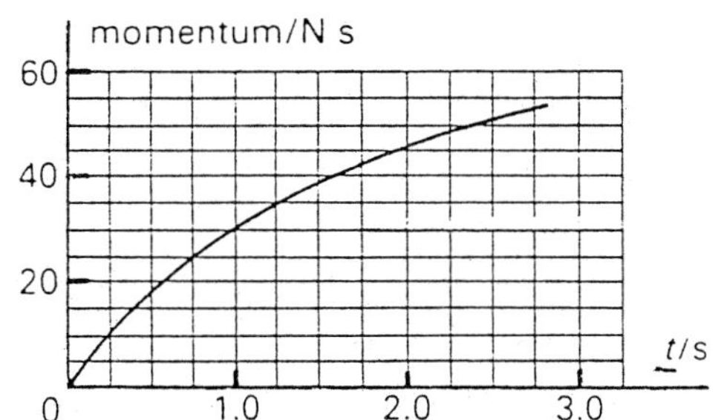

2.68 A wind of speed $10\,m\,s^{-1}$ blows horizontally and at right angles to a flat cricket sightscreen which measures 4.0 m by 10 m.
Estimate the force which the wind exerts on the sightscreen, explaining any assumptions you make.
Density of air = $1.3\,kg\,m^{-3}$.

2.69 A female water skier, whose weight (plus board) is 680 N, is moving at a constant velocity behind a speedboat. If the pull of the tow on her is 120 N draw a free-body force diagram of the skier and her board, marking all the forces on her. What produces the backward push on her?
If the pull of the tow suddenly fell to zero, calculate her initial acceleration. Why would this acceleration not be constant as she slowed down?

2.70 A simple rocket motor which can be demonstrated in the laboratory is shown in the figure. The Sparklets CO_2 cylinder is strapped to the trolley with tape and the end pierced with a tap from a hammer on a nail with the trolley held at rest.

(a) Explain what happens as the CO_2 rushes out through the hole.

(b) If the total mass of the trolley and cylinder is 0.40 kg when the hole is first made and the rocket starts to accelerate at $5.0\,m\,s^{-2}$ as measured by a ticker-timer, calculate the accelerating force, that is the push of the exhaust gases on the rocket.

(c) Someone suggests that the trolley may have a slightly increasing acceleration rather than a constant acceleration. Do you agree?

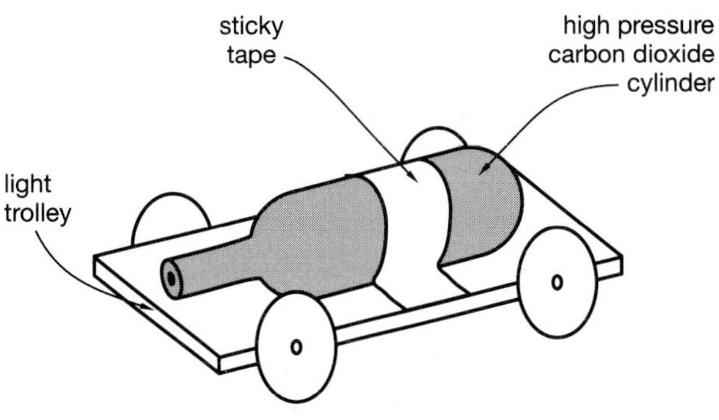

2.71 In heavy rain a depth of 30 mm of water might fall in one hour. If the rain falls vertically and its terminal speed is $8.0\,m\,s^{-1}$, calculate the average force on a flat roof of area 25 m^2 caused by the *falling* rain (assume no water lies on the roof). The density of water is $1000\,kg\,m^{-3}$.

2.72 The table gives some data about three rockets. Copy and complete it.

rocket	thrust/N	mass flow/kg s^{-1}	exhaust speed/m s^{-1}
V2	2.5×10^5	180	
Atlas	1.8×10^6		1800
Saturn V		1.4×10^4	2400

2.73 A capsule containing 5.0 g of liquid carbon dioxide at a high pressure is attached to a laboratory trolley which is placed on a friction-compensated runway in a laboratory. The end of the capsule is then pierced so that the carbon dioxide emerges rapidly, and the trolley accelerates in the opposite direction. Assume that the emission of carbon dioxide occurs at a constant rate of $3.0\,g\,s^{-1}$. What is the exhaust speed of the carbon dioxide if the acceleration of the trolley (of mass 0.80 kg) is found to be a constant $0.25\,m\,s^{-2}$?

2.74 If 70 kg of air passes through a jet engine each second, and the exhaust speed of the air is $600\,m\,s^{-1}$ greater than the intake speed, calculate the forward push on an aircraft fitted with four such engines.
As always, when a force pushes a body, some other body must be doing the pushing. In this situation what is it that is pushing?

3 Energy and its conservation

Data $g = 9.81\,\mathrm{N\,kg^{-1}} = 9.81\,\mathrm{m\,s^{-2}}$

3.1 Fuels and energy

3.1 The table gives the rate at which energy is used by a typical human being in some common activities. Estimate

(a) the energy you use in a day

(b) the heating power of a class of 15 pupils.

activity	power/W	activity	power/W
sleeping	80	typewriting	160
lying down (awake)	90	walking ($2\,\mathrm{m\,s^{-1}}$)	250
sitting still	120	running fast	700
standing	140	rowing in a race	1400

3.2 *(a)* A man doing heavy manual labour converts energy at a rate of about 1500 W. *If* he could keep up this rate of working for a working day of 8 hours, how much work would he have done?

(b) Electrical energy is available at a cost of about 8p per kW h. What would be the cost of the energy equal to the work done by the man? Does your answer help to explain the improvement in the standard of living in developed countries in the past 200 years?

3.3 In 1988 it was estimated that the total usable mass of oil in the world was about 340×10^{12} kg. At that time the world's oil consumption was about 4×10^{12} kg per year and was increasing by 6% annually.

(a) Plot a graph to show the world's oil consumption over 40 years from 1988, assuming the 6% growth rate is maintained.

(b) Use your graph to estimate how long the world's usable reserves will last at this rate of consumption.

3.4 'With a few exceptions we derive all our energy ultimately from the Sun.' Discuss whether you agree or disagree with this statement, paying attention to both renewable and non-renewable resources.

3.5 In 1988 the following renewable alternative technologies were seen to be promising:
– estuarine tidal energy
– shoreline wave energy
– land-based wind energy.
Choose one of these and describe the way in which the energy is harnessed.

3.2 The principle of conservation of energy

3.6 A motor car (internal combustion) engine is said to be 25% efficient, i.e. 75% of the chemical energy in the fuel is converted into useless internal energy. List the parts of the car where this conversion occurs. What happens to the 25% which is 'usefully' converted?

3.7 Gas and oil can be burnt in houses with an efficiency of over 85%. When their chemical energy is converted to electrical energy in power stations the efficiency of this process is less than 40%. Comment on the following points of view:

(a) Electrical energy should be used only when it is necessary, e.g. in electric motors. Gas and oil should be burnt in homes and factories for space heating.

(b) The use of gas and oil should be reserved for the chemical industry to use for manufacturing purposes (e.g. to make plastic materials).

3.8 Construct an energy flow or Sankey diagram for a car travelling at a constant speed along a level road. Make the diagram as quantitative as possible for a car where the power from the fuel is 60 kW and the power loss at the exhaust is 48 kW, the remaining power losses being frictional losses in the gearbox, driveshaft and wheels.

3.9 On August 23rd, 1977, cyclist Bryan Allen became the first man to achieve a man-powered flight round a figure-of-eight course in the 'Gossamer Condor'. In doing so he won for the craft's designer Paul McCready a prize of £60,000.

Draw an energy-flow diagram ***(a)*** for the take-off part of the flight and ***(b)*** for the middle part of the flight which was at constant speed.

3.10 The radiation received from the Sun at the Earth's surface at the latitude of Great Britain is typically about $600\,\mathrm{W\,m^{-2}}$ (in the absence of cloud).

(a) What area of solar panel would be needed to replace a power station of output 2.0 GW, if the solar panels used could convert solar radiation to electrical energy at an efficiency of 20%?

(b) What percentage is this area of the total area of the British Isles (which is $3 \times 10^{11}\,\mathrm{m^2}$)?

(c) If the total power station capacity (1989) is about 120 GW, what percentage of the surface of Great Britain would be covered by solar panels if all the power stations were to be replaced? Comment on your answer.

3.11 There is a possibility of creating a *tidal barrage* in the Severn Estuary. Water from the incoming tide would pass through sluices and be trapped behind the barrage; it would then be released through turbines to produce electricity. Estimate the average power output from a power station using such turbines, given that there are two tides each day, that the area of the water behind the barrage is $70\,\mathrm{km^2}$ with an average depth at high tide of 6 m, and that the overall efficiency of the conversion process is 80%. The density of water is $1000\,\mathrm{kg\,m^{-3}}$

3.12 The graph shows the demand for electrical energy in a particular region during a 24-hour period.

(a) Estimate the mean demand rate during this period. Explain how you made your estimate.

(b) Calculate the energy demand in (i) one minute (ii) one hour during the mid-morning period.

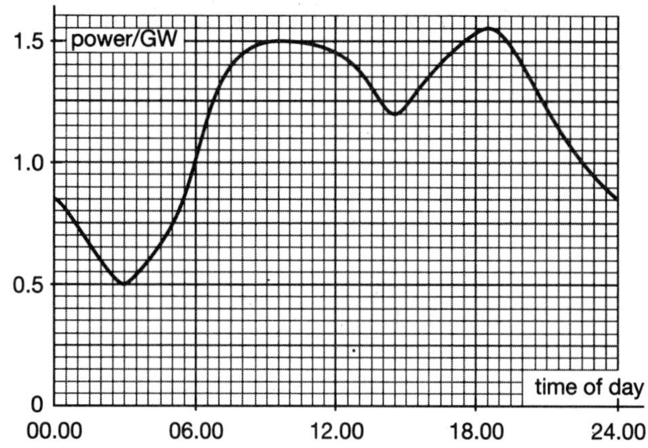

3.13 It would obviously be desirable for the power station in the previous question to be able to work at a constant rate, equal to this demand rate.

It is therefore proposed to construct the main power station to work at this mean demand rate. During periods when the availability of energy is greater than the demand, the energy should be used at a pumped-storage power station to pump water from a low to a high reservoir. It would then be released to help drive the power station turbines when demand is greater than the mean demand rate.

Assuming an efficiency of 80% in the pumping process, *estimate* the mass of water which would be needed, if the reservoir were 300 m above the power station. Assume the maximum power output of the main station to be 1.4 GW.

3.3 Work and power

3.14 To cut a lawn, Mum has to push a lawnmower 80 m. If her average horizontal push on the mower is 100 N, how much work does she do on the lawnmower? As the mower has no kinetic energy when she has finished the task, how much work is done on the lawnmower by frictional forces?

3.15 Draw a free-body force diagram for a block of mass 6.0 kg which is being pulled across a rough horizontal table by a horizontal force of 30N. The maximum frictional force which the table can exert on the block is 20N. Find the work done by each of the forces in a horizontal displacement of 0.80m.

3.16 During the first 0.6m of the lift a super-heavyweight weightlifter produced an upward pull on the barbell of 3800N. If the mass of the barbell was 240kg, calculate

(a) the work done by the weightlifter on the barbell
(b) the work done by the pull of the Earth on the barbell.

What can you deduce about the barbell after it had been raised 0.6m?

3.17 A simple pendulum consists of a thread of length 700mm and a bob of mass 60g. The bob is pulled to one side until its *vertical* height above its lowest position is 20mm, and is then released. What is the size of the pull of the Earth on the bob? Draw a free-body force diagram for the bob when it is moving, and calculate the work done by each of the forces on the bob while

(a) it moves to its lowest point
(b) it moves from its lowest point to its extreme position on the other side.

3.18 To measure the work which can be done by a motor, a *band brake* is sometimes used, as shown in the figure. The two spring balances measure the tensions in the rope on either side of the pulley, and the difference between the readings gives the frictional force which the rope exerts on the pulley.

(a) Write down an expression for the work done by the motor in one revolution.
(b) If the spring balance readings are 9.5N and 1.0N when the motor is turning at 1200 revolutions per minute, and the radius of the pulley is 50mm, what is the power of the motor?

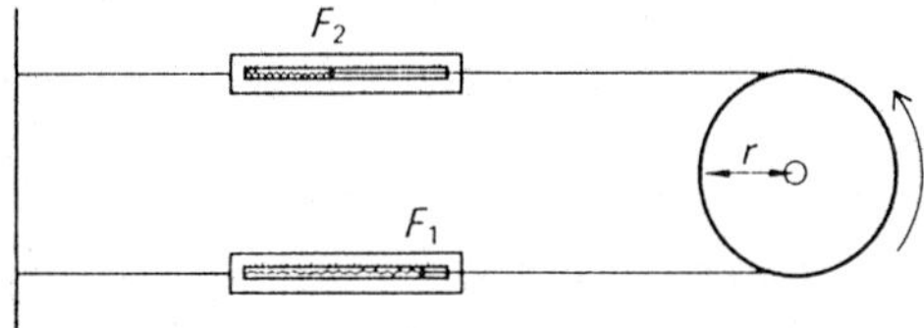

3.19 A man does 20 press-ups (i.e. lying on his front, he straightens his arms to lift his shoulders from the ground) in 50s. Estimate the power of the muscles which he is using.

3.20 A spring of constant stiffness $40\,\mathrm{N\,m^{-1}}$ is fixed at one end. A man pulls the other end horizontally.

(a) How much work does the man do in stretching the spring from its unstretched position (i) 0.20m (ii) a further 0.20m?
(b) Explain why the answer to (ii) is not the same as the answer to (i).

3.21 The figure below shows a force-extension graph for a wire which breaks at B.

(a) How much work has to be done on the wire to break it?
(b) How much work would have been needed if the wire had broken at A?

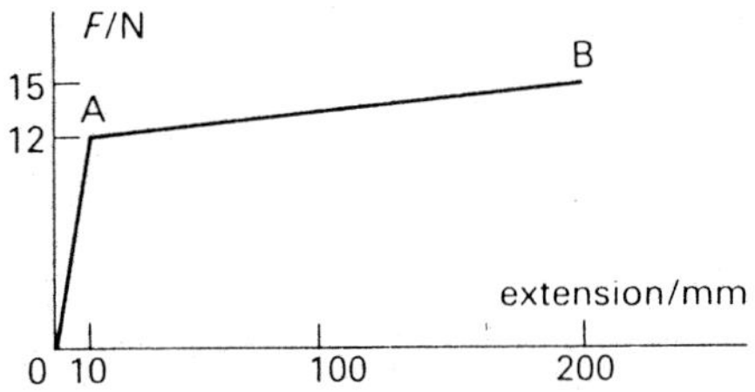

3.22 Corresponding values of force and extension for a particular rubber band are shown in the table.

force /N	0	0.25	0.50	0.75	1.0	2.0	3.0	4.0	5.0
extension /mm	0	20	40	50	55	64	66	68	70

Plot a graph of force (on the *y*–axis) against extension (on the *x*–axis). How much work is done in stretching the rubber band 70mm?

3.23 The table below shows how the Moon's gravitational pull F on a particular spacecraft varies with distance r from the centre of the Moon (radius 1.74×10^6 m).

$r/10^6$ m	1.74	2.0	2.4	2.8	3.2
$F/10^4$ N	6.5	4.9	3.4	2.5	1.9

Estimate the work done by this force as the spacecraft rises from the Moon's surface to a distance of 3.2×10^6 m from the centre of the Moon.

3.24 A piano of mass 300 kg is being lifted to a window 12 m above the ground using a system of pulleys and a diesel motor.

(a) If the motor has an output power of 800 W, how long will it take to raise the piano to the window?

(b) How much chemical energy is converted by the motor during the lift if its efficiency is 20%?

3.25 A motor drives a pulley which lifts a box of mass 5.0 kg at a steady speed of 2.0 m s^{-1}. What is the power output of the motor?

3.26 The power of the electric motor of a locomotive pulling a train at a constant speed of 50 m s^{-1} is 2.5 MW. What is the total resistance force on the train?

3.4 Kinetic energy

3.27 Estimate the kinetic energy of

(a) a tennis ball which has just been served. Tennis balls have a mass of 58 g, and the serving speed might be 30 m s^{-1}.

(b) a rifle bullet. It has a mass of 10 g, and the speed might be 300 m s^{-1}.

(c) a man sprinting. The world record for the 100 metres is less than 10 s.

(d) a loaded articulated lorry on a motorway. Its mass might be 40 tonnes, and 70 m.p.h. is roughly equal to 32 m s^{-1}.

3.28 *(a)* A car of mass 800 kg reaches a speed of 20 m s^{-1} in a distance of 100 m, as a result of internal forces doing work on the car. What constant external force would have been needed to do the same amount of work?

(b) If its motor is then switched off, and frictional forces equivalent to a constant horizontal force of 200 N act on it, in what distance will it stop?

3.29 To push start a car on a winter's morning (its battery is flat), two people each push with a force of 300 N. After pushing for 15 m the car's engine starts. If at that moment the car's kinetic energy was 7500 J, calculate

(a) the work done by the push of the people on the car

(b) the work done by frictional forces on the car.

3.30 *(a)* A large oil tanker has a mass, when fully loaded, of half a million tonnes, that is 5.0×10^8 kg. What is the k.e. of the tanker when it travels at its full speed of 11 m s^{-1}?

(b) In an emergency the tanker can stop, from full speed ahead, in a distance of 6.0 km. What average force is required to achieve this and what produces this force?

3.31 An object of mass 300 g falls from rest for 2.5 m in a vacuum.

(a) How much work is done by the pull of the Earth on it?

(b) What is its final speed?

When it fell in air its final speed was 6.8 m s^{-1}.

(c) How much work was done by the air resistance?

3.32 A climber of mass 70 kg falls vertically off a cliff. She is attached to a rope which allows her to fall freely for 20 m. Then it becomes taut, but stretches, bringing her to rest in a further 4.0 m. An energy-flow diagram for this accident would show gravitational p.e. being converted to k.e while she is falling freely and, while she is being slowed down, the k.e., and some more g.p.e., being converted into internal energy in the rope. Draw this energy-flow or Sankey diagram, attaching numerical values to the boxes for g.p.e and k.e. Calculate the internal energy in the rope, and the average force exerted on her by the rope.

3.33 During a single human heart-beat, 20 g of blood is pushed into the main arteries.

(a) If this blood is accelerated from a speed of

0.20 m s^{-1} to 0.34 m s^{-1}, calculate the increase in kinetic energy of this blood.

(b) If the heart is pulsing at 60 beats per minute, what is the average power of the heart pump?

3.34 A pendulum bob of mass 30 g is drawn to one side so that it is raised to a *vertical* height of 35 mm, and released.

(a) How fast is it moving when it passes through its lowest point?

(b) Does this speed depend on the mass of the bob? Explain your answer.

3.35 The figure shows a block of mass 4.0 kg sliding down a ramp of length 5.0 m. The frictional force is a constant 15 N.

(a) How much work is done by the weight of the block?

(b) How much work is done by the frictional force?

(c) If the block was given a speed of 1.0 ms^{-1} at the top of the ramp, what is its speed at the bottom?

(d) If the block was required to slide down the ramp at constant speed, how much work would have to be done by the frictional force?

(e) *Hence* calculate the frictional force needed.

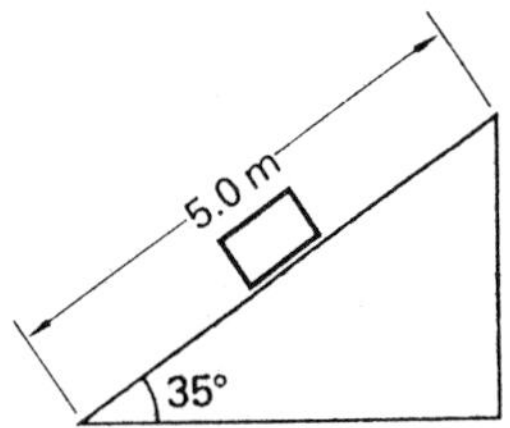

3.36 The figure shows part of a roller coaster at a fairground. If a car of mass 250 kg has a speed of 2.0 m s^{-1} at A, and the combined frictional and air resistance forces are constant, what is the maximum value of these forces if the car is to pass over the hump at C?

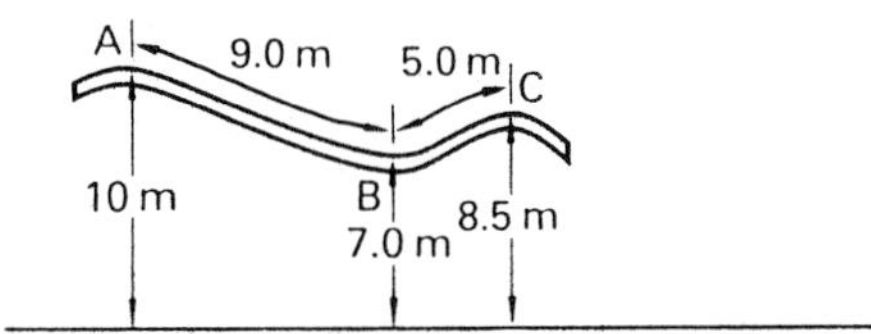

3.37 In a game of cricket a fielder throws a cricket ball from the boundary to the wicket. It leaves his hand with a speed of 20 m s^{-1}. How fast is it moving when it has risen a vertical height of 5.0 m? Explain whether the answer depends on the angle to the horizontal at which the ball is thrown?

3.38 The compression spring in a pinball machine has a stiffness of 100 N m^{-1}. The spring is compressed 40 mm and when released fires a ball of mass 30 g. With what speed does it leave the spring?

3.5 Potential energy

3.39 A squash ball of mass 25 g is allowed to fall from a height of 1.0 m onto a hard surface, and it bounces up to a height of 0.20 m.

(a) What is its initial gravitational p.e.?

(b) What is its final gravitational p.e.?

(c) How do you account for the difference?

3.40 A cross-country skier of mass 80 kg is skiing along level ground at 6.0 m s^{-1}. He comes to a short uphill section 6.0 m long which rises 1.5 m, as shown in the figure.

(a) Calculate his gain of g.p.e. as he skis up the slope.

(b) What is his k.e. (i) at P and (ii) at Q, assuming the slope exerts no frictional forces on his skis.

(c) If there was a constant frictional push of the ground on his skis of 40 N, calculate what his speed would now be at Q.

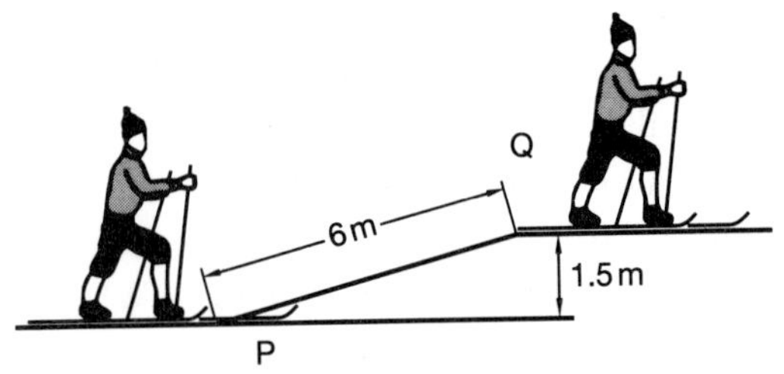

3.41 The figure shows two experiments to compare the power output of different sets of muscles in the body. Suppose that the bodyweight of both the girl and the boy doing the exercises is 600 N. In (i) her step-up distance is 45 cm and in (ii) the pull-up (or 'chin') lifts his centre of mass 0.35 m. The results are as follows: (i) 24 step-ups in the first 50 s, and (ii) 8 pull-ups in the first 30 s.

(a) Calculate the work done during one step-up and one pull-up and hence find the power developed in each exercise.

(b) It was found that while the girl doing the step-ups could continue at the same rate for another 50 s, the boy doing the exercise had to stop after 8 pull-ups. What does this tell you about the sets of muscles used in these experiments?

3.42 A man attaches a load of mass 5.0 kg to the lower end of a vertical steel wire, supporting the load as he does so until the whole weight of the load is carried by the wire. The extension of the wire is then 4.0 mm. What is

(a) the loss of gravitational p.e. of the load

(b) the gain of elastic p.e. of the wire?

Why are these answers different?

3.43 The figure below shows an energy-flow diagram. Suggest a process to which it might refer, giving numercial information where possible.

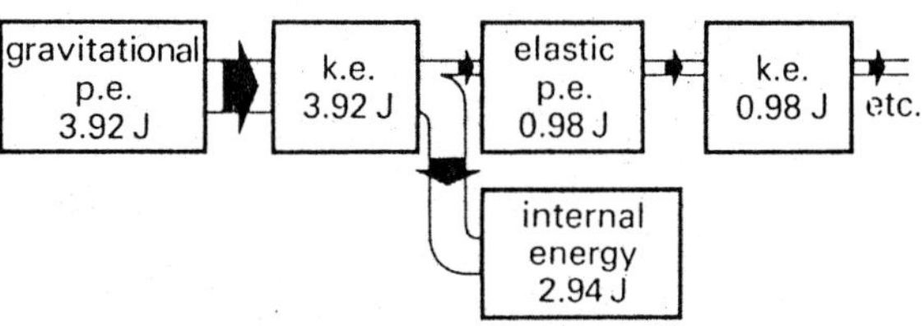

3.44 *(a)* The figure shows a catapult which consists of two posts A and B, and a rubber band. When the band is placed round A and B it is not stretched. The middle point of the rubber band is then pulled back to X (AX = XB = 90 mm); the force needed to hold the rubber band in this position is 5.0 N.
(i) What is the tension in the rubber band?
(ii) Calculate the elastic p.e. now stored in it.

(b) A pellet of mass 3.0 g is then placed at X, and the band is released, pushing the pellet to Y. Calculate the speed of the pellet when it loses contact with the rubber band at Y.

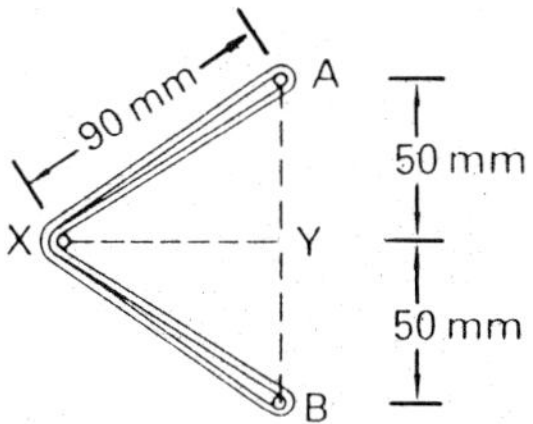

3.45 A lump of weight 4.0 N is held stationary at the bottom of a vertical spring of stiffness 20 N m^{-1}; the spring is not stretched. The lump is then released. When it has fallen 0.20 m, find the changes in

(a) the gravitational potential energy of the lump

(b) the elastic potential energy of the spring,

(c) the kinetic energy of the lump.

The lump passes through this position. When it has fallen a total distance of 0.40 m find the change (from the initial values)

(*d*) in the gravitational potential energy of the lump
(*e*) in the elastic potential energy of the spring.
What can you deduce from these figures?

3.46 A trampolinist falls vertically from a height of 3.0 m: on the rebound she rises to a height of 3.5 m. Discuss the energy changes quantitatively and draw an energy-flow diagram for the process.

3.47 Describe in detail how you would measure the percentage of elastic potential energy stored in a catapult which is transferred to the kinetic energy of a stone when the catapult is fired.
You should draw a diagram of the experimental arrangement, state all the measurements you will take and explain how you will process these measurements to achieve the aim of the experiment.
Discuss the uncertainty likely in the measurements you take and deduce an overall likely error in your final result.

3.6 Collisions

3.48 A railway wagon of mass 15 tonnes which has a velocity of 5.0 m s^{-1} north collides with a wagon of mass 10 tonnes which has a velocity of 2.0 m s^{-1} south. They couple together on impact.
(*a*) Find their velocity after the collision.
(*b*) Calculate the kinetic energy converted into other forms of energy.

3.49 Refer to the photograph which accompanied question *2.11* on page 7. Is that an elastic collision? Explain your answer.

3.50 An air track glider of mass 200 g, moving at 0.30 m s^{-1}, makes an elastic collision with stationary gliders of mass (*a*) 200 g (*b*) 400 g. What are the velocities of the two gliders after the collision in each case?

3.51 A bullet of mass 10 g is fired into a block of wood of mass 4.0 kg which is supported by vertical threads. After the bullet had become embedded in the block, the block swings and rises (vertically) 50 mm.
(*a*) What was the speed of the bullet?
(*b*) How much internal energy was produced?

3.52 A car of mass 1000 kg which has a velocity of 10 m s^{-1} east collides at a crossroads with a car of mass 800 kg which has a velocity of 5.0 m s^{-1} north. If the cars lock together after the collision, find their initial velocity afterwards. How much kinetic energy is converted in the collision? [Hint: the momentum after the collision in the northerly direction is the same as it was before the collision.]

3.53 In some situations an electron and a gas atom can collide eleastically. Suppose the atom has a mass which is 1.0×10^5 times greater than that of the electron.
(*a*) Find the velocities of the electron and the gas atom after a collision in which (i) an electron of speed u hits, head-on, a stationary gas atom (ii) a gas atom of speed u hits, head-on, a stationary electron. [You will find it sensible to make some approximations.]
(*b*) For (i) find the kenetic energy of the electron after the collision. For (ii) find what fraction of the k.e. of the atom is given to the electron.

3.7 High energy physics

3.54 How fast must a particle be moving for its mass to increase by (*a*) 1% (*b*) 10% (*c*) 50%? Express your answers as fractions of the speed of light c.

3.55 In lists of fundamental particles the units of mass are often given as MeV (1 MeV = 1.6×10^{-13} J. For example:

particle	rest mass/MeV
electron	0.512
proton	938

Express these masses in kilograms.

3.56 When one mole of hydrogen molecules reacts with half a mole of oxygen molecules in the chemical reactions $H_2 + \frac{1}{2}O_2 = H_2O$ the internal energy produced is 2.8×10^5 J. Express the loss in mass

(a) in kilograms

(b) as a fraction of the total mass of the original materials. (One mole of hydrogen molecules has a mass of 2.0 g; one mole of oxygen molecules has a mass of 32 g.)

(Take $c = 3.0 \times 10^8\,\mathrm{m\,s^{-1}}$.)

3.57 In a certain experiment electrons (of rest mass 9.11×10^{-31} kg) were accelerated to a very high speed and then allowed to travel at constant velocity for a distance of 5.00 m. The time t taken to travel this distance was recorded for different amounts of work W done (by electrical forces) in accelerating the electrons.

$W/10^{-14}$ J	0.50	1.00	2.00	3.00	4.00	5.00	6.00
$t/10^{-8}$ s	4.99	3.67	2.80	2.45	2.25	2.13	2.04

(a) Assuming k.e. $= \frac{1}{2}mv^2$ and using only the first row of figures, predict the speed v of the electrons for those amounts of work done on it, and plot v^2 (on the y–axis) against W (on the x–axis). Since $W = \frac{1}{2}mv^2$ this graph should be a straight line of slope $2/m$.

(b) Calculate the actual speed v_a of the electron from the above measurements of time t. Plot the values of v_a, squared, on the same graph. The slope of this graph decreases. What does this suggest about the mass of the electron at very high speeds?

4 Structure of matter

Data Avogadro constant L (N_A) = $6.02 \times 10^{23}\,\mathrm{mol^{-1}}$
mass of proton = mass of neutron = 1.66×10^{-27} kg
mass of electron = 9.11×10^{-31} kg
unified atomic mass unit u = 1.66×10^{-27} kg
relative atomic masses (r.a.m.): sodium 23, chlorine 35.5, iron 56, silver 108, gold 197 relative molecular masses: hydrogen 2, helium 4, nitrogen 28, oxygen 32
electronic charge $e = 1.60 \times 10^{-19}$ C
$g = 9.81\,\mathrm{N\,kg^{-1}}$

4.1 Atoms and molecules

4.1 The diameters of most atoms are about 3×10^{-10} m. Roughly how many atoms thick is:

(a) a piece of gold foil, of thickness 6×10^{-7} m

(b) a strand of the copper wire (diameter 0.10 mm) used to make flexible electrical connecting wire?

4.2 Describe how you would perform an experiment to measure the length of a molecule of a fatty acid (e.g. oleic acid, palmitic acid). Include labelled diagrams in your description, draw attention to any difficulties in the experiment, and state any assumptions you make. What other information would you need in order to find the diameter of one of the carbon atoms in the molecule?

4.3 *(a)* Estimate the size of the full stop at the end of this sentence.

(b) If this dot represents the nucleus of an atom, how large, on this scale, would an atom be?

4.4 An atom of uranium–238 has 92 protons, 146 neutrons and 92 electrons.

(a) What fraction of the mass is not in the nucleus?

(b) If the nucleus of this atom may be thought of as a sphere of radius 7.4×10^{-15} m, what is the average density of the material of the nucleus?

4.5 The atomic number Z of carbon is 6; the neutron numbers N of its three common isotopes are 6, 7 and 8. Write down

(a) the mass numbers A of these isotopes
(b) the atomic mass of the most massive isotope.

4.6 The three common isotopes of silicon have mass numbers of 28, 29 and 30. Their percentage abundances are 92.2%, 4.7% and 3.1% respectively. Calculate the relative atomic mass of silicon by finding the weighted average of these mass numbers.

4.7 In one type of mass spectrometer positive ions of an element are all given the same kinetic energy and are then moving horizontally. They enter an evacuated horizontal tube, and while in the tube the only force which acts on them is the pull of the Earth. The time taken for them to reach the end of the tube is measured, and it is found that when potassium ions are used the ions arrive at two different times corresponding to the isotopes of potassium which have mass numbers 39 and 41.

(a) Explain which kind of ion arrives first.

The initial k.e of the ions is 5.00×10^{-18} J, and the length of the tube is 0.600 m.

(b) What was the initial speed of each type of ion
(c) What was the time of flight of each type of ion?

4.8 Using data on page 23, find the mass of

(a) one mole of electrons
(b) 10 moles of oxygen molecules
(c) 20 moles of oxygen atoms.

4.9 Using data on page 23, explain which of the following contains the greatest number of molecules, and find that number:

(a) 20 g of hydrogen (H_2)
(b) 20 g of helium (He)
(c) 200 g of nitrogen (N_2).

4.10 Using data on page 23, find the relative molecular mass of palmitic acid, $C_{16}H_{32}O_2$, and use the value of L to calculate the mass of one molecule.

4.11 The relative atomic mass of gold is 197.

(a) What is the mass of one atom of gold? The density of gold in the solid state is 1.93×10^4 kg m^{-3}.
(b) How many atoms of gold are there in a volume of 1.00 m^3?
(c) Treating a gold atom as if it occupied a cubical volume, what is the volume of such a cube?
(d) What is the length of the side of such a cube?

This is an approximate measure of the 'diameter' of a gold atom. Repeat this calculation for an atom of aluminium, for which the relative atomic mass is 26.9 and the density 2.70×10^3 kg m^{-3}. Comment on the two values of diameter.

4.12 Using data on page 23, find the number of

(a) gold atoms in a gold ring which has a mass of 25 g
(b) iron atoms in an iron mass of one kilogram
(c) sodium chloride (NaCl) molecules in 100 g of sodium chloride
(d) sodium atoms in 100 g of sodium chloride.

4.2 Atomic forces

4.13 What evidence is there, in everyday life, that atoms attract each other and also repel each other?

4.14 What are the four most common types of bonding between atoms? Explain the mechanism of each, and give an example of a material formed by each type.

4.15 Atoms are electrically neutral: how is it possible for them to attract each other?

4.16 For some kinds of atoms which form solids, when their separation is r, the force of attraction F_a between them could be given by the equation $F_a = -A/r^2$, and the force of repulsion F_r by the equation $F_r = A/r^7$.

(a) Taking, for convenience, $A = 1$, calculate the values of F_a and F_r for values of r from 0.80 to 1.30 at intervals of $r = 0.10$.
(b) On the same axes, plot graphs of F_a and F_r against r.

(c) Also plot the graph which shows how $(F_a + F_r)$ varies with r.
The graphs indicate how the forces of attraction and repulsion between certain kinds of atom, and the resultant force, vary with separation.

(d) What is the significance of the value of r for which $(F_a + F_r) = 0$?
(If you have access to a programmable calculator or a computer you might try calculating F_a, F_r and $(F_a + F_r)$ for values of r from 0.60 to 1.50 at intervals of $r = 0.05$. A computer could be programmed to plot the graphs.)

4.17 Repeat the processes of the last question (using a computer if possible) for

(a) values of r from 0.97 to 1.03 at intervals of $r = 0.01$ and plot a graph of $(F_a + F_r)$ against r.

(b) values of r from 0.997 to 1.003 at intervals of $r = 0.001$ and plot a graph of $(F_a + F_r)$ against r.

What features of these graphs explain why Hooke's Law (extension is proportional to force) is obeyed by many solids for small extensions? Up to what fractional change in length (i.e. extension/original length) would you expect Hooke's Law to be obeyed?

4.18 Neighbouring ions in a crystal of sodium chloride are 2.8×10^{-10}m apart. If the repelling force F_r on an ion is proportional to $1/r^{10}$, and the attracting force F_a is proportional to $1/r^2$, and each is 5.1×10^{-9}N when an ion is in equilibrium, find the values of F_r and F_a, and the resultant force

(a) when $r = 2.4 \times 10^{-10}$m

(b) when $r = 3.2 \times 10^{-10}$m.

In each case state whether the resultant force is attractive or repulsive and comment on their sizes.

4.19 The diagram shows how the force of repulsion and the force of attraction, between adjacent atoms in a crystal of a metallic element vary with their separation r. Copy the graphs on to graph paper, and add to them a graph to show the resultant force acting on each atom. (Note: at the separation r_0 the sizes of the attraction and repulsion forces are the same.)

(a) What is the significance of the separation r_0?

(b) Using the graph of resultant force, explain what happens when forces are exerted on the crystal to (i) stretch it, (ii) compress it

(c) Also explain why the crystal obeys Hooke's law for small stresses.

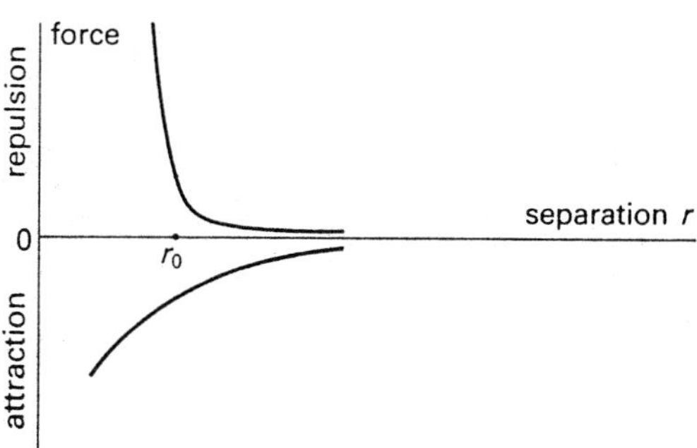

4.20 The atoms in a particular kind of crystal have potential energies E when they have a separation r as shown in the table:

$r/10^{-10}$m	2.0	2.2	2.5	2.8	3.0	3.5	4.0	4.5	5.0
$E/10^{-19}$J	13.1	−4.2	−11.6	−12.7	−12.4	−11.2	−9.9	−8.9	−8.0

(a) Draw a graph of $E/10^{-19}$J against $r/10^{-10}$m.

(b) The p.e. is a minimum when $r = 2.8 \times 10^{-10}$m. What is the significance of this separation?

(c) Using a larger scale for the p.e. (e.g. 20mm = 1.0×10^{-19}J) draw again the p.e. against separation graph for $r = 2.5 \times 10^{-10}$m to $r = 3.0 \times 10^{-10}$m. If the atoms have a k.e. of 0.2×10^{-19}J when $r = 2.8 \times 10^{-10}$m, what are their maximum and minimum separations in their oscillation?

(d) Looking at the general shape of the graph, are the amplitudes of oscillation on each side of the equilibrium position exactly equal? How does the average separation of the molecules when they are oscillating compare with their separation when they are not oscillating? What does your answer predict about the way in which the solid behaves when it is heated?

(e) Draw tangents to the original graph at $r/10^{-10}$m = 2.5 and 2.8 and find their slope. What do the slopes represent?

4.21 *(a)* Sketch a graph to show how the potential energy of a pair of atoms varies with their separation.

(b) Indicate on your graph the equilibrium separation of the atoms.

(c) What feature of the graph indicates the energy needed to separate the atoms completely?

4.3 The solid phase

4.22 'Crystals have shiny surfaces. Glass has a shiny surface. Therefore glass is crystalline.' What experiments could you do to prove that glass is *not* crystalline?

4.23 Metals are not obviously crystalline (e.g. they do not have naturally shiny surfaces). Explain why we say they are polycrystalline.

4.24 Describe how you would use a bubble raft to model the formation of crystalline materials. What properties of the bubbles allow them to be used for this purpose?

4.25 Why is it nowdays common to find the following items made of a plastic material (previously-used material in brackets)?

(a) Washing-up bowls (enamelled iron)

(b) Rainwater pipes (cast iron)

(c) Electric light switches (brass with ceramic inserts).

4.4 The liquid and gaseous phases

4.26 Give a description, as if you were talking to a 10-year-old brother or sister, of the way in which we think the atoms of a crystalline material are behaving when the material is in the solid phase. Also describe what happens as the temperature of the material is raised until it melts, and eventually evaporates.

4.27 What would be the effect on the Brownian motion of ash particles in air when

(a) using smaller ash particles

(b) warming the air?

4.28 Assuming that the kinetic energies of the air molecules and ash particles in Brownian motion are roughly equal, estimate a typical speed for an ash particle, given that the air molecules have a speed of about $500\,\mathrm{m\,s^{-1}}$, the mass of an air molecule is about $5 \times 10^{-26}\,\mathrm{kg}$ and the mass of an ash particle is about $1 \times 10^{-18}\,\mathrm{kg}$.

4.29 When liquid bromine is released at the bottom of a wide vertical tube containing air, it evaporates to form a brown gas, but the colour spreads *slowly* up the tube. It takes perhaps 10 minutes to spread about 250 mm. Yet the bromine molecules typically have speeds of $200\,\mathrm{m\,s^{-1}}$. Explain why the colour moves so slowly.

4.30 An air molecule leaves the floor of a room, travelling vertically upwards at a speed of $500.00\,\mathrm{m\,s^{-1}}$. Assuming that it does not collide with any other molecule, what is its speed when it reaches the ceiling, which is 2.5 m above the floor? Is it reasonable to ignore gravitational effects when we are considering the pressure which air exerts on different surfaces?

4.31 The mean free path of air molcules at room temperature and normal pressure is about $10^{-7}\,\mathrm{m}$. Their speeds are about $500\,\mathrm{m\,s^{-1}}$. It can be shown that when a molecule takes N 'steps' in random directions it reaches, on average, a distance of $\sqrt{N}$ steps from its starting point. If there were no air currents in the room, how long would it be likely to take one molecule to move from one end to the other of a room which is 5.0 m long?

4.32 The density of liquid oxygen at 90 K (its normal boiling point) is $1.14 \times 10^{3}\,\mathrm{kg\,m^{-3}}$, and the density of gaseous oxygen at the same temperature is $3.79\,\mathrm{kg\,m^{-3}}$.

(a) If the 'diameter' of an oxygen molecule is d, the volume it occupies in the liquid phase is, roughly, d^3. In terms of d^3, how much space does a molecule take up when it is in the gaseous phase at 90 K?

(b) What would be the side of a cube of this volume, in terms of d?

5 Performance of materials

Data Avogadro constant $L\ (= N_A) = 6.02 \times 10^{23}\,\text{mol}^{-1}$
mass of proton = mass of neutron = $1.66 \times 10^{-27}\,\text{kg}$
$g = 9.81\,\text{N kg}^{-1}$

5.1 Materials in tension

5.1 Two tug-of-war teams each pull on a rope with a force of 5000 N. The rope is horizontal. What is the tension in the rope

(a) at its mid-point
(b) a quarter of the way along its length?

5.2 What is the tensile stress in

(a) one of the supporting cables of a suspension bridge which has a diameter of 40 mm and which pulls up on the roadway with a force of 30 kN
(b) a nylon fishing line of diameter 0.35 mm which a fish is pulling with a force of 15 N
(c) a tow rope of diameter 6.0 mm which is giving a car of mass 800 kg an acceleration of $0.40\,\text{m s}^{-2}$ (other horizontal forces on the car being negligible)?

5.3 What is the tensile strain when

(a) a copper wire of length 2.0 m has an extension of 0.10 mm
(b) a rubber band of length 50 mm is stretched to a length of 150 mm?

5.4 A mass of 6.0 kg is placed at the lower end of a vertical wire; the upper end is fixed to a ceiling. What is the tension in the wire

(a) at its lower end
(b) at its upper end?

What assumption do you have to make to be able to answer *(b)*?

5.5 The mass of 6.0 kg referred to in question 5.4 is now supported by a uniform rope which has a mass of 1.0 kg. What is the tension in the rope

(a) at its lower end
(b) at its upper end
(c) at its mid-point?

5.6 A rectangular strip of polythene is 0.10 mm thick and 10 mm wide (and several centimetres long). When it is stretched it deforms so that the ends still have their original width and thickness, but there is a central section which is still 0.10 mm thick but only 5.0 mm wide. If the force with which each end is being pulled is then 50 N, find the tensions and the tensile stresses in *(a)* the wide and *(b)* the narrow part of the strip.

5.7 *(a)* Two wires of the same material but of different lengths and diameters are joined end-to-end and hung vertically and support a load. Explain which of the following quantities must be the same for both wires: tensile force, tensile stress, strain, extension.
(b) Two other wires of the same material are now hung vertically side-by-side with their ends joined together; these wires have the same length but different diameters. Explain which of the following quantities must now be the same for both wires: tensile force, tensile stress, strain, extension.

5.8 Suppose a girl of mass 55 kg jumps off a wall, which is 3.0 m above the ground.

(a) What is her speed on reaching the ground?
(b) If she takes 25 ms to stop when she reaches the ground, what is the *average* force exerted on her by the ground?
(c) Estimate the *maximum* force exerted on her by the ground.
(d) The main bone in her leg is the tibia. If the minimum cross-sectional area of one of her tibia is $2.4 \times 10^{-4}\,\text{m}^2$, what is the maximum compressive stress in each of her tibia during the landing, assuming that the force is distributed equally between the two legs?
(e) This value is quite a large fraction of the maximum

compressive stress of bone (about 16×10^7 Pa). What would you advise her to do when she reaches the ground?

5.9 What is the minimum radius of a nylon fishing line which is required to lift a fish of mass 5.0 kg vertically at a steady speed? If the fish struggles (and therefore accelerates) the force may be increased by a factor of 10. What minimum radius is now required? (Ultimate tensile stress of nylon filament = 60 MPa.)

5.10 A lift of mass 3000 kg is supported by a steel cable of diameter 20 mm. The maximum acceleration of the lift is 2.5 m s^{-2}. Calculate

(a) the maximum tension in the cable

(b) the maximum stress in the cable

(c) the maximum strain in the cable (E for steel = 200 GPa).

5.11 A copper wire and a tungsten wire of the same length are hung vertically side by side. The cross-sectional areas of the wires are 0.10 mm^2 and 0.15 mm^2 respectively. Equal steadily increasing forces are applied to each wire. The Young modulus E and ultimate tensile stress σ_u are given in the table:

	E/GPa	σ_u/MPa
copper	130	220
tungsten	410	120

Which of the wires will ***(a)*** break first, ***(b)*** have the larger extension at that time?

5.12 A pressure vessel has a cylindrical cross-section of radius 100 mm and a lid which is fixed down by means of 8 steel bolts. The pressure in the vessel may rise to 2500 kPa above atmospheric pressure. The ultimate tensile stress of the steel is 100 MPa.

(a) What is the maximum total tension in the 8 bolts?

(b) What is the minimum diameter of each bolt?

(c) If bolts of the minimum diameter were used, and one bolt (perhaps because of a fault in the material) broke, what would happen?

(d) Calculate the minimum diameter of each bolt if the lid is to remain fastened if two bolts break?

5.13 The Young moduli of copper and aluminium are 130 GPa and 70 GPa respectively. Bars of the same length and diameter are made from each material. Explain which bar would be the easier to bend.

5.14 Two students A and B perform experiments on copper wire. Both wires have the same length, but B's has twice the diameter of A's. Explain which of the following statements are true:

(a) when they apply the same stress they get the same strain

(b) when they apply the same load A's strain is 4 times B's

(c) when they apply the same load A's extension is four times B's.

5.15 A copper wire of length 1.2 m and cross-sectional area 0.10 mm^2 is hung vertically; for copper E = 130 GPa. A steadily increasing force is applied to its lower end to stretch it. When the force has reached a value of 10 N

(a) what is the stress in the wire

(b) what is the strain in the wire

(c) what is the extension of the wire?

5.16 A garage intends to tow a lorry, using a steel wire. Explain to what extent the garage need consider each of the following factors: the Young modulus of the steel, the ultimate tensile stress of the steel, the length of the wire, the cross-sectional area of the wire.

5.17 Wires of many ductile materials form a neck just before they break, i.e. the wire narrows at one point of the wire. Explain, correctly using terms like force, stress and strain, why the wire must inevitably break where the neck first forms. Sketch stress-strain and force-extension graphs describing the behaviour of the wire before and after the neck forms, and explain why these graphs differ in shape.

5.18 Sketch stress-strain graphs for typical examples of the following: a ductile material, a brittle material, a glass, a polymer and a rubber.

5.19 Describe how you would measure the Young modulus for copper, assuming that copper wires of different diameters and lengths are available. You should say which instruments you would use to make the measurements, and explain which measurements would have the greatest uncertainty in them.

5.20 The table gives the corresponding values of load and extension when masses were hung on a wire of length 2.0 m and diameter 0.40 mm.

mass/kg	0	0.20	0.40	0.60	0.80	1.00	1.10	1.12
extension/mm	0	1.0	2.1	3.1	4.2	5.4	7.3	9.0

(a) Plot a graph of load (on the *y*–axis) against extension (on the *x*–axis).

(b) Hence calculate the Young modulus of the material.

(c) Estimate the probable final extension of the wire after the load of 1.12 kg is removed.

[Note: keep your answers for a later question.]

5.21 A successfully designed road bridge will be *strong*, *stiff* and *elastic*. Explain why it needs to have each of these properties, making clear the meaning of each of the words in italics.

5.22 Examine some pieces of plywood to see how the grain lies in adjacent layers. Explain why it is put together in this way. (The Young modulus of all woods is about ten times greater along the grain than across the grain.)

5.23 In many practical situations the bending of a piece of material (e.g. a concrete beam) produces tension in the material. Draw a diagram of a concrete beam which is supported only at its ends, and mark on it the parts of the beam which have tensile stress in them, and the parts which have compressive stress in them. The ultimate tensile stress of concrete is about ten times less than the ultimate compressive stress. Mark on your diagram where you would place steel reinforcing bars.

5.2 A molecular view

5.24 Explain, in terms of behaviour at the molecular level why

(a) the stiffness of rubber is low when the applied stress is low

(b) rubber becomes stiffer as the applied stress increases

(c) cooling rubber makes it stiffer.

5.25 Graphite is a form of carbon in which there are layers of atoms strongly held together in a hexagonal pattern. There are only weak forces between the layers. Explain why this molecular structure makes graphite suitable as a lubricant (and for pencil 'leads').

5.26 Draw a graph to show how the force which two atoms exert on each other varies with their separation. What features of your graph account for

(a) the elasticity of solid materials

(b) the fact that for small stresses solid materials obey Hooke's law for both tension and compression?

5.27 Suppose, for simplicity, that the copper atoms in a wire are arranged in a simple cubic lattice, the distance between the rows (and therefore also between the centres of atoms) being *d*. The Avogadro constant $L\,(= N_A) = 6.02 \times 10^{23}\,\text{mol}^{-1}$ and the r.a.m. of copper is 63.5.

(a) Calculate the mass of one copper atom.

(b) The density of copper is $8930\,\text{kg}\,\text{m}^{-3}$. Calculate the volume occupied by one copper atom and hence the value of *d*.

(c) If the wire has a cross-sectional area of $1.0\,\text{mm}^2$, how many atoms are there in any cross-section?

(d) If the whole wire is pulled with a force of 20 N, with what force does each atom pull its neighbour?

Now consider the wire as a whole:

(e) What is the stress in the wire?

(f) If *E* for copper is 130 GPa, what is the strain for the wire as a whole?

(g) Without further calculation write down the strain for a pair of atoms.

(h) Use your value of *d* to calculate how far each atom moves apart from its neighbour.

(i) What is the stiffness *k* (i.e. the ratio of force to extension) for a pair of atoms?

5.28 The diagram below shows how the potential energy E of a pair of atoms in a crystalline solid varies with their separation r for two elements A and B. Describe and explain how the following physical properties differ in the solid form of the two elements, assuming that they both have the same type of crystal structure:

(a) the size of the atoms
(b) the Young modulus
(c) the ultimate tensile stress.

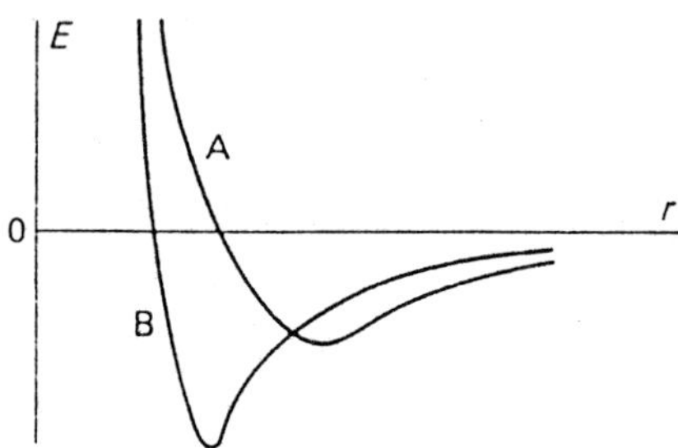

5.29 Suppose an element exists in crystalline form in which the atoms form a simple cubical arrangement, and that the atoms are separated by a distance d (i.e. their diameter is d). A particular block of this material has m atoms along one horizontal edge, n atoms along the other horizontal edge, and is l atoms high. Vertical forces P are applied at top and bottom to stretch the block.

(a) Calculate the tensile stress in the block.
(b) If the change in separation of the atoms, when the stress is applied, is d, write down an expression for the strain in the material.
(c) Write down an expression for the Young modulus E.
(d) What is the force which each atom exerts on its neighbour?
(e) Now think of the atoms as if they were held together by springs of stiffness k: use $F = kx$ and your answer to ***(d)*** to find an expression for the additional separation d when the block is stretched.
(f) Use your answers to ***(c)*** and ***(e)*** to find a relationship between E, k and d.
(g) If for copper $E = 130$ GPa and $d = 0.24$ nm, calculate k for the inter–atomic 'springs' of copper.
(h) What differences are there between the stretching of a real copper wire, and the stretching visualised in the model described above?

5.3 Failure mechanisms

5.30 *(a)* Draw a diagram to show the presence of a simple (edge or line) dislocation in a crystal.
(b) With a further diagram show how the dislocation may be made to move by applying a stress to the crystal.
(c) How does the presence of the dislocation make the material weaker?

5.31 Explain the following observations:

(a) Newly drawn glass fibres are stronger than fibres which have been handled a few times.
(b) Newly drawn glass fibres are sometimes treated by evaporating a layer of metal (a few atoms thick) on to their surfaces.
(c) If a glass fibre is bent into a semi-circular arc, it may break if touched on the outside of the arc (e.g. by another glass fibre) but not if it is touched on the inside.

5.32 Glass shatters but metals bend. Explain how the molecular structure of these materials accounts for their different behaviour.

5.4 Energy stored in stretched materials

5.33 The common 'expendable' springs often found in laboratories have a stiffness of $30\,\mathrm{N\,m^{-1}}$. What is the stiffness of

(a) three of these springs connected end-to-end?
(b) two of these springs connected side-by-side?
(c) a spring made by cutting one of these springs into two equal halves?

5.34 How much energy is stored in a steel wire of initial length 1.5 m and diameter 0.50 mm when it is pulled with a force of 45 N? Assume that Hooke's law is obeyed: E for the steel = 200 GPa.

5.35 A copper wire is stretched with a steadily increasing force: Hooke's law ceases to be obeyed when the force reaches 80 N. The extension is 5.0 mm when the force is 20 N. How much elastic potential energy is stored in the wire when the force is ***(a)*** 20 N, ***(b)*** 40 N, ***(c)*** 60 N?

5.36 Refer to question 5.20.

(a) Estimate the work which has been done in stretching the wire up to the point where it carries a load of 1.12 kg.

(b) Estimate how much of this energy has become internal energy, and how much is stored as elastic p.e. (and therefore recoverable).

5.37 The diagram below shows idealised forms of the force-extension curve for specimens (of the same shape) of high tensile steel and mild steel up to the point where each specimen breaks.

(a) Explain which is the *stronger* material.

(b) By considering, in each case, the area between the graph and the extension axis, find the work which must be done to break each specimen.

(c) Explain which is the *tougher* material.

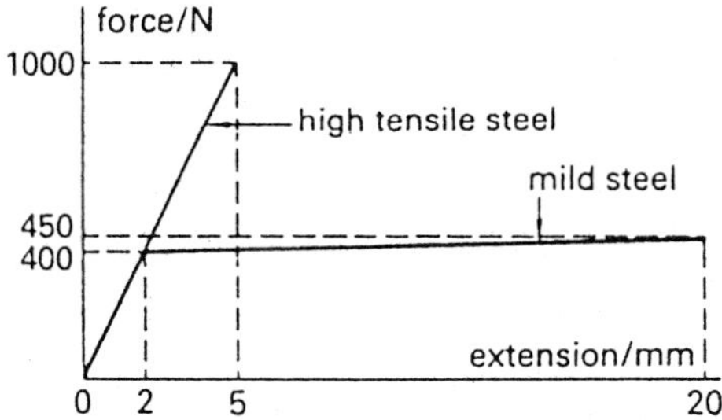

5.38 The diagram shows a force-extension graph for a length of rubber cord which is loaded and then unloaded.

(a) Which curve, the lower or the upper, describes the loading?

(b) What name is given to the fact that the two curves do not coincide?

(c) Explain how this effect causes heating in motor car tyres.

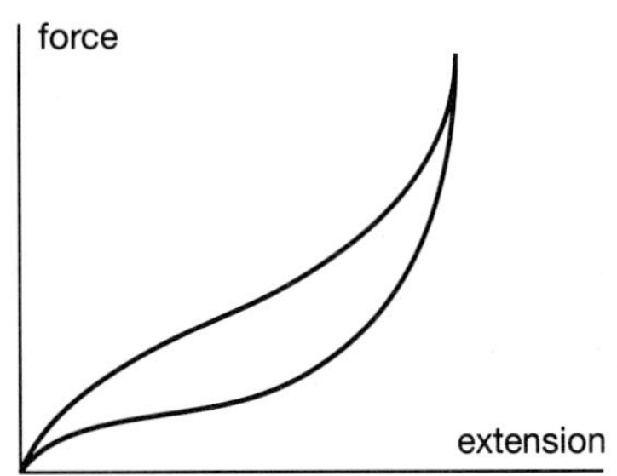

5.39 A rubber band was supported so that it hung vertically. The extensions of the band for various loads, when the band was loaded and unloaded, are shown in the table:

load/g	0	200	400	600	800	1000	1200
extension (when loading)/mm	0	70	245	410	530	600	650
extension (when unloading)/mm	0	190	550	610	630	650	650

(a) Plot a graph of load against extension for loading and unloading.

(b) Estimate the area beneath each graph and find (i) the work done in stretching the rubber band (ii) the internal energy generated in the rubber band.

5.40 Laboratory experiments involving the oscillations of masses supported by springs are common, but similar experiments using masses supported by rubber bands are rarely attempted.

(a) Why is this?

(b) Sketch a graph to show how the amplitude might vary with time for a mass supported by a rubber band.

5.41 Consider a wire of original length l, cross-sectional area A, which stretches by an amount x when pulled with a force F. The elastic limit is not exceeded.

(a) Show that the energy stored in it is $\frac{1}{2}Fx$, and that this may be written as $\frac{1}{2}kx^2$.

(b) Show that the energy stored in it per unit volume $= \frac{1}{2}$(stress)(strain).

5.42 A spring has a length of 0.25 m and stiffness 400 N m^{-1}.

(a) What is the tension in it when its length is 0.30 m?

(b) How much work is done on it when its length is increased from (i) 0.30 m to 0.35 m (ii) 0.35 m to 0.40 m?

6 Fluid behaviour

Data atmospheric pressure = 101 kPa
densities/kg m^{-3}: air 1.29, water 1000, mercury 13 600
$g = 9.81\,\text{N kg}^{-1}$

6.1 Pressure

6.1 A building brick has a mass of 2.8 kg and measures 230 mm by 110 mm by 75 mm. What pressure does it exert when stood, in turn, on each of its three faces on a horizontal surface?

6.2 Referring to the pressure which the objects produce when they are used correctly, explain the construction of *(a)* skis, *(b)* drawing pins, *(c)* football boots.

6.3 Estimate the average difference of pressure there must be between the upper and lower surfaces of the wings of an airliner, if the loaded plane has a mass of 350 tonnes and the wings have a total area of about 500 m^2.

6.4 If air were not easily compressible, the atmosphere would consist of a uniformly dense (1.29 kg m^{-3}) layer of air which ended abruptly at a certain height above the Earth's surface. What height would this be?

6.5 A U-tube manometer contains oil of density 780 kg m^{-3} and has one side (A) connected to a gas supply. The other side (B) is open to the atmosphere. The difference in levels in the tubes is 230 mm.

(a) On which side is the oil higher?

(b) What is the pressure of the gas supply, if the atmospheric pressure is 101.2 kPa?

(c) What is the advantage of using oil in the tube, rather than water?

6.6 The heart pumps blood through our arteries; as it does so the pressure rises and falls. The usual method of measuring the pressure of the blood is to wrap an air sack round the patient's upper arm and increase the pressure in it until the blood flow stops: this gives the maximum blood pressure (the systolic pressure), which is recorded as a difference in levels (in mm) on a mercury manometer; the air in the sack is then released until the blood begins to flow again, and the pressure (the diastolic pressure) when this happens is again recorded.

(a) If a patient has blood pressure measurements of '120/80', what are these pressures in kPa?

(b) Assuming that the density of blood is similar to that of water, estimate the systolic pressure in the arteries of this person's foot when he is sitting down.

6.7 An increase in pressure of 2.1 GPa reduces the volume of seawater, and hence increases the density, by 1%. The density of seawater is 1025 kg m^{-3}.

(a) What is the percentage increase in density at depths of (i) 100 m, (ii) 1000 m?

(b) The depth of the deepest ocean is 11 km. Is the

water significantly denser there than it is at the surface?

6.8 The simplest form of mercury barometer consists of a vertical tube closed at its upper end. Its lower end is beneath the surface of some mercury in an open dish, and the atmospheric pressure has pushed mercury up the tube. The space above the mercury in the tube is empty except, inevitably, for a very little mercury vapour. Explain

(*a*) why the internal diameter of the tube does not matter
(*b*) whether the bore of the tube need be uniform
(*c*) whether the tube need be exactly vertical
(*d*) whether in an accurate measurement of atmospheric pressure you would need to take account of (i) the thermal expansion of mercury, (ii) the thermal expansion of the glass, (iii) the pressure of water vapour in the air above the mercury in the dish
(*e*) how you would test for the presence of air above the mercury in the tube, without using another barometer.

6.9 The type of pump which used to be seen in the streets of towns and villages to raise water from a well is called a lift pump. The diagram shows the essential features: V_1 and V_2 are valves which open upwards only. Suppose that there is some water in the cylinder, as shown.

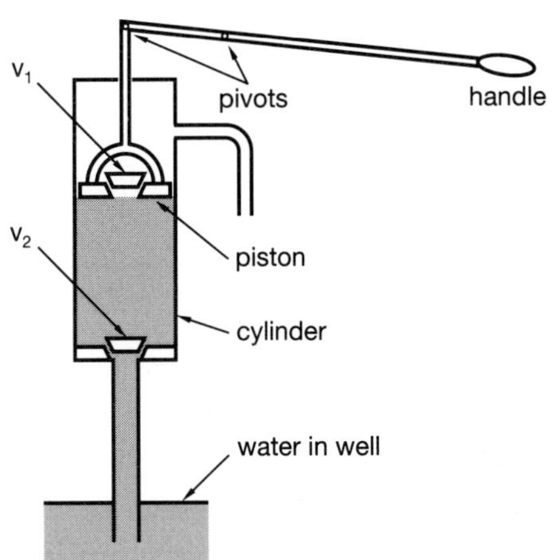

(*a*) Explain what happens when the handle is pulled up.
(*b*) Explain what happens when the handle is then pushed down.
(*c*) Explain whether there is any limit to the depth from which it can draw up water.

6.10 The figure shows two pistons P and Q which fit into tubes of cross-sectional area $4.0 \times 10^{-4}\,m^2$ and $1.0 \times 10^{-2}\,m^2$ respectively. The space between the pistons is completely filled with a liquid which may be assumed to be incompressible.

(*a*) If P is pushed with a force of 20 N, and Q is held stationary, what is the increase in pressure in the liquid?
(*b*) What force must be exerted on Q to keep it stationary?
(*c*) It is clear that with this arrangement a small push on one part of the machine can cause the machine to exert a much larger push elsewhere. Are we getting 'something for nothing'?
(*d*) State one advantage this type of machine will have over other machines which consist entirely of solid moving parts.

6.11 Oak has a density of about $700\,kg\,m^{-3}$. Draw a free-body diagram for a piece of oak floating in water, and explain fully why 0.7 of its total volume is submerged.

6.12 A mixture of ice and water is poured into a beaker until it is completely full. Explain whether there will be an overflow when the ice melts.

6.13 The airship R101 (which burst into flames when the hydrogen in it ignited) had a volume of $1.38 \times 10^5\,m^3$. Using data given above, calculate *(a)* the upthrust on it

(b) the weight of the gas in it if it is filled with (i) hydrogen (density $0.0880\,kg\,m^{-3}$), (ii) helium (density $0.176\,kg\,m^{-3}$)

(c) the differences between the upthrust and these two weights.

6.14 *(a)* What is the Archimedean upthrust on a body of volume $0.20\,m^3$ when it is suspended, completely immersed, in a tank of water?

(b) Why is the upthrust exactly the same when it rests on the bottom of the tank?

6.15 *(a)* In a misguided attempt to measure the density of air a student found the mass of a deflated balloon, blew it up (making sure that the air in it was at atmospheric pressure) and found the new mass. He found that the two masses were identical. Why was this?

The masses of a table tennis ball and a squash ball were found by placing them on a top pan balance. The readings were 2.39 g and 23.82 g respectively, and the balls' diameters were 38.6 mm and 40.6 mm.

(b) Using data given above, calculate (i) the upthrust of the air on the balls, and (ii) their true masses.

(c) In each case what is the percentage error in the mass?

(d) In what type of situation is it necessary to consider the upthrust of the air on a body?

6.16 *(a)* A piece of cork of volume $2.0 \times 10^{-5}\,m^3$ and density $250\,kg\,m^{-3}$ is kept submerged below the surface of some water in a tank by means of a thread of negligible mass. Draw a free-body force diagram for the cork and find the tension in the thread.

(b) What would be the tension in the thread if the tank were (i) falling freely, (ii) on the surface of the Moon (where $g = 1.6\,N\,kg^{-1}$)?

6.17 A stone is supported from a spring balance, and is gently lowered into a beaker of water resting on a top pan balance until the stone rests on the bottom of the beaker, completely immersed.

(a) Draw free-body force diagrams for the stone when it is (i) suspended in air, (ii) suspended in the water, (iii) resting on the bottom of the beaker.

(b) Draw free-body diagrams for the water when the stone is in each of these positions.

(c) Describe what happens to the readings of the spring balance and top pan balance during the process.

(d) The experiment is repeated with the beaker replaced by a Eureka can (i.e. a can fitted with a spout near its top). Initially the water is level with the lip of the spout so that as soon as the stone is lowered into the can, water begins to overflow clear of the top pan balance. Describe what happens to the reading on the top pan balance as the stone is lowered into the can.

6.18 An aqueduct is a bridge which carries a canal or a river. Is the downward force on the aqueduct greater when a barge is passing over it? Explain.

6.2 Flow

6.19 A horizontal pipe A of cross-sectional area $4.0 \times 10^{-4}\,m^2$ narrows into a second horizontal pipe B of cross-sectional area $1.0 \times 10^{-4}\,m^2$. The pipes are full of water, and the speed of the water in pipe A is $0.20\,m\,s^{-1}$.

(a) What is the speed in pipe B?

(b) What is the rate of flow of volume in (i) pipe A, (ii) pipe B?

(c) Explain how the water in pipe B has been able to be accelerated.

6.20 Suppose your kitchen tap delivers $500\,cm^3$ of water in 2.5 s, and at the tap the diameter of the stream of water is 1.2 cm.

(a) At what speed does the water emerge from the tap?

(b) How fast is it moving when it has fallen 0.20 m?

(c) Calculate the diameter of the stream of water when it has fallen that distance.

6.21 Photographs of wind surfers often show the sail with a curved shape, but the wind is blowing across the surface of the sail, not into it, as might have been expected: see the diagram. Explain why the sail is curved in this way.

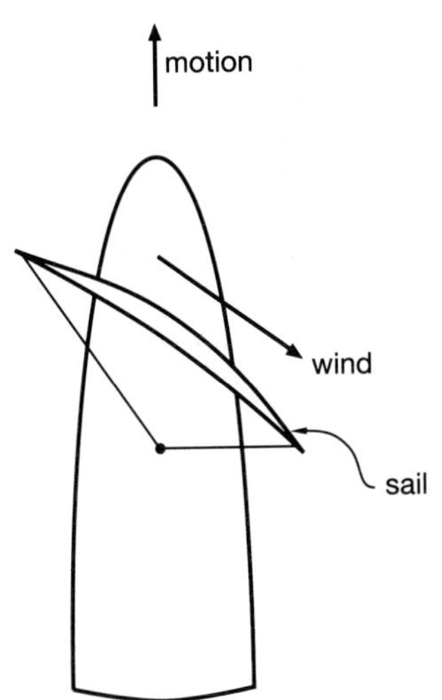

6.22 A table tennis ball may be supported on an upward jet of air produced by a hair drier. The molecules of air which hit the ball are pushed downwards, and by Newton's third law, the ball is pushed upwards. But why does the ball return to the centre of the jet if it is pushed sideways slightly?

6.23 Explain why

(a) a car being overtaken by a long high-sided lorry may be pulled towards the lorry

(b) a strong wind blowing along the outside of a garden wall may cause the wall to fall forwards.

6.24 When you stir a cup of coffee the circular motion of the coffee ceases after a short time. Why is this?

6.25 Why is a pump needed to keep liquid flowing along a horizontal pipe?

6.26 A small ball bearing may be released at the top of a tall jar containing a transparent viscous liquid such as glycerol. Describe how you would perform an experiment to check whether the ball bearing reaches a terminal speed. If so, describe how the terminal speed could be measured.

7 Electric currents, energy and power

Data electronic charge $e = 1.60 \times 10^{-19}$C

Electric current

7.1 What is the average electric current in a wire when a charge of 150C passes in 30s?

7.2 The current in a small torch bulb is 0.20A. What is the total electric charge which passes through a point in the circuit in 12 minutes? How many electrons pass through this point in this time?

7.3 In the circuit shown in the diagram below the bulbs are identical. The current at P is 0.20A. What are the currents at ***(a)*** Q, ***(b)*** R, ***(c)*** S, ***(d)*** T?

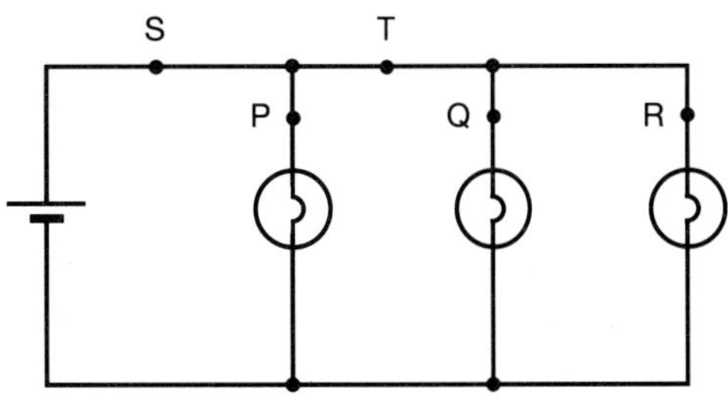

7.4 In the circuit the three bulbs are identical and reach full brightness when the current is 0.20 A. Bulb B is observed to be at full brightness. Which (if any) of the other bulbs will be at full brightness, and what is the current in each of them?

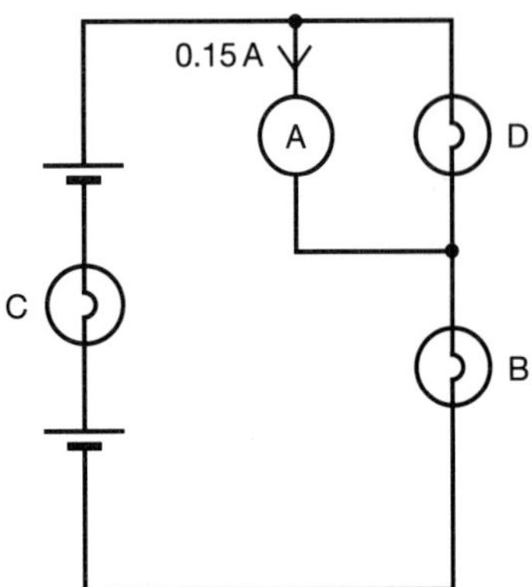

7.5 A new electric cell was joined in series with a bulb and an ammeter. The initial current was 0.30 A. At subsequent intervals of 1 hour the readings on the ammeter were: 0.27 A, 0.27 A, 0.26 A, 0.25 A, 0.23 A, 0.19 A, 0.09 A, 0.03 A, and at 9 hours the ammeter reading had become negligibly small.

(a) Plot a graph of current against time.

(b) What does the area under the graph represent?

(c) How much electric charge passes through the circuit when a current of 0.10 A passes for 1 hour?

(d) What is the total electric charge which passes through the cell in the 9 hours?

7.6 In a gas discharge tube containing hydrogen the current is carried partly by (positive) hydrogen ions and partly by electrons. An ammeter in series with the tube indicates a current of 1.5 mA. If the rate of passage of electrons past a particular point in the tube is $6.0 \times 10^{15}\,s^{-1}$, find the number of hydrogen ions passing the same point per second.

7.2 Currents in solids

7.7 Some copper fuse wire has a diameter of 0.22 mm and is designed to carry currents of up to 5.0 A. If there are 1.0×10^{29} electrons per m^3 of copper, what is the mean drift speed of the electrons in the fuse wire when it carries a current of 5.0 A?

7.8 A wire carrying an electric current will overheat if there is too large a current: the accepted value for the maximum allowable current in a copper wire is 1.2×10^7 A per square metre of cross-section of the wire. If there are 1.0×10^{29} electrons per m^3 of copper, calculate the mean drift speed of the electrons in the wire when the current reaches this value.

7.9 Two copper wires of diameter 2.00 mm and 1.00 mm are joined end-to-end. What is the ratio of the average drift speeds of the electrons in the two wires when a steady current passes through them? In which wire are the electrons moving faster?

7.10 A copper wire joins a car battery to one of the tail lamps and carries a current of 1.8 A. The wire has a cross-sectional area of 1.0 mm^2 and is 6.0 m long. If there are 1.0×10^{29} electrons per m^3 of copper, calculate how long it takes an electron to travel along this length of wire.

7.3 Electrical energy

7.11 A cell has an e.m.f. of 1.50 V.

(a) How much energy is converted when an electric charge of 20 C passes through the cell?

(b) What form of energy is there less of afterwards, and what forms of energy is there more of?

7.12 A battery of e.m.f. 6.0 V passes a current of 0.30 A through a torch bulb for 5 minutes. How much energy is converted by the cell?

7.13 A lead-acid cell of e.m.f. 2.0 V can drive a current of 0.50 A round a circuit for 10 hours.

(a) How much chemical energy is converted to electrical energy in this time?

(b) How long would you expect the same cell to maintain a current of 0.20 A?

7.14 *(a)* It is estimated that the average electric charge transported in a lightning flash is 30 C. If the energy converted is 2.4×10^{10} J, what is the p.d. between the cloud and the ground?

(b) In a typical thunderstorm lightning flashes strike the ground at intervals of about 3 minutes. Over the whole surface of the Earth the total current carried in this way between the atmosphere and the ground averages 1800 A. Estimate the average number of thunderstorms taking place at any instant over the whole Earth.

7.15 A battery has an e.m.f. of 3.0 V and is connected to a bulb. The current in the bulb is 0.30 A and the potential difference between its ends is 2.8 V.

(a) In 5 minutes how much chemical energy is converted to electrical energy in the battery?

(b) In the same time how much electrical energy is converted into internal energy in the bulb?

(c) How do you account for the fact that these two answers are not the same?

7.16 The e.m.f. of a small cell is 1.5 V and it can pass a current of 20 mA for 10 hours before its chemical energy is completely converted.

(a) How much chemical energy does the cell have?

(b) How much energy would be converted if the same total charge were passed by three such cells connected (i) in series, (ii) in parallel?

7.17 In the circuit shown in the figure a voltmeter reads 1.46 V when connected across the cell and 0.67 V when connected across the bulb. If the wires have negligible resistance,

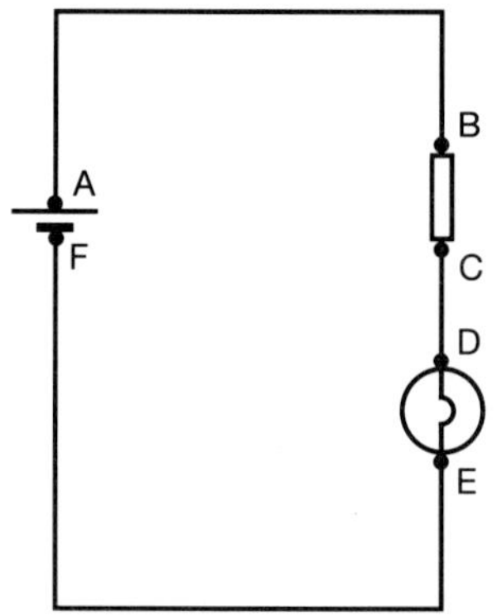

(a) what will the voltmeter read when connected between (i) A and B, (ii) C and D, (iii) E and F?

(b) what will the voltmeter read when connected across the resistor?

7.18 If point F in the circuit (see previous figure) is earthed, i.e. its potential is taken to be zero

(a) what are the potentials of the other labelled points?

(b) where are the points which have potentials of (i) 1.30 V, (ii) 0.70 V, (iii) 0.64 V?

7.19 Draw circuit diagrams to show two identical bulbs connected to a 6.0 V battery so that

(a) each has a p.d. of 3.0 V across it

(b) each has a p.d. of 6.0 V across it.

7.20 The circuit below shows a bulb, a resistor and a motor connected in parallel across a battery. A voltmeter connected across the battery reads 2.89 V. What does it read when connected across (a) the bulb, (b) the resistor, (c) the motor?

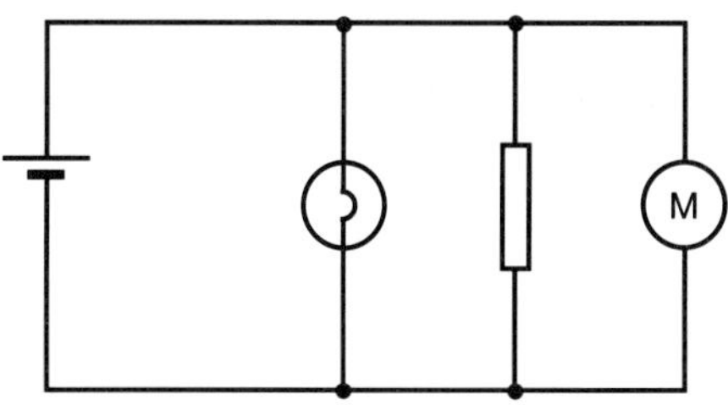

7.21 In the circuit below the p.d. across the battery is 5.86 V, and the p.d. across the bulb is 2.45 V. If the

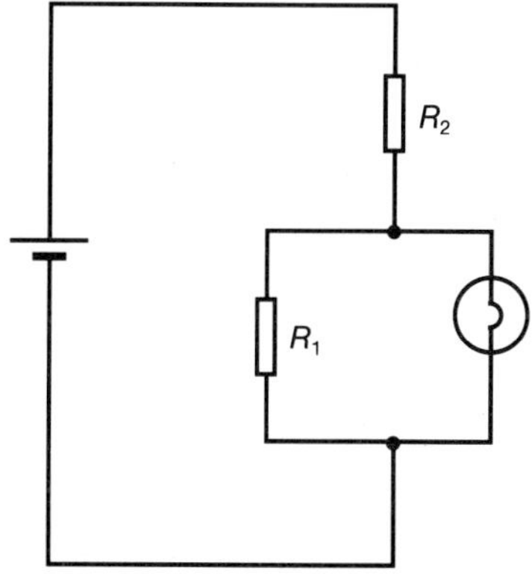

wires have negligible resistance, what is the p.d. across

(a) resistor R_1

(b) resistor R_2?

7.22 Five resistors are connected to a cell as shown below. The p.d.s across R_1 and R_2 are 0.60 V and 0.75 V respectively, and the other three resistors are identical. The potential at point A is zero.

(a) What are the potentials at (i) point G, (ii) point E?

(b) State the p.d. between (i) B and E, (ii) B and F, in each case saying which point has the higher potential.

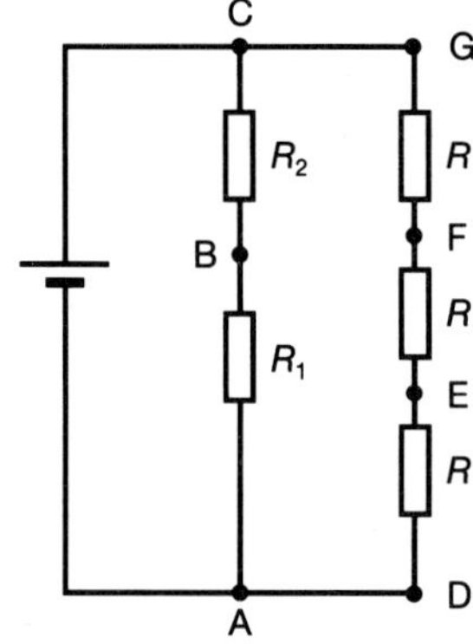

7.23 Two identical cells of e.m.f. 1.50 V are connected to two identical resistors in the circuits shown. In each case point C is earthed.

(a) What are the potentials at A, B and D in circuit (i) and in circuit (ii)?

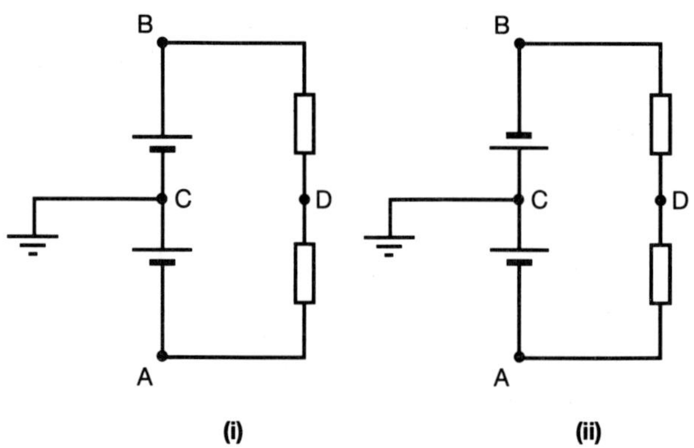

(b) In each case what would be the effect of connecting a wire between C and D?

7.24 The figure shows a circuit in which a 1.0 Ω resistor and a 2.0 Ω are connected in series with a battery which provides a p.d. of 3.0 V.

(a) If point C is earthed, what are the potentials at A and B, and what is the current in the 1.0 Ω resistor?

(b) If point A is earthed, what are the potentials at B and C, and what is the current in the 1.0 Ω resistor?

(c) If point B is earthed, what are the potentials at A and C, and what is the current in the 1.0 Ω resistor?

(d) If points A and B are both earthed, what is the potential at C, and what are the currents in the two resistors?

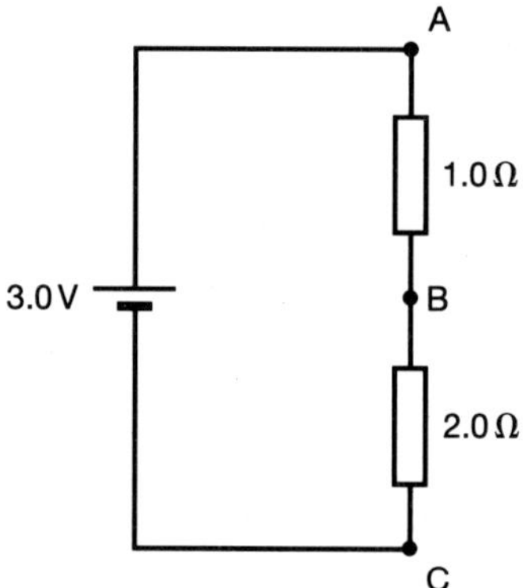

7.25 *(a)* How many nicad cells each of e.m.f. 1.2 V are needed to provide a 6.0 V battery for a calculator?

(b) In fitting these cells the user puts one of the cells in the wrong way round by mistake. What is the e.m.f. of the battery now?

7.4 Electrical power

7.26 A lead acid battery of e.m.f. 12.0 V is supplying a current of 10 A to some car headlamps. What is the rate of conversion of chemical energy to electrical energy?

7.27 An electric toaster is labelled 800 W. How much

energy is converted in it in 3 minutes?

7.28 The current in a small immersion heater is 3.8 A and the p.d. across its terminals is 11.9 V. How much electrical energy is converted to internal energy in 20 minutes?

7.29 An electric light bulb is labelled 100 W and is designed to be used with a p.d. of 240 V. What current flows in it, and how much energy is converted in 1 hour?

7.30 The energy of a single flash of light from a stroboscopic lamp is 0.60 J. The p.d. across the bulb is 240 V.

(a) How much charge passes through the lamp during the flash?

(b) If the flash lasts for 10 μs, what is the average current?

(c) What is the average power?

7.31 An electric motor is being used to raise gravel through a height of 30 m from a quarry at a rate of 500 kg per minute.

(a) What is the rate at which the motor does work on the load?

(b) If the efficiency of the motor is 70%, what is the electrical power input to the motor?

(c) If the p.d. across the motor is 400 V, what is the current in the motor?

7.32 A power station generates electrical energy at a p.d. of 25 kV and an average rate of 500 MW.

(a) What is the current leaving the power station?

(b) How much energy is generated in one day?

(c) If the efficiency of the power station is 40%, how much internal energy is delivered to the surroundings in one day?

8 Electrical resistance

Data electronic charge $e = 1.60 \times 10^{-19}$ C
resistivities/$10^{-8}\,\Omega$ m: copper 1.7, aluminium 3.2, steel 14, nichrome 130, carbon 4000

8.1 Resistance

8.1 There is a current of 0.20 A in a wire when the potential difference between its ends is 5.0 V. What is its resistance?

8.2 The opposite faces of a sheet of polythene are covered with metal foil. When the potential difference between the two layers of foil is 12 V, the current through the polythene is 1.4×10^{-10} A. What is the resistance of the polythene?

8.3 What potential difference must be applied to a resistance of 10 MΩ to drive a current of 5.0 μA through it?

8.4 The current I in a resistor was measured for various values of the applied p.d. V and the values shown below were obtained:

V/V	50	100	200	300	400
I/mA	0.60	1.15	2.20	3.15	4.04

(a) Plot a graph of I against V.

(b) Was the resistor made from a metal or from carbon?

(c) What was the resistance of the resistor at an applied p.d. of 200 V?

(d) Estimate the value of the resistor (i) for an applied p.d. of 400 V, (ii) a very small applied p.d.

8.5 A rheostat consists of resistance wire uniformly wound on a former of length 300 mm: the resistance of the wire is 100 Ω. Initially the slider is at the centre of the rheostat (so that its resistance is 50 Ω, and the rheostat is connected in series with a battery which provides a constant p.d. of 6.0 V across the rheostat.

(a) What is the current in the circuit initially?

(b) The slider is now moved 30 mm to reduce the resistance of the rheostat. What is now the resistance of the rheostat, and the current in the circuit?

(c) The slider is now moved 30 mm on three more occasions, each time in the direction which reduces the resistance. What are the new resistances, and the currents?

(d) Comment on the suitability of the rheostat for adjusting the current in the circuit.

8.6 A lamp bulb is connected to the mains supply by twin cable, each wire of which has a resistance of 0.025 Ω per metre. If the length of the cable between the supply and the lamp is 8.0 m, what is

(a) the resistance of each wire

(b) the p.d. between the ends of each wire when the current in it is 0.60 A

(c) the power then in the cable?

8.7 Two lamp bulbs are labelled '240 V 100 W' and '240 V 60 W'. What do these markings mean, and what is the current in each of them when it is working normally?

8.8 The heating element of one kind of toaster contains of a ribbon of nichrome wire which is wound round an insulating support. A girl finds that it is broken and decides to mend it by twisting the two broken ends together (thus making the ribbon shorter). Explain whether the power of the toaster will be larger or smaller than before.

8.9 When the current through a resistor is 2.0 A its power is 10 W. Assuming that the resistance is unchanged, what does the power become when the current is increased to 6.0 A?

8.10 Two resistors R_1 and R_2, of constant resistance 10 Ω and 15 Ω, respectively, are each in turn connected to a power supply which provides a constant p.d. of 6.0 V. Which resistor provides the greater power, and what is that power?

8.11 Two resistors, of resistance 3.3 Ω and 4.7 Ω are connected first in series and then in parallel to a power supply which provides a constant p.d. of 6.0 V. Which resistor has the greater power, and what is that power, when the resistors are *(a)* in series, *(b)* in parallel?

8.12 A car headlamp bulb has a power of 60 W when it is connected to a potential difference of 12 V.

(a) What is the resistance of the filament?

(b) If its resistance remained constant, calculate the power if a p.d. of 6.0 V were connected across it?

(c) Its resistance will not remain constant: how will it change, and will the power of the bulb be larger or smaller than the power calculated in *(b)*?

8.13 The resistance of some wire is 14 Ω per metre. What length is needed to provide a power of 20 W when a p.d. of 12 V is available?

8.14 *(a)* What is the resistance, at full brightness, of (i) a 240 V 60 W bulb, (ii) a 12 V 60 W bulb?

(b) How many 12 V bulbs must be connected in series across a 240 V supply if each is to work at full brightness?

(c) What will happen if two 240 V 60 W bulbs are connected in series across a 240 V supply?

(d) What will happen if a 240 V 60 W bulb and a 12 V 60 W bulb are connected in series across a 240 V supply?

8.15 A factory (represented by the resistor R in the figure below) is supplied with electrical power from a generator through two long cables AB and CD each of resistance 3.0 Ω. The generator (connected at A and D) delivers 200 kW of electrical power at a potential difference of 6.0 kV.

(a) Calculate the current delivered by the generator.

(b) If D is earthed, calculate potentials at A, B and C.

(c) What is the potential difference between B and C?

(d) Calculate the rate at which electrical energy is converted to internal energy in the pair of cables.

(e) What percentage of the power is lost as internal energy?

(f) If a generator delivering the same power at 2.0 kV had been used instead, what would have been the percentage power loss in the cables? Comment on the result.

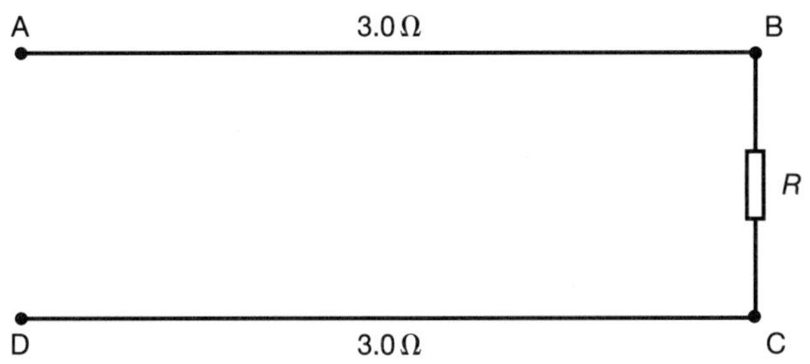

8.16 Resistances of 10 Ω and 15 Ω are joined ***(a)*** in series, ***(b)*** in parallel. What is the total resistance in each case?

8.17 Calculate the combined resistance of each of the arrangements of standard resistors shown in the figure below.

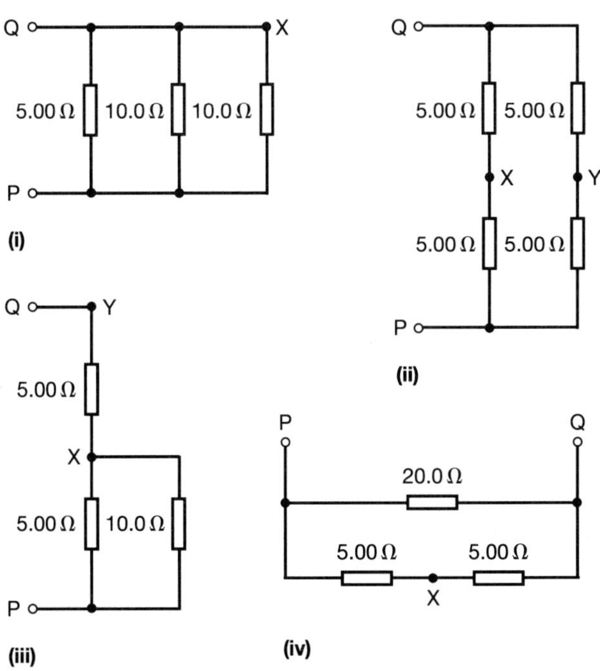

8.18 Each of the arrangements of resistors in question *8.17* is joined to a power supply, so that P is earthed and Q is at a potential of 6.0 V.

(a) What is the potential at X in each case?

(b) In (ii) and (iii) what are the potential differences between X and Y?

8.19 A connecting lead of length 1.0 m used in a laboratory consists of 55 strands of wire. If each strand has a resistance of 2.3 Ω, what is the resistance of the complete wire?

8.20 What is the total resistance when ***(a)*** two, ***(b)*** ten, 10 Ω resistors are connected in parallel?

8.21 In the two arrangements ***(a)*** and ***(b)*** of resistors shown in the figure, is the combined resistance about 100 Ω, between 1 Ω and 100 Ω, or less than 1 Ω? What general rule could you state for calculating a rough value of the resistance of resistors connected in parallel?

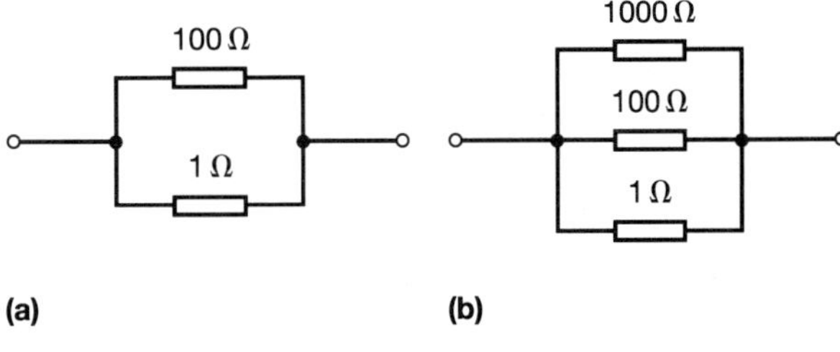

8.22 Calculate the combined resistance of each of the arrangements of resistors in the figure for question *8.21*.

8.23 What is the smallest number of resistors you need to provide a resistance of

(a) 5 Ω, given a supply of 3 Ω resistors

(b) 7 Ω, given a supply of 4 Ω resistors?

In each case draw a diagram to show how you would connect them.

8.24 The circular loop of wire shown in the figure below has a resistance round the loop of 10 Ω.

(a) Calculate the resistance between the point P and each of the other equally spaced points on the loop.

(b) Plot a graph of the resistance between P and Q for the full range of possible values of the distance l from P to Q.

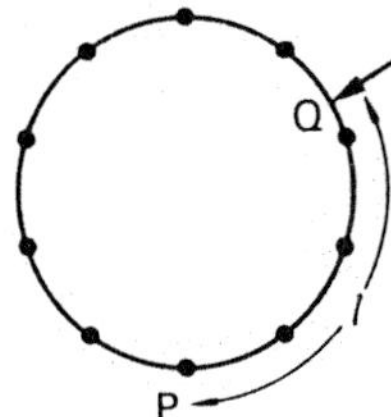

8.25 The diagram below shows a resistor used as a shunt for an ammeter. The resistor consists of a metal film mounted on a plastic base. It is difficult to make the film of exactly the required thickness, so the resistance is adjusted by cutting through the film at points like A, B etc. Explain whether this will make the resistance larger or smaller.

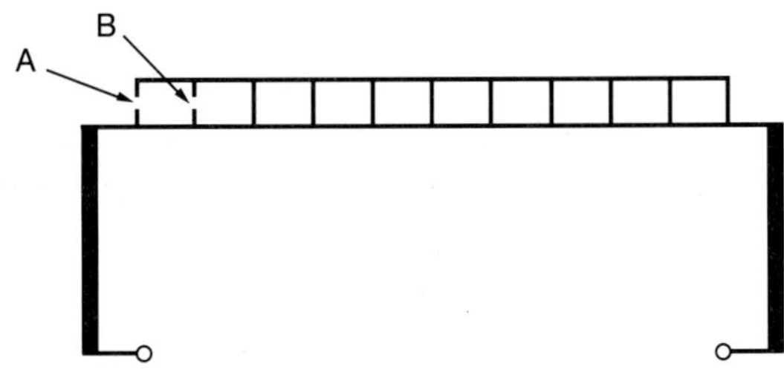

8.26 What is the current in each of the resistors shown in the diagram below?

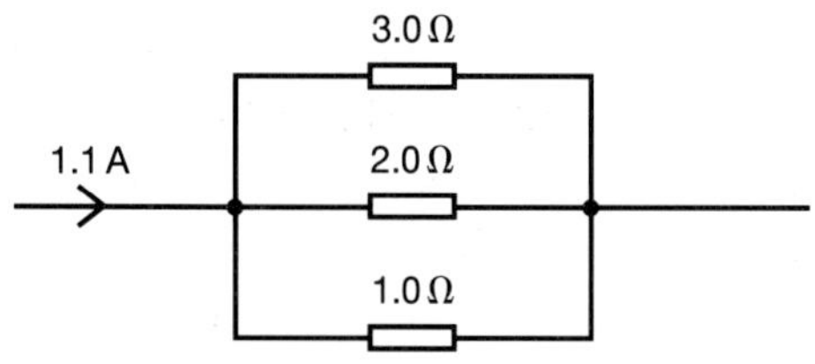

8.27 A tungsten filament bulb, and a carbon filament bulb, are connected (separately) to a variable power supply, and the current measured as the p.d. is varied.

The table shows the readings obtained:

V/V	0	50	100	150	200	250
tungsten I/A	0	0.11	0.16	0.20	0.23	0.26
carbon I/A	0	0.07	0.16	0.26	0.37	0.51

(a) Plot graphs to show how current varies with p.d. for each of these filaments.

(b) What is the power of each lamp when the p.d. across it is 240 V?

(c) When the p.d. is set at 200 V, what is the current drawn from the supply if the bulbs are connected (i) in parallel, (ii) in series, with the supply?

(d) What p.d. is needed to draw a current of 0.25 A from the supply if the bulbs are connected in series?

(e) What p.d. is needed to draw a current of 0.50 A from the supply if the bulbs are connected in parallel with the supply?

8.28 The following readings are obtained for the p.d. across a silicon diode and the current in it:

V/V	−0.40	0	0.40	0.50	0.55	0.60	0.63	0.65	0.68	0.70	0.72	0.75
I/mA	0	0	0	1	3.5	9	18	29	52	73	130	210

(a) Plot the characteristic of the diode, i.e. a graph of I against V.

(b) What is the resistance of the diode when the p.d. across it is (i) 0.25 V, (ii) 0.64 V, (iii) 0.74 V?

(c) Estimate the resistance of the diode when the p.d. across it is 10 V.

8.29 A silicon diode is connected to two resistors as shown in the figure.

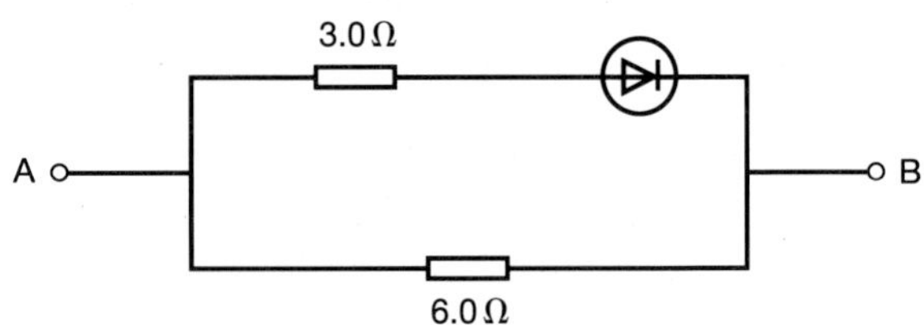

(*a*) First assume that the silicon diode has zero resistance in the forward direction, and infinite resistance in the reverse direction. The p.d. between A and B is varied from −3.0 V to +3.0 V. Draw a graph to show how the current between A and B varies with p.d.

(*b*) Now assume that the diode behaves as a 'real' diode, with the performance shown in the table for question 8.28. Sketch (no detailed calculations required) on the same axes how the current between A and B varies with p.d.

8.2 Resistivity

8.30 A wire has a resistance of 6.0 Ω. It is then doubled back on itself. What now is the resistance between the ends of the doubled wire?

8.31 One of the copper wires in a three-core power cable has a cross-sectional area of $0.50\,\text{mm}^2$. Using data given above, find the resistance of a 10 m length of this wire.

8.32 A power cable (for the grid system) consists of six aluminium wires enclosing a central steel wire. The purpose of the steel wire is to give the cable strength: the current in it may be assumed to be negligible. If each of the aluminium wires has a diameter of 4.0 mm, calculate, using data given above

(*a*) the cross-sectional area of each wire, in mm^2

(*b*) the resistance of 1.0 km of one of the aluminium wires

(*c*) the resistance per km of the whole cable.

8.33 The heating element of an electric toaster consists of a nichrome ribbon which is 1.0 mm wide and 0.050 mm thick. Using data given above, find the length of ribbon needed to provide a power of 800 W when the element is connected to a p.d. of 240 V.

8.34 A slice of silicon which measures 30 mm by 30 mm and which is 0.50 mm thick has conducting strips fitted to two opposite edges AB and CD.

(*a*) If the resistivity of silicon is $4.0 \times 10^3\ \Omega\,\text{m}$, calculate the resistance of the sheet measured between AB and CD.

(*b*) What would be the resistance of a similar sheet, measuring 15 mm by 15 mm, of the same thickness?

8.35 The resistance of the heating element of an electric fire is measured at 0°C and found to be 50 Ω. When it is connected to a 240 V supply the power delivered is 1.0 kW. If the temperature coefficient of resistance of the metal is $1.7 \times 10^{-4}\,\text{K}^{-1}$, calculate the temperature of the heating element when it is working normally.

8.36 Draw a circuit diagram to show how you would use a power supply, a rheostat, an ammeter and a voltmeter to investigate how the current *I* through a 12 V bulb varies with the applied potential difference *V*. The set of readings obtained in such an experiment is shown below:

V/V	0.2	0.5	1.0	2.0	4.0	6.0	8.0	10.0	12.0
I/A	0.10	0.17	0.22	0.26	0.32	0.37	0.42	0.46	0.50

Plot the characteristic of the bulb, i.e. a graph of *I* against *V*. (Keep your graph for question 8.53 later.)

(*a*) Deduce from your graph the resistance of the bulb at room temperature.

(*b*) By what factor does the resistance increase between room temperature (assume this to be about 300 K) and the maximum temperature (assume this to be 2400 K)?

(*c*) Is this in agreement with the observation that for some metals resistivity is proportional to kelvin temperature?

8.37 The resistance of the tungsten filament of an electric lamp is found to be 27 Ω at 0°C. If the average temperature coefficient of resistance for tungsten is $5.6 \times 10^{-3}\,\text{K}^{-1}$, calculate

(*a*) the resistance of the filament at its working temperature of 2400 K

(*b*) the ratio (power of lamp when first switched on)/(power of lamp at working temperature)

8.38 Explain why the power of a filament lamp falls during the first few milliseconds after it is switched on.

8.3 Circuit calculations

8.39 A circuit contains a battery, a bulb, a 15 Ω resistor, and an ammeter in series. The ammeter reads 0.23 A. A voltmeter connected across the battery terminals reads 5.7 V: when connected across the bulb it reads 2.4 V.

(a) What is the p.d. across the bulb?
(b) What is the resistance of the bulb?

8.40 A catalogue states that when a particular light-emitting diode is used with a 5.0 V supply a 270 Ω resistor must be connected in series with it to limit the current to 10 mA. Calculate

(a) the p.d. across the resistor
(b) the resistance of the LED in these conditions.

8.41 A power supply which provides a constant p.d. of 6.0 V is connected in series with a resistor of constant resistance 100 Ω and a thermistor. The resistance of the thermistor is 380 Ω at 25°C but falls to 28 Ω at 100°C. Calculate the p.d. between the ends of the resistor at *(a)* 25°C and *(b)* 100°C.

8.42 The figure below shows a circuit in which a battery provides a p.d. of 2.9 V. The p.d. across the 22 Ω resistor is found to be 1.2 V.

(a) What is the p.d. across (i) bulb A, (ii) bulb B?
(b) What is the current in the resistor?
(c) If the bulbs have the same resistance, how many times greater is the current in B than the current in A (leave your answer as a fraction)?
(d) What is the current in the battery?

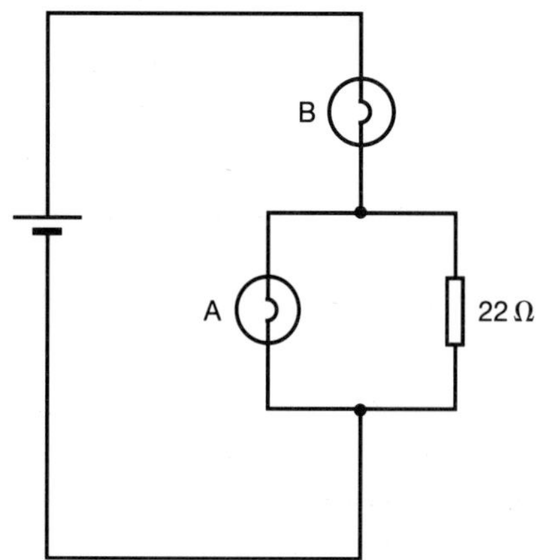

8.43 In the circuit in the previous figure the fixed resistor is replaced by a rheostat of maximum resistance 22 Ω. Explain what happens to the brightness of each bulb as the resistance of the rheostat is reduced from 22 Ω to zero.

8.44 Three resistors, of resistance 4.7 Ω, 10 Ω and 15 Ω respectively, are connected to a battery as shown in the figure below. A voltmeter connected across the battery reads 5.7 V.

(a) Calculate the resistance of the circuit between B and C.
(b) Calculate the p.d. between (i) A and B, (ii) B and C.
(c) Calculate the current through (i) the 4.7 Ω resistor, (ii) the 10 Ω resistor, (iii) the 15 Ω resistor.

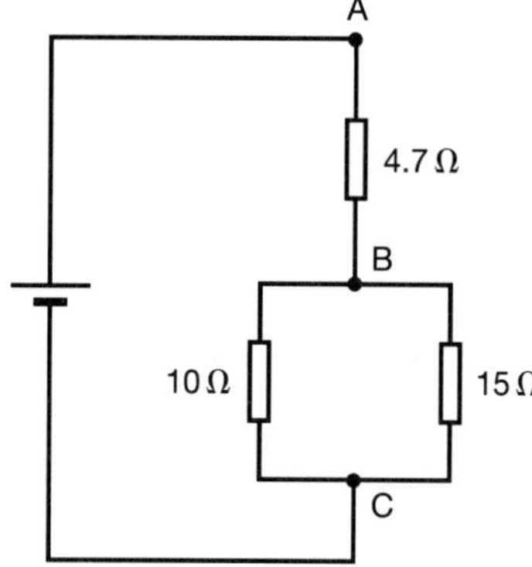

8.45 A bulb which is labelled 2.5 V 0.2 A is connected in series with a rheostat of maximum resistance 50 Ω and a battery. Assume that the battery has a constant p.d. of 3.0 V between its terminals.

(a) Calculate the resistance of the bulb when it is working normally.
(b) Assume that the resistance of the bulb is constant, and calculate the minimum current which may be obtained by adjusting the rheostat.
(c) The resistance of the bulb is not constant: is the actual minimum current larger or smaller than your answer to *(b)*?

8.46 A power supply which provides a constant p.d. of 12 V is connected across two resistors R_1 and R_1 in series. Calculate the p.d. across each when

(a) $R_1 = 120\,\Omega$, $R_2 = 120\,\Omega$

(b) $R_1 = 120\,\Omega$, $R_2 = 470\,\Omega$

(c) $R_1 = 680\,\Omega$, $R_2 = 470\,\Omega$

(d) $R_1 = 1.5\,\text{k}\Omega$, $R_2 = 470\,\Omega$.

8.47 If the negative terminal of the power supply in the previous question is connected to R_1 and earthed, what is the potential of the point between the resistors for each of the four cases?

8.48 You are provided with a battery which can provide a constant p.d. of 6.0 V, a rheostat and a voltmeter. Draw a circuit diagram to show how p.d.s. of all values between zero and 6.0 V may be obtained and measured.

8.49 A rheostat of maximum resistance 100 Ω is connected as a potential divider to a power supply which provides a constant p.d. of 12 V. The slider is moved until a voltmeter (of very high resistance) measures the 'output' of the potential divider to be 3.0 V.

(a) Draw a circuit diagram of this arrangement.

(b) A 47 Ω resistor is now connected across the output of the potential divider, and the voltmeter reading falls. What is the new voltmeter reading?

(c) What is then the current in (i) the 47 Ω resistor, (ii) the part of the rheostat in parallel with the 47 Ω resistor, (iii) the power supply?

8.50 A rheostat of maximum resistance 50 Ω is connected as a potential divider to a battery which provides a constant p.d. of 3.0 V. A student adjusts the slider on the rheostat until the p.d. available, as measured by a voltmeter, is 2.5 V. He then connects a 2.5 V 0.2 A bulb in parallel with the voltmeter but finds that the bulb does not light. Explain this result.

8.51 A light-dependent resistor and a fixed resistor (of resistance 10.0 kΩ) are connected as shown below in series between the terminals of a power supply which provides a constant p.d. of 5.0 V. The negative terminal of the power supply is earthed, i.e. may be taken to be 0 V. In the dark the potential of the point X is 0.21 V; when more light falls on the LDR the potential of X rises to 4.2 V. Calculate the resistance of the LDR in these two situations.

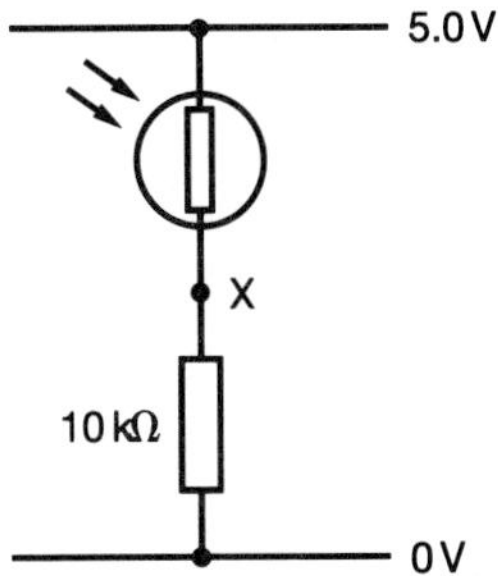

8.52 The diagram shows two identical resistors connected to the same cell in two different ways. In which case, *(a)* or *(b)*, is the total power greater, and how many times greater is it? Assume that the cell has no internal resistance, and that the resistors have constant resistance.

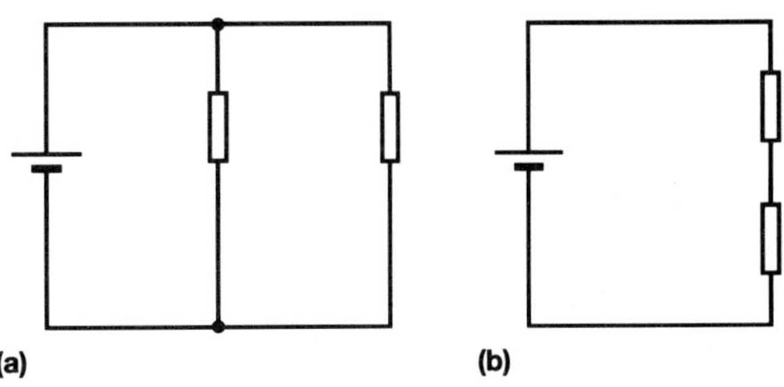

8.53 When connected to a 240 V mains supply the current in an electric lamp is 0.25 A. The current in an electric heating element connected in parallel to the same mains supply has a current in it of 5.0 A.

(a) Calculate the resistances of the devices when connected in this way (i.e. at their normal working temperatures).

(b) Assuming, in this part of the question, that the resistance of the devices remains constant, what will be the current in them when they are connected in series to the same supply, and what will be their powers?

(c) What will be the appearance of the two devices in

these conditions?

(d) In practice the resistances will not have remained the same. Will they be greater or smaller when the devices are connected in series? Which device will have the greatest change of resistance?

8.54 A mains lamp labelled '240 V 60 W' and a car headlamp bulb labelled '12 V 60 W' are connected in series to a 240 V supply. What will happen? [Hint: calculate the resistances of the lamp filaments when the lamps are in normal use.]

8.55 A mains lamp labelled '240 V 60 W' and a torch bulb labelled '1.25 V 250 mA' are connected in series to a 240 V supply. What will happen?

8.56 On the graph of question 8.36 draw also the characteristic of a wire of constant resistance 20 Ω.

(a) At what p.d. does the bulb have a resistance of 20 Ω?

(b) If the bulb and the wire were joined in series, what p.d. would be needed to drive a current of 0.40 A through them?

(c) If the bulb and the wire were joined in parallel, what p.d. would be needed to drive a current totalling 0.40 A through them?

(d) What p.d. would be required to drive a current of 0.35 A through two such bulbs in series?

(e) What would be the total current if a p.d. of 11 V were applied across two such lamps in (i) series, (ii) parallel?

8.57 Each lamp in a string of Christmas tree lamps is labelled '12 V 0.1 A' and the whole string is designed to be connected to a 240 V supply.

(a) How many lamps are there in the string? Draw a circuit diagram to show how the lamps are connected.

(b) What is the power of each lamp?

(c) What is the current drawn from the 240 V supply?

(d) When one lamp fails the others do not go out: how might this result be achieved? Assuming that your solution is correct, what would happen if several lamps failed?

8.58 Your electric fan heater is not working and you need to draw a circuit diagram to help you find out what is wrong. All you know is that there are three simple on-off switches: one switches on the fan without heating, and the other two provide different powers. You assume that the circuit is arranged so that the heating cannot be switched on if the fan is not on, and that there are two separate heating elements.

(a) Draw a possible circuit diagram.

(b) The maximum power of the heater is stated to be 1.0 kW when it is connected to a 240 V supply. What is the resistance of each heater, assuming they are the same?

8.4 Circuits for measurement

8.59 The diagram shows two ways of connecting an ammeter and a voltmeter to measure the resistance of a bulb. It could be argued that in neither circuit are the meters going to measure what is required, i.e. the current through the bulb *and* the p.d. across the bulb. Explain.

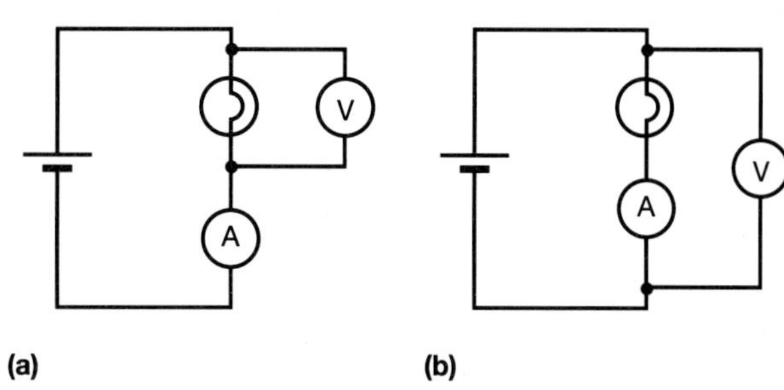

8.60 If in the circuits shown in the previous diagram the bulb has a resistance of 20 Ω, the ammeter has a resistance of 0.10 Ω and the voltmeter a resistance of 100 kΩ, which method would you choose? (No detailed calculations are required.)

8.61 The diagram shows a Wheatstone bridge network. The bridge is balanced. If the resistances of P, R and S are 15 Ω, 33 Ω and 22 Ω, what is the resistance of Q?

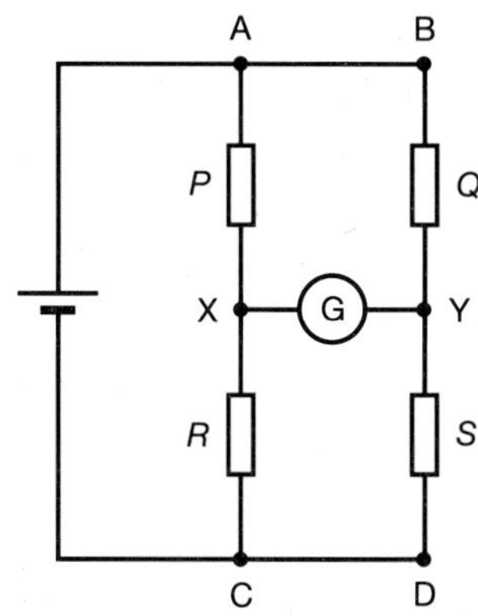

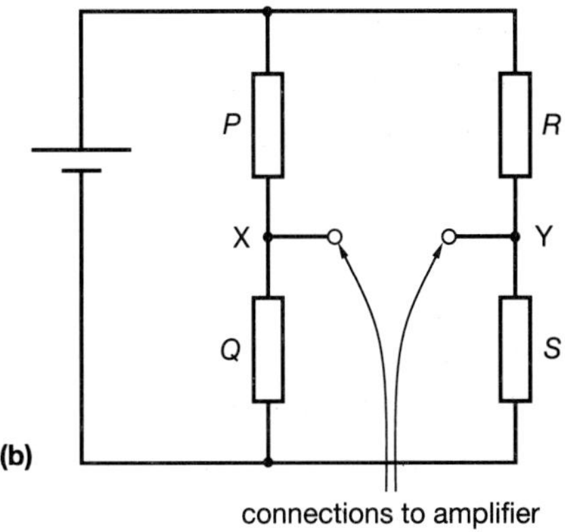

Explain why, if P and R are unchanged, and Q and S are increased to 100 Ω and 220 Ω, the bridge is still balanced. If the resistance of Q is now increased slightly, explain in which direction the current will flow in the meter.

8.62 A strain gauge consists of 80 mm of copper-nickel foil and has a resistance of 120 Ω.

(a) If the resistivity of the foil is $50 \times 10^{-8}\,\Omega\,\mathrm{m}$, calculate the cross–sectional area of the foil in mm^2.

A resistance bridge network is constructed from four strain gauges connected as a 'rosette' as shown in part (a) of the figure; the electrical connections are as shown in (b). The rosette is connected to a steel girder whose axis is parallel to the direction of the wires in P and S.

(b) What is the purpose of the gauges Q and R?

(c) What is the advantage of having both P and S connected in the circuit?

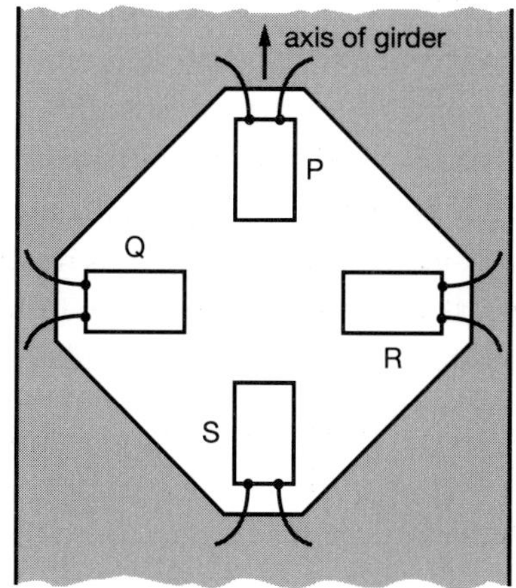

(d) If the girder is placed in tension, in which direction will current flow in the leads to the amplifier?

8.63 A potentiometer circuit contains a lead-acid cell, and a length of resistance wire, as shown in the diagram. A student calibrates the potentiometer by connecting a standard cell C to the circuit. This cell is known to have an e.m.f of 1.0186 V at the temperature of the laboratory, and the balance length is found to be 534 mm. The student then connects, in turn, the four dry cells from a battery pack in place of the standard cell, and the new balance lengths are found to be 687 mm, 754 mm, 752 mm and 761 mm. What are the e.m.f.s. of these four cells?

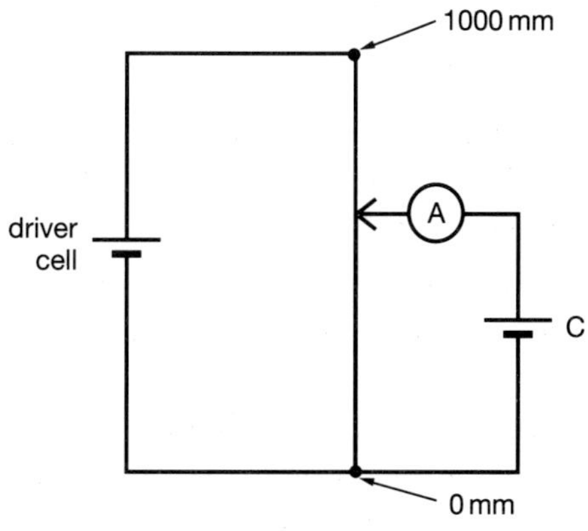

8.64 Why, when using a potentiometer circuit,

(a) must the driver cell have a constant e.m.f. while the experiment is being performed?

(b) is it not necessary to know the internal resistance of the driver cell?

(c) must the resistance wire have a constant resistance per unit length?

(d) is it the e.m.f. of the test cell, and not just its terminal p.d., which is being measured?

(e) does the resistance of the meter not need to be known?

8.65 You need to measure the e.m.f. of a thermocouple, using a potentiometer circuit. The e.m.f. of the thermocouple is known to vary between zero and 5 mV.

(a) Explain why the potentiometer circuit shown in the previous diagram would not be suitable.

(b) Explain why the e.m.f. could be measured if a suitable resistor were connected in series with the driver cell and the resistance wire.

(c) If the e.m.f. of the driver cell were 2.0 V, and the resistance of the wire were 5.0 Ω, what value of series resistor would be suitable?

9 Cells and meters

Data electronic charge $e = 1.60 \times 10^{-19}$ C
mass of electron $m_e = 9.11 \times 10^{-31}$ kg

9.1 Electric cells

9.1 Five identical cells each provide an e.m.f. of 1.5 V. What does a voltmeter read when connected between A and B when the cells are arranged as shown in the diagram?

(a)

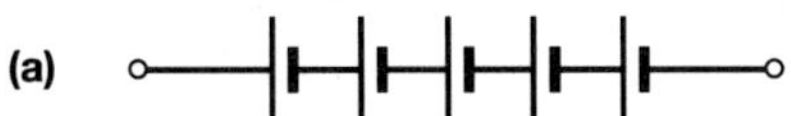

(b)

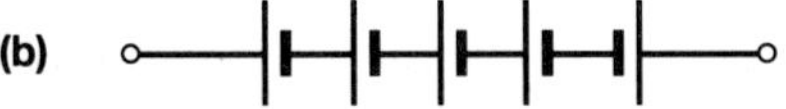

(c)

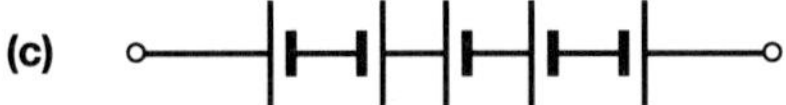

9.2 A radio cassette recorder might need six 1.5 V cells to make it work. The diagram shows what one cell would look like. Draw a diagram to show how they would be arranged if

(a) they were all side by side

(b) they were in two side-by-side 'columns' each of which consisted of three cells.

In each diagram show the points between which you could connect a voltmeter so that it would read 4.5 V.

9.3 Two cells of e.m.f. 2.0 V are connected (i) in series and (ii) in parallel to a resistor of resistance 10 Ω. The cells may be assumed to have negligible resistance.

(a) What is the total e.m.f. of the cells, and the current in the resistor (i) when connected in series, (ii) when connected in parallel?

(b) What are the answers to these questions if one of the cells is replaced by a rechargeable nicad cell of e.m.f 1.2 V in series with a 1.0 Ω resistor?

9.4 Prove that the combined e.m.f of two cells of e.m.f $\mathscr{E}_1$ and $\mathscr{E}_2$ is $\mathscr{E}_1 + \mathscr{E}_2$ when they are connected in series.

9.2 Internal resistance

9.5 A bulb of resistance 14 Ω is connected to a dry cell of e.m.f 1.50 V and internal resistance 0.80 Ω. Calculate

(a) the current in the circuit

(b) the p.d. across the bulb.

(c) the p.d. across the cell.

9.6 A voltmeter of resistance 100.0 Ω is used in an attempt to measure the e.m.f. of a cell.

(a) If the cell has an e.m.f. of 1.500 V and its internal resistance is 1.0 Ω, what reading does the voltmeter give for the e.m.f.?

(b) What would be the reading if the voltmeter had a resistance of 10000 Ω?

9.7 A student wants to measure the internal resistance of a cell and connects it in series with an ammeter and a variable resistor. The student then connects a voltmeter across the variable resistor and, for different settings of the variable resistor, obtains the following readings:

V/V	1.43	1.41	1.39	1.33	1.20
I/mA	143	176	231	333	600

Plot a graph of V against I and deduce the internal resistance and e.m.f. of the cell.

9.8 A dry cell is connected in a circuit in series with a switch and a resistor of resistance 2.0 Ω. A high-resistance voltmeter is connected across the cell. With the switch open the initial reading of the voltmeter is 1.52 V. The switch is then closed and the subsequent readings V of the voltmeter are plotted on a graph as

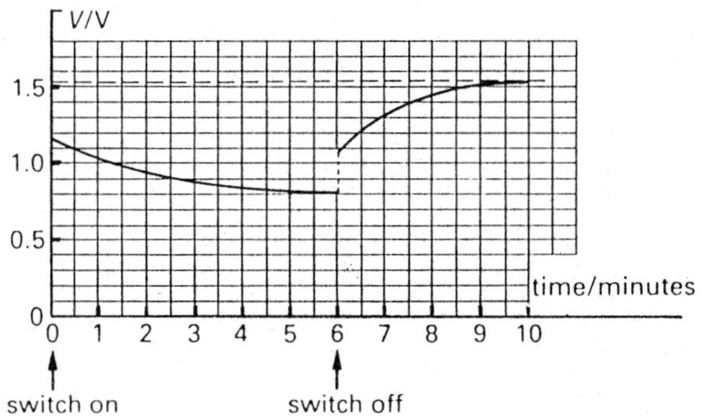

shown. After 6 minutes the switch is again opened and the readings are continued, as shown. What are the e.m.f. and internal resistance of this cell

(a) before any current has been taken from it, and

(b) after it has been driving a current in the circuit for 6 minutes?

9.9 Two cells, each of e.m.f. 1.50 V and internal resistance 0.50 Ω, are connected ***(a)*** in series, ***(b)*** in parallel. In each case what is the combined e.m.f. and internal resistance?

9.10 A cell of e.m.f. 1.55 V and internal resistance 0.50 Ω is connected to a resistor of resistance 10 Ω. What is

(a) the current in the circuit?

(b) the p.d. across the resistor?

(c) the power of the cell?

(d) the power of the resistor?

Your answers to *(c)* and *(d)* should not be the same: explain why.

9.11 A small torch bulb is marked '2.5 V 0.3 A'.

(a) What is its resistance at its normal working temperature?

(b) What resistance would you put in series with it to run it from a 6 V battery?

(c) When the torch bulb is run directly from a battery of e.m.f. 3.0 V, the correct p.d. of 2.5 V is produced across it. What is the internal resistance of the battery?

9.12 A cell of e.m.f. $\mathcal{E}$ and internal resistance r is connected to a resistor of resistance R, and there is then a current I in the circuit and a p.d. V across the resistor (and the cell). The power of the cell is $\mathcal{E}I$, the power of the resistor is VI: these measure rates of conversion of energy *from* one kind (W_1) *to* another kind (W_2).

(a) For the rate of conversion $\mathcal{E}I$, what are W_1 and W_2?

(b) For the rate of conversion VI, what are W_1 and W_2?

(c) Explain why $\mathcal{E}I > VI$ in this situation. Using the symbols given in the question, write down an expression for X in the equation $\mathcal{E}I = VI + X$.

9.13 A student uses the circuit shown in the diagram. R is a resistance box which gives known values of resistance. For various values of R the current I is measured, and the table gives the results:

R/kΩ	8.0	6.0	4.0	2.0	1.0	0.80	0.60
I/mA	167	214	300	500	750	833	938

Calculate the power of the resistor for each value of R.

(a) Predict the power of the resistor when R is zero and when R is infinitely large.

(b) Plot a graph of power against resistance.

(c) For what value of R is the power a maximum?

(d) The internal resistance of the cell is known to be 1.0 Ω. Comment on the shape of the graph.

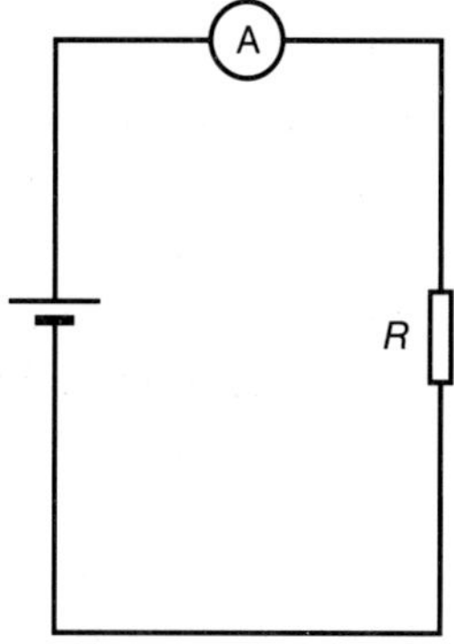

9.14 A battery B_1 consists of three cells, each of e.m.f. 2.0 V and internal resistance 0.10 Ω. A second battery B_2 consist of two of the same kind of cell. They are connected in a series circuit with a resistor of resistance 1.5 Ω as shown in the diagram. Calculate

(a) the current in the circuit

(b) the p.d.s. across B_1, B_2 and the resistor

(c) the rates of working of B_1 and B_2

(d) the rates of production of internal energy in B_1, B_2 and the resistor.

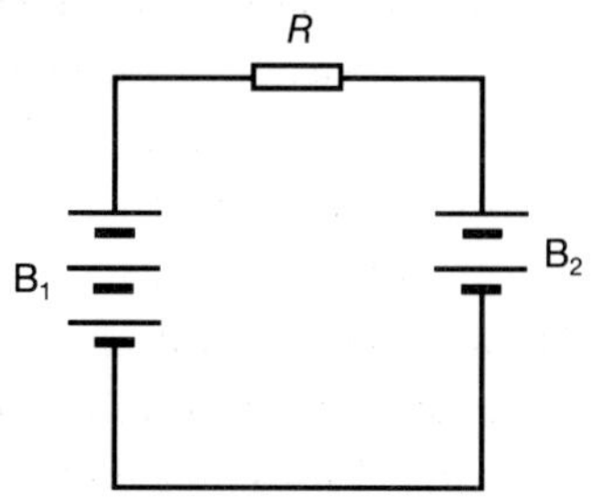

9.15 A laboratory power supply is designed to provide p.d.s. of up to 6.0 kV; it is provided with an internal resistance of 50 MΩ.

(a) What current will flow if the power supply is set at 6.0 kV and connected to a resistor of resistance 100 MΩ?

(b) What will happen if the power supply is again set at 6.0 kV, and an ammeter of resistance 100 kΩ is connected directly across the power supply's terminals, with no other resistance in the circuit?

9.16 The diagram shows two cells C_1 and C_2, of e.m.f. 2.0 V and 1.5 V, connected to a resistor R whose value is 1.0 Ω. Each cell has an internal resistance of 1.0 Ω. The currents in the various branches of the circuit are labelled a, b and $a+b$.

(a) The p.d. V_{C1} across C_1 could be written as $V_{C1} = 2.0\,V - (1.0\,\Omega)\,a$. Write down similar expressions for the p.d. across C_2 and the resistor.

(b) These three p.d.s. are the same. Hence show that $a = 0.83$ A and $b = 0.33$ A and show that the p.d. is 1.17 V.

(c) The resistance of R is now steadily increased until the value of b falls to zero. What is then the p.d. across C_2?

(d) What is then the p.d. across C_1 and R?

(e) What is then the resistance of R?

(f) What will happen if R is increased further?

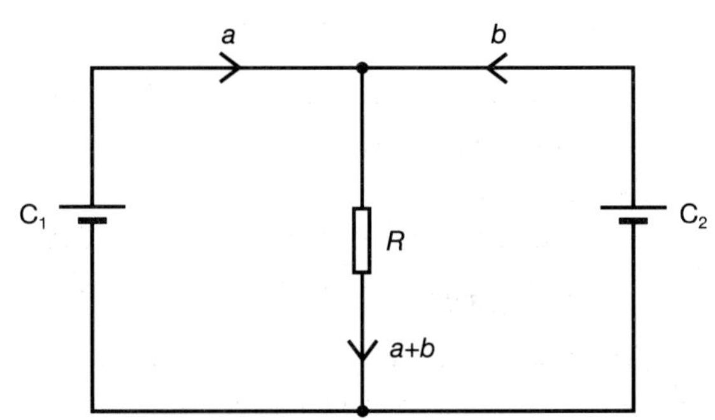

9.17 A battery manufacturer makes three different D size 1.5 V cells. Their capacities are 5.2 A h, 7.9 A h and 16 A h. Calculate the energy stored in each of these cells, assuming that the cells provide an e.m.f. of 1.5 V throughout their lives. If the total masses of the cells are 79 g, 100 g and 131 g respectively, calculate the energy per unit mass for each of the cells.

9.18 The same manufacturer makes other cells using the same materials as in the high-capacity cell in the previous question. The C, AA and AAA size cells have capacities of 7.2 A h, 2.2 A h and 1.0 A h, and their masses are 64 g, 22 g and 11 g respectively. Calculate the energy stored per unit mass, and comment on your answers.

9.19 A car battery has an e.m.f. of 12 V, negligible internal resistance and a capacity of 70 A h. It is connected, through a series resistor of 1.2 Ω, to a battery charger which provides a p.d. of 16.5 V. If the battery initially has no energy stored in it, how long will it take to fill it with chemical energy?

9.3 Meters

9.20 A moving-coil meter has a resistance of 100 Ω and a full-scale deflection of 1.0 mA. If, without fitting a multiplier, it is used as a voltmeter, what is the maximum p.d. it may measure?

9.21 A moving-coil meter has a resistance of 1800 Ω and a full-scale deflection of 100 μA. What must be connected to it if it is to be used as

(a) an ammeter with a full-scale deflection of 10 mA?
(b) a voltmeter with a full-scale deflection of 1.0 V?

9.22 A moving-coil meter has a resistance of 75 Ω and a full-scale deflection of 1 mA. What must be connected to it if it is to be used as

(a) an ammeter with a full-scale deflection of 100 mA?
(b) a voltmeter with a full-scale deflection of 10 V?

9.23 A laboratory technician needs to construct a shunt to enable a meter, which has a resistance of 100 kΩ and a full-scale deflection of 100 μA, to measure currents up to 1 A. He does this by connecting a length of nichrome wire, which has a resistance per unit length of 37 Ω m^{-1} across the terminals of the meter and putting the adapted meter in series with another meter which has already had a shunt fitted, so that he can check whether the adaption is correct.

(a) What length of wire does he need?
(b) He fixes approximately this length to the meter and finds that when the newly adapted meter reads 0.95 A the other reads 1.00 A. Explain whether he should make the wire longer or shorter.

9.24 A student measures the p.d. between the terminals of a battery of negligible internal resistance and finds that it is 6.0 V. She then connects the battery to two 100 kΩ resistors as shown in the diagram, and uses a voltmeter to measure the p.d. across each of them in turn. She expects the voltmeter to record a p.d. of 3.0 V across each of them, but to her surprise the recorded p.d.s. are each only 2.0 V. Her teacher tells her that 'this is because the voltmeter has a resistance of only 100 kΩ'. Why does this remark explain the readings?

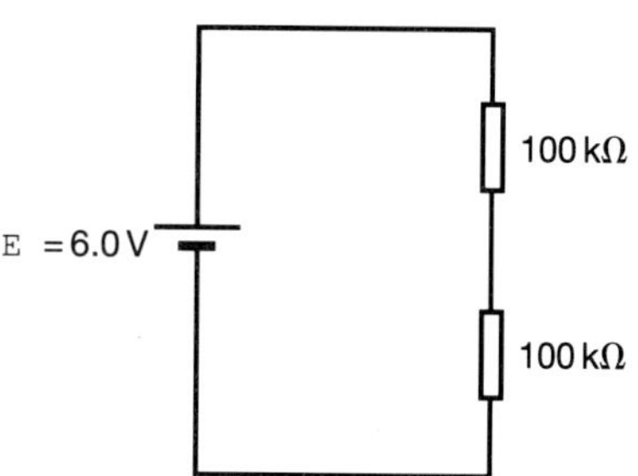

9.25 A cell of e.m.f. 1.5 V is connected in series with two resistors of resistance 47 kΩ and 68 kΩ respectively (see the diagram overleaf). The p.d. across the 68 kΩ resistor is measured with an analogue meter of resistance 100 kΩ and a digital meter of resistance 100 MΩ. What readings does each meter record when

(a) the analogue meter is used by itself?
(b) the digital meter is used by itself?
(c) both meters are used simultaneously, both being connected in parallel across the resistor?

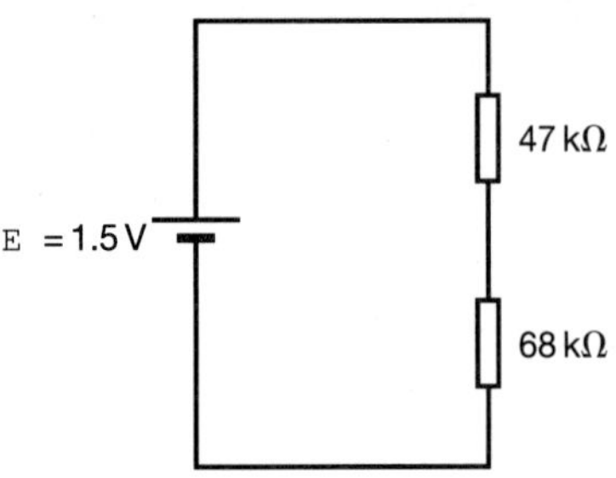

9.26 A student wants to find the resistance of a bulb which is known to be about 20 Ω. He has available a battery which has negligible internal resistance and an e.m.f. of 6.0 V, an ammeter which has a resistance of 10 Ω and a voltmeter which has a resistance of 100 kΩ. His first three attempts at connecting up a circuit, shown in the diagram, are wrong. In each case what do the meters read?

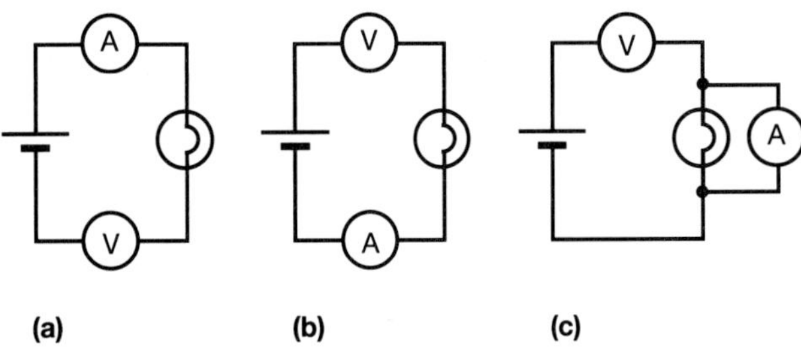

9.27 The diagram shows a circuit containing two resistors of resistance 10.00 Ω, connected in series with a cell whose e.m.f. is 1.500 V and internal resistance 0.500 Ω. A voltmeter is connected across one of the resistors, as shown. The two resistors are then replaced by two 100.0 Ω resistors, two 1.000 kΩ resistors and two 10.00 kΩ resistors, and in each case the voltmeter readings are recorded, as shown:

resistance/Ω	10	100	1000	10000
p.d./mV	732	748	746	714

(a) Account qualitatively for the variation in the voltmeter readings.

(b) Show that the measurements are consistent with the voltmeter having a resistance of 100 kΩ.

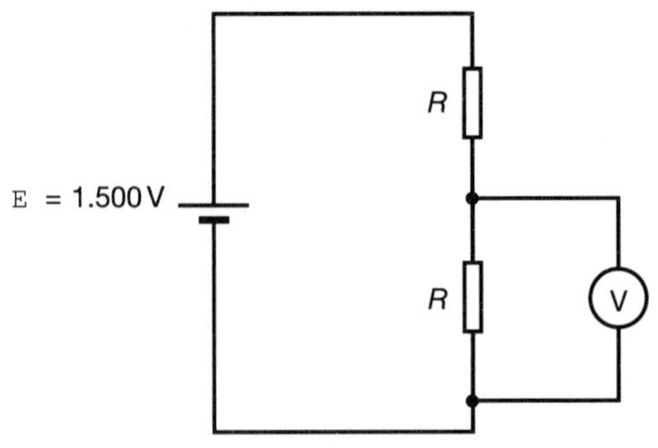

9.4 The cathode ray oscilloscope

9.28 An oscilloscope has its sensitivity control set to 2.0 V div^{-1} and its time base switched off. Initially the spot is at the centre of the screen. What is the size and direction of the movement of the spot when the c.r.o. is connected to the following points in the circuit shown in the diagram (in each case the positive terminal of the c.r.o is connected to the first-named point)? The battery has an e.m.f. of 6.0 V and negligible internal resistance, and all the resistors are identical. Indicate upward and downward movements with + and − signs respectively.
(a) A and B, *(b)* B and C, *(c)* B and D,
(d) A and E, *(e)* E and F, *(f)* B and F, *(g)* C and F?

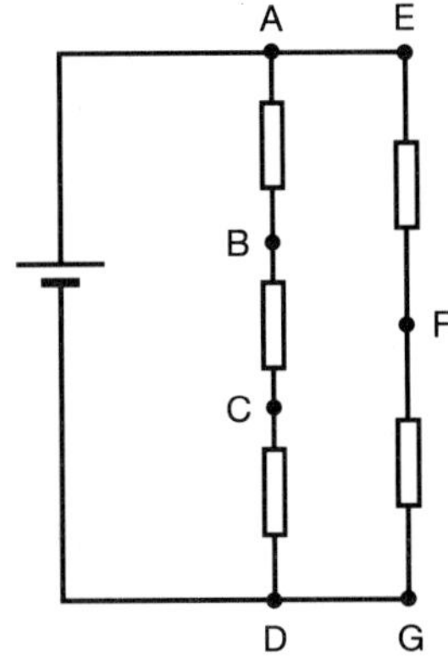

9.29 The diagram shows some traces on an oscilloscope screen. What is the frequency of the alternating p.d. if in each case the time base speed is 5.0 ms div^{-1}?

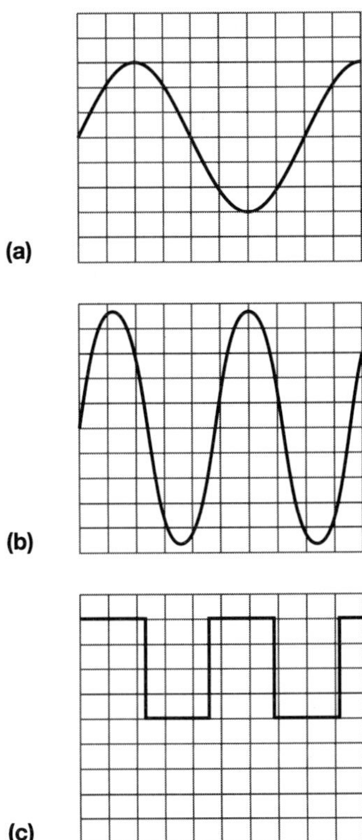

9.30 In a cathode ray oscilloscope the final anode is at zero potential and the cathode is at a potential of −800 V. At one setting of the brilliance control, 1.0×10^{16} electrons are leaving the cathode each second.

(a) How much electrical potential energy does an electron lose when it moves between the cathode and the anode?

(b) With what speed does each electron leave the anode?

(c) What is the electric current between cathode and anode?

(d) If the screen is at zero potential, what is the speed of an electron when it reaches the screen?

(e) If the process of converting kinetic energy to light when the electrons hit the screen is 30% efficient, what is the rate of emission (in W) of light from the screen?

9.31 The time base is switched off in an oscilloscope, and the X and Y inputs have the same sensititivites of 2 V div^{-1}. The spot is initially at the centre of the screen. Draw diagrams to show the positions of the spot when the earth socket is connected to the negative terminal of the battery as shown in the diagram for question 9.28 and the X and Y inputs are connected as follows:

(a) X to point C and Y to point F

(b) X to point B and Y to point F

(c) X to point D and Y to point E.

9.32 The time base is switched off in an oscilloscope, and the X and Y inputs have the same sensitivities of 2 V div^{-1}. The spot is initially at the centre of the screen. Draw diagrams to show the trace observed on the screen when the pairs of alternating p.d.s. are connected to the X and Y inputs as shown in the diagram.

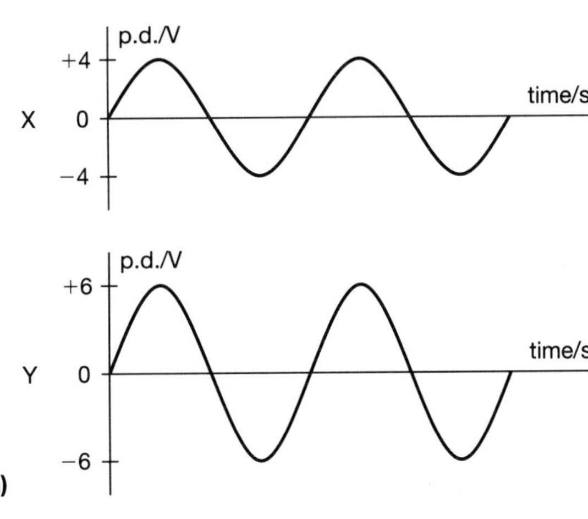

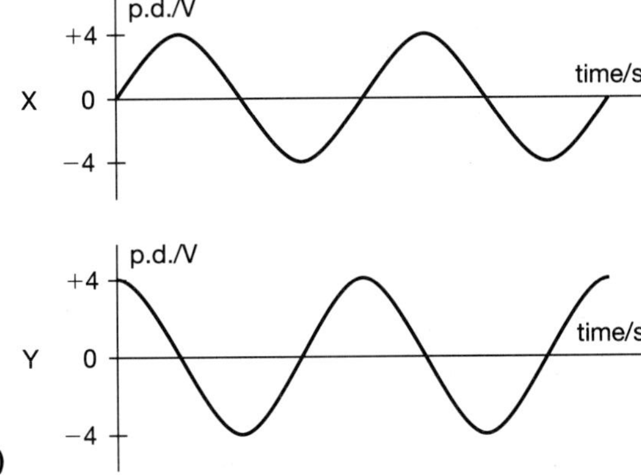

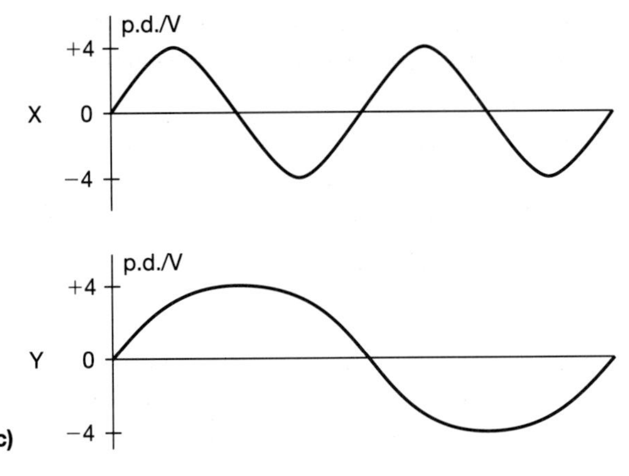

9.33 The time base is switched off in an oscilloscope, and the X and Y inputs have the same sensitivities. Two signal generators, apparently set to the same frequency, are connected to the X and Y inputs of the oscilloscope. The screen initially shows a line at 45° to the horizontal. The line slowly changes to an ellipse, whose axis is at 45° and then to a circle.

(a) Explain why this happens.

(b) Draw diagrams to show what is next seen on the screen.

10 Heating solids and liquids

Data $g = 9.81\,\text{N kg}^{-1}$
specific heat capacities/J kg^{-1}K^{-1}: copper 385, iron and steel 420, aluminium 910, expanded polystyrene 1400, rubber 1600, ice 2100, concrete 3350, water 4200
specific latent heat of fusion of ice: $0.334\,\text{MJ kg}^{-1}$
specific latent heat of vaporisation of water $= 2.26\,\text{MJ kg}^{-1}$

10.1 Measuring temperature

10.1 Two copper blocks, placed together in good thermal contact, will soon reach the same temperature. Explain whether the blocks necessarily have the same amount of internal energy.

10.2 In a mercury thermometer why is

(a) the bore narrow

(b) the bulb relatively large

(c) the glass of the bulb thin

(d) mercury preferred to other liquids

(e) the inside evacuated?

10.3 *(a)* Does a thermometer read its own temperature or the temperature of its surroundings? Suppose a mercury thermometer was put in a place shaded from direct sunlight, and reached a steady temperature. Another identical thermometer placed in direct sunlight would give a higher steady temperature.

(b) What are these two thermometers measuring? Explain, making reference to the rates of emission and absorption of energy by the bulbs, why the readings are different.

10.4 One mercury thermometer is designed to measure temperatures from −10°C to 110°C; another is designed to measure temperatures from −10°C to 400°C. They have the same length: what differences would you expect to find in their construction?

10.5 *(a)* The length of a mercury column in a mercury

thermometer is 15.3 mm at the ice point and 47.8 mm at the steam point. What is the temperature on the centigrade scale of this thermometer when the length of the column is 21.6 mm?

(b) The resistance of a piece of platinum is 3.254 Ω at the ice point and 4.517 Ω at the steam point. It is used to measure the same temperature as in *(a)* and its resistance is then 3.494 Ω. What is then the temperature on the centigrade scale of *this* thermometer?

(c) Comment on the discrepancy between your two answers.

10.6 What type of thermometer would you use to measure each of the following? In each case explain the reasons for your choice.

(a) the boiling point of water on a mountain

(b) the temperature just after ignition in a cylinder of an internal combustion engine

(c) the temperature of the filament of an electric lamp

(d) the normal melting point of zinc.

10.2 Internal energy

10.7 Write down a statement of the First Law of Thermodynamics, using the symbols ΔU, ΔQ and ΔW, and explain what each symbol means.

10.8 What is meant by the internal energy of a body? If a car is stopped by being braked, in what sense is the increase of energy of the molecules of the brake drums, tyres, road, etc., different from the original kinetic energy of the car?

10.9 Would you describe the following energy exchanges as heating or working? Identify in each case (i) the body losing the energy, and the kind of energy lost; (ii) the body gaining the energy, and the kind of energy gained.

(a) A can of beer is taken from a refrigerator and put in a warm room.

(b) A cabinetmaker sandpapers a block of wood: its temperature rises.

(c) A night storage heater cools down during the day.

(d) A tennis ball is dropped and after several bounces comes to rest.

(e) The coffee in a mug has just been stirred, and is rotating: later it comes to rest.

(f) A cyclist pumps air into a bicycle tyre: the pump and air become hotter.

10.10 When a car's brakes are applied frictional forces do 0.20 MJ of work. Because they are hot they lose 0.080 MJ of energy to the surroundings. What are *(a)* ΔW, *(b)* ΔQ, *(c)* ΔU for this process?

10.11 For each of the following bodies undergoing the stated processes state whether the quantities (i) ΔU, (ii) ΔQ, (iii) ΔW are positive, zero or negative:

(a) water which is boiling at a constant rate in a kettle

(b) water in a waterfall which may be assumed to lose all its kinetic energy when it hits the rocks at the bottom of the waterfall

(c) a rubber band which is released after being stretched

(d) a steel ball which is falling at a steady speed through a tall jar of motor oil.

10.12 A battery drives a current through a bulb. During the first few milliseconds, while the filament is still warming up, are ΔU, ΔQ and ΔW positive, negative or zero for the filament?
Are they positive, negative or zero when the filament has reached its steady temperature?

10.3 Heat capacity

10.13 Using data given above, find the heat capacities of the following:

(a) 2.0 litres of water

(b) a kettle which consists of 0.25 kg of aluminium and a heating element which contains 0.20 kg of iron

(c) a copper calorimeter of mass 0.10 kg

(d) an expanded polystyrene cup of mass 5.0 kg.

10.14 In a steel-making furnace 5 tonnes of iron have to be raised from a temperature of 20°C to the melting point of iron (1537°C). Using data given above, find how much energy (in GJ) is needed to do this.

10.15 Make a rough calculation of the cost of using electrical energy to heat water for a bath, if about 0.3 m^3 of water have to be heated from 5°C to 35°C. Assume that the cost of 3.6 MJ of electrical energy is about 7.4 pence.

10.16 The bit of a soldering iron is made of copper and has a mass of 3.3 g. If the power of its electrical heater is 45 W, how long will it take to raise its temperature from 15°C to 370°C, assuming that there are no energy losses to the surroundings? Use data given above.

10.17 An instant gas hot water heater is capable of raising the temperature of 2.0 kg of water by 50 K each minute.

(a) What is its power?

(b) What problem might there be in designing an instant electric water heater which is to work from the ordinary mains supply and achieve the same rate of heating?

10.18 A power station needs to get rid of energy at a rate of 600 MW and does so by warming up a river which flows past it. If the river is 30 m wide, 3.0 m deep, and flows at an average speed of 1.2 $m\,s^{-1}$, how much warmer is the river downstream of the power station?

10.19 An electric kettle has a heat capacity of 450 $J\,K^{-1}$ and an element whose power is 2.25 kW. Ignoring losses of energy to the surroundings, what is the rate of rise of temperature when the kettle contains 1.0 kg of water?

10.20 It is sometimes said that the cost of running an upright freezer is greater than the cost of running a chest freezer because each time the door of an upright freezer is opened the cold air falls out. Consider an upright freezer of capacity 0.20 m^3 and discuss whether there is any truth in this statement. The temperature inside a freezer may be assumed to be about −18°C, and the s.h.c. of air (under these conditions) is 600 $J\,kg^{-1}\,K^{-1}$.

10.21 A 100 W immersion heater is placed in 200 g of water in a plastic cup (of negligible heat capacity). Ignore the heating of the surroundings: how fast, in $K\,min^{-1}$, does the temperature rise?

10.22 How long would it take a 2.0 kW heater to warm the air in a room which measures 4 m by 3 m by 2.5 m from 5°C to 20°C. (The s.h.c. of air under these conditions is about 1000 $J\,kg^{-1}\,K^{-1}$.)
Give at least two reasons why in practice it takes much longer (perhaps an hour?) for the heater to warm such a room.

10.23 A car of mass 800 kg moving at 20 $m\,s^{-1}$ is braked to rest 10 times. If 20% of the car's kinetic energy is retained by the steel brake discs, what is their rise in temperature, if each of the four has a mass of 1.5 kg?

10.24 A squash ball of mass 46 g is struck so that it hits a wall at a speed of 40 $m\,s^{-1}$; it rebounds with a speed of 25 $m\,s^{-1}$. Use data given above.

(a) What is its rise in temperature?

(b) Why is it unnecessary to know its mass?

(c) What will happen to its temperature if the players continue to hit it against the wall?

10.25 You could measure the s.h.c. of a substance by putting some of it in a vertical tube, about 1 metre long, which was then closed at both ends. If the tube was then inverted, the substance would fall and its gravitational potential energy would be converted into internal energy, thus warming the substance. Describe how you would use this method, indicating what measurements you would make, what instruments you would use to make them, and how you would design the experiment to minimise errors in the result (e.g., what would influence your choice of substance, and the amount you used?)

10.26 James Joule is said to have measured the temperature at the top and bottom of a waterfall as part of his investigation into energy. What temperature rise would you expect there to be at the bottom of a waterfall 50 m high, if the water loses all its kinetic energy on arriving at the bottom of the waterfall?

10.27 Water has a relatively high s.h.c. What effect does this have on

(a) climate

(b) the cost of heating water for baths and showers

(c) the volume of water in a car's cooling system

(d) the running costs of a water-filled central heating system?

10.28 A packet of soup designed for slimmers is said to 'contain 60 calories'. In fact this means 60 kilocalories, and the conversion rate between calories and joules is 4.2 J cal^{-1}. The soup is to made by adding 200 ml of water. Assume the soup is at a temperature of 60°C when you drink it, and your body temperature is 38°C. What amounts of energy (in kJ) are delivered to you

(a) by you digesting the soup

(b) by the soup cooling down? (Assume its s.h.c. is the same as that of water.)

10.29 1.0 kg of water at a temperature of 95°C is poured into a copper saucepan of mass 0.70 kg which is at a temperature of 20°C. What is the temperature of the water before it starts to lose energy to the surroundings?

10.30 A block of copper of mass 400 g is raised to a temperature of 450 K and lowered into 500 g of water contained in a vessel of heat capacity 200 J K^{-1}; these were initially at a temperature of 290 K. If the final temperature of the water was 300 K, what value do these measurements give for the s.h.c. of copper?
Discuss whether this procedure could be used as a method of measuring the s.h.c. of materials in solid form, explaining any precautions you would need to take. Would it matter if the material was a bad conductor of energy?

10.31 *(a)* A copper can of mass 300 g is at room temperature, which is 18.0°C. 200 g of water, at a temperature of 65.0°C, are poured into it, and the final temperature is found to be 59.4°C. What is the s.h.c. of copper?

(b) Find the heat capacity of the can and the water.

(c) Some glass beads, of mass 400 g, at room temperature, are immediately dropped into the water in the can. After waiting for the beads to warm up, the final temperature is found to be 50.5°C. What is the specific heat capacity of the glass?

10.32 A kettle of heat capacity 500 J K^{-1} contains 1.5 kg of water at 12°C. If its power is 2.5 kW

(a) how long will it take for the kettle and water to reach 100°C, ignoring losses of energy to the surroundings?

If, in practice the kettle was switched off at 100°C and its temperature fell to 96°C in 50 seconds. What was

(b) the average rate of loss of energy during these 50 s

(c) the rate of loss of energy at 98°C

(d) the average temperature while it was being heated?

Use your answers to *(c)* and *(d)* to deduce

(e) the average rate of loss of energy while it has being heated

(f) the loss of energy while it was being heated.

10.33 A 30 W immersion heater was placed in an aluminium block of mass 1.0 kg, and switched on for 6.0 minutes: the initial temperature of the block and the surroundings was 12.3°C. At successive one-minute interbals, the following temperatures were recorded: 14.1°C, 15.9°C, 17.7°C, 19.5°C, 21.2°C, 22.9°C, 22.8°C, 22.7°C, 22.6°C, 22.5°C.

(a) Estimate the maximum temperature which would have been reached if the block had not been heating the surroundings.

(b) Hence calculate the s.h.c. of aluminium.

10.34 Suppose you were given an immersion heater, a power supply, an ammeter, a voltmeter, a stop clock, a thermometer and a plastic beaker which you could fill with water, and you could ask for any other (simple) apparatus which you might need. Describe what you would need to measure the s.h.c. of the water, and how you would measure it, paying particular attention to the precautions you would take to ensure a reliable result.

10.35 Suppose you were asked to design a night storage heater, i.e. a device consisting of a set of blocks (similar to concrete) which is heated at night (when for 7 hours between midnight and 7 a.m. electrical energy is relatively cheap) and which releases its energy during the day. Discuss as many aspects of the design as possible, including: drawing a temperature–time graph for a 24–hour cycle, estimating the power of the heater you would need, estimating the mass of the blocks, and drawing attention to any disadvantages of this form of heating.

10.36 A student measures the temperature of a plastic mug of water and draws a temperature-time graph. The mass of water is 153 g and the heat capacity of the mug is negligible. He draws a tangent to the curve at the point where the temperature is 80°C and finds that the line shows a fall in temperature of 25°C in 9.6 minutes.

(a) What is the rate of loss of energy at this temperature?

(b) Room temperature was 18°C. Estimate the rate of loss of energy when the temperature of the water had fallen to 60°C.

10.37 In an experiment to measure the rate of flow of energy along a copper bar, thin copper tubing carrying water is wrapped round one end of the bar. This keeps that end of the bar cool because energy flows into the water which is passing through the tubing. It is found that the inlet and outlet temperatures of the water are 15.6°C and 34.3°C respectively when the rate of flow of water is such that 430 g are collected in 5 minutes. Calculate the rate of flow of energy into the water.

10.38 An immersion heater is fitted to a hot water tank in a house. In the summer months hot water is needed only for washing. One member of the family says it is better to keep the heater running all the time because if the water is allowed to cool down there will be extra energy needed to warm it up again. A second member of the family says it is best to have the heater switched on only when it is needed. Decide which of these people you think is right and explain why.

10.4 Latent heat

10.39 Using data given above, find how much energy must be

(a) given to 2.0 litres of water at 100°C to evaporate it

(b) taken from 0.50 kg of water at 0°C to freeze it.

10.40 How long will it take

(a) a 1000 W heater to evaporate 1.0 kg of water which is already at 100°C, its normal boiling point

(b) a refrigerator to freeze 1.0 kg of water which is already at 0°C, its normal freezing point, if it can remove energy at a rate of 75 W?

10.41 Using the values of s.h.c. and s.l.h. given at the start of this section, draw a graph, with labelled axes, to show how the temperature varies with time when a block of ice, of mass 2.0 kg has an immersion heater of power 200 W placed in it. The ice is initially at −10°C; continue the graph until the temperature of the water vapour is 110°C. S.h.c. of water vapour under these conditions = 1400 J $kg^{-1} K^{-1}$.

10.42 ***(a)*** Two lumps of ice, at 0°C, each of mass 20 g, are added to a glass containing a mixture of alcohol and water at a temperature of 15°C. The heat capacity of the glass and its contents is 600 J K^{-1}. When the system has reached equilibrium how much ice is left?

(b) What would have been the result if only one lump of ice had been used?

10.43 A coffee machine in a café passes steam at 100°C into 0.18 kg of cold coffee (s.h.c. the same as that of water) to warm it. If the initial temperature of the coffee is 14°C, what mass of steam must be supplied to raise the temperature of the coffee to 85°C?

10.44 The mass of liquid nitrogen in an open beaker is found to have decreased by 46.3 g in 10 minutes. If the s.l.h. of vaporisation of nitrogen at its boiling point is 1.99×10^5 J kg^{-1}, at what rate were the surroundings heating the beaker? Why is the heat capacity of the beaker irrelevant?

10.45 The following temperatures θ were taken for 0.25 kg of a substance cooling in surroundings which were at a steady temperature. During the cooling the substance solidified.

t/min	0	1	2	3	4	5	6	30	31	32	33	34
θ/°C	82.0	80.0	78.0	76.1	74.2	72.7	72.4	72.4	71.3	67.8	64.6	61.7

Draw graphs of θ against t for the first 6 minutes and the last 4 minutes and from them estimate what the slopes of these two parts of the cooling curve would have been at 72.4°C if the substance had not solidified. These are the rates of fall of temperature which the liquid and the solid would have had at 72.4°C.
If the s.h.c. of the substance in the liquid phase was 1850 J kg^{-1} K^{-1} what was

(a) its s.h.c. in the solid phase
(b) its rate of loss of energy at 72.4°C
(c) its s.l.h. of fusion, assuming that it was solidifying for 26 minutes?

10.46 Describe how you would measure

(a) the s.l.h. of fusion of water
(b) the s.l.h. of vaporisation of water. In each case (i) explain how you would calculate the result, (ii) state the factors which lead to uncertainty in the result, (iii) describe the precautions you would take to make your result as accurate as possible.

10.47 Discuss some of the effects on everyday life if we lived on a planet in which the values for water of the following quantities were one-tenth of their present value:

(a) the s.h.c.
(b) the s.l.h. of fusion
(c) the s.l.h. of vaporisation.

10.48 A thermocouple probe connected to a multimeter gave a reading of 20.5°C for room temperature on a particular day. Explain the following observations:

(a) When the probe was placed in some ethanol in a watch glass the recorded temperature fell to 14.8°C.
(b) When the probe was removed from the ethanol and placed in the air again the temperature fell further to 6.8°C, but after a few seconds the temperature began to rise again, eventually reaching 20.5°C.

10.49 An open dish of liquid is very slightly cooler than its surroundings. Why? Your explanation should include an account of why its temperature is steady, and the factors which determine the steady temperature.

10.50 Explain the following:

(a) If you have just finished taking some exercise you should put on a track suit, even if you feel warm. It is particularly important to do this on a windy day.
(b) A bottle of milk is sometimes put under an upturned earthenware pot which is standing in a bowl of water. The pot is porous and water seeps up it. In this way the milk is kept cool.
(c) Snow and ice lie on the ground for some days after the air temperature has risen above 0°C.
(d) A large tub of water placed in a cellar will make it less likely that the temperature in the cellar will fall below 0°C.

10.51 *(a)* A female runner of mass 60 kg generates internal energy at a rate of 800 W. Assuming that she loses no energy, and that the average s.h.c. of her body is the same as that of water, at what rate, in K min^{-1}, will her temperature rise?
(b) If she loses energy through conduction, convection and radiation at a rate of 300 W, at what rate, in K min^{-1}, will her temperature rise?
(c) Ideally her temperature should remain constant. Evaporation (from skin and through exhaled air from the lungs) is an additional mechanism by which she can lose energy. At what rate, in g min^{-1}, must she evaporate water in order to keep her temperature constant?
(d) When she stops running she generates internal energy at a rate of 100 W, but continues to lose energy at a rate of 800 W. At what rate (in K min^{-1}) will her body temperature fall?

10.52 When a 100 W heater was embedded in some substance in the solid phase the temperature rose to 70°C and remained steady for 4.0 minutes before rising further. Later, with the heater switched off, the temperature fell to 70°C and remained steady for 16 minutes before falling further.

(a) What can you deduce from these readings?

(b) If the mass of substance was 80 g, what was its s.l.h. of fusion?

10.53 In the liquid phase benzene has a density of $800\,\text{kg}\,\text{m}^{-3}$ at its normal boiling point (353 K) and in the vapour phase at that temperature it has a density of $2.69\,\text{kg}\,\text{m}^{-3}$. What is the volume of 0.100 kg of benzene at 353 K

(a) in the liquid phase

(b) in the vapour phase?

The work done by a substance when its volume increases by ΔV is $p\Delta V$, where p is the external pressure.

(c) What is the work done when 0.100 kg of benzene evaporates at 353 K, and atmospheric pressure (101 kPa)?

The s.l.h. of vaporisation of benzene at 353 K is $3.94 \times 10^{5}\,\text{J}\,\text{kg}^{-1}$.

(d) How much energy is needed to evaporate 0.100 kg of benzene at this temperature?

(e) How do you explain the difference between your answers to *(c)* and *(d)*?

(f) What would be the s.l.h. of vaporisation of benzene if the external pressure had been 50 kPa?

(g) Why would pressure have very little effect on the value of the s.l.h. of fusion of benzene?

11 Energy transfer

Data $g = 9.81\,\text{N}\,\text{kg}^{-1}$

11.1 Convection

11.1 ***(a)*** Why is an immersion heater always fitted at the bottom, and not the top, of a hot water tank?

(b) Some hot water tanks have a second immersion heater fitted near the top. What is a possible explanation for this?

11.2 In this question you are asked to find the acceleration of the heated air in a convection current. Consider a volume of 1.000 litre of air: at a room temperature of 15°C its density is $1.293\,\text{kg}\,\text{m}^{-3}$. Suppose it is heated to a temperature of 30°C.

(a) If the density of the air is inversely proportional to the kelvin temperature, calculate its density at 30°C.

(b) What is the weight of the air?

(c) What is the upthrust on the air?

(d) What is the air's initial acceleration?

(e) What factors will affect the air's subsequent acceleration?

11.3 Explain why smoke from a blown-out candle

(a) initially rises vertically in a narrow column

(b) later disperses.

11.2 Conduction

11.4 Central heating radiators do radiate some energy into their surroundings, but radiation is not the main mechanism of energy transfer. Describe and explain how energy is transferred from the radiator to the room.

11.5 What is the rate of flow of energy through a window if the glass is 4 mm thick, and measures 1.0 m by 1.2 m? Take the temperatures of the two faces to be 11.2°C and 9.7°C respectively. The thermal conductivity of glass is $1.0\,\text{W}\,\text{m}^{-1}\,\text{K}^{-1}$.

11.6 The water in most modern central heating systems is contained in a closed system. It is heated by being passed through a heat exchanger in the tank which holds the hot water which is used for washing. The surfaces of the heat exchanger are made of copper, have an area of $1.5\,m^2$, and a thickness of 1.5 mm. When the water in the tank is at 75°C, and the central heating water flows through the heat exchanger at a rate of 3.0 litres per minute, the temperature of the central heating water rises from 10°C to 56°C. The thermal conductivity of copper is $385\,W\,m^{-1}\,K^{-1}$.

(a) Calculate the rate of flow of energy from the hot water tank to the central heating water.

(b) *Hence* calculate the average temperature difference between the surfaces of the heat exchanger.

(c) How would you explain why your answer to (b) is not much greater, e.g. 75°C minus the average of (10°C + 56°C)?

11.7 The fabric of a hot-air balloon is 2.5 mm thick and has a thermal conductivity of $0.050\,W\,m^{-1}K^{-1}$. The surface area of the fabric is $1200\,m^2$.

(a) What is the rate of loss of energy from the balloon when there is a temperature difference of 1.5 K between the inner and outer surfaces?

(b) The temperature is maintained by igniting 500 kW gas burners at regular intervals for periods of 5.0 seconds. What length of time is there between each supply of energy?

11.8 Suppose a metal bar is lagged well enough for escape of energy from its sides to be negligible. Initially the whole bar is at room temperature. One end of the bar is then left exposed to the air, and the other end is kept at a steady temperature of about 50 K above room temperature. Describe what happens to the temperature at different points along the bar. You should explain why the temperature of the bar does not become uniform, and why the final temperature of the exposed end of the bar is above room temperature.

11.9 Sketch graphs to show how the temperature varies with distance along a metal bar when one end is kept at a high temperature and the other exposed to the air in the room if

(a) the bar is uniform and well lagged

(b) the bar is uniform and not lagged

(c) the bar is well lagged but tapers towards the cooler end.

11.10 A pond has a surface area of $30\,m^2$; on its surface is a layer of ice which is 10 mm thick and increasing at a rate of 1.35 mm per hour. If the upper and lower surfaces of the ice are at −0.50°C and 0.00°C respectively, calculate

(a) the rate, in $kg\,s^{-1}$, at which ice is being formed (density of ice $= 920\,kg\,m^{-3}$)

(b) the rate of transfer of energy through the ice

(c) the thermal conductivity of ice.

Explain whether you would expect the thickness of the layer of ice to increase uniformly with time, if the two temperatures remain constant.

11.11 The ends of a well-lagged bar are kept at temperatures of 80°C and 10°C. The thermal conductivity of copper and iron are $385\,W\,m^{-1}K^{-1}$ and $80\,W\,m^{-1}K^{-1}$ respectively. What is the rate of flow of energy along the bar when it is

(a) made of copper, is 0.20 m long, and has a cross-sectional area of $4.0\,cm^2$

(b) made of copper, is 0.20 m long, and has a cross-sectional area of $2.0\,cm^2$

(c) made of copper, is 0.40 m long, and has a cross-sectional area of $2.0\,cm^2$

(d) made of iron, is 0.20 m long, and has a cross-sectional area of $4.0\,cm^2$?

11.12 Two metal discs A and B are placed one on top of the other in good thermal contact. The outer face of A is kept at 80°C and the outer face of B is kept at 20°C. What is the temperature of the interface between the discs if

(a) A and B are made from the same metal, and have the same thickness

(b) A and B are made from the same metal, but the thickness of A is twice that of B

(c) A and B have the same thickness, but the thermal conductivity of A is half that of B

(d) the thickness of A is twice that of B, but the thermal conductivity of A is half that of B?

11.13 The figure shows a lagged iron pipe which carries hot water. The dashed circles are drawn at radii of 50 mm and 100 mm. The length of the pipe is 3.0 m and the radius of the lagging is 150 mm.

(a) If the rate of escape of energy from the lagging is 18 W, what is the outward rate of flow of energy across the circumference of (i) radius 20 mm, (ii) radius 100 mm?

(b) If the thermal conductivity of the lagging is $0.035\,\mathrm{W\,m^{-1}\,K^{-1}}$, what is the temperature gradient $\Delta\theta/\Delta r$ in the lagging at a radius of (i) 50 mm, (ii) 100 mm?

(c) Give a physical reason why your answer to (b)(i) is half your answer to (b)(ii).

(d) Sketch a graph to show the variation of $\Delta\theta/\Delta r$ with r, if the pipe has an external radius of 20 mm.

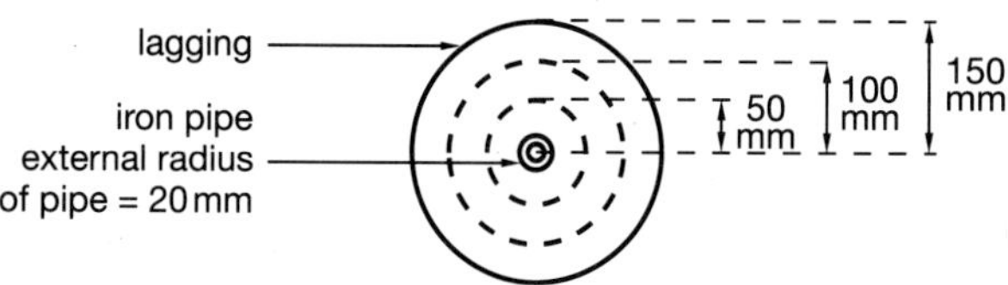

11.14 In an experiment to measure the thermal conductivity of copper, a well-lagged bar of diameter 38.0 mm was heated at one end. At the other end, cooling water was passed through tubing wrapped round the bar. No measurements were made until the temperatures of all parts of the bar were steady. Then 435 g of water were collected in 10.0 minutes, and the inlet and outlet temperatures were 12.7°C and 34.2°C. At two points 100 mm apart along the length of the bar the temperatures were 73.2°C and 58.6°C. What value do these readings give for the thermal conductivity of copper?

11.15 A hot water storage tank in a house has a surface area of $1.6\,\mathrm{m^2}$ and contains water at 70°C. Assume that the outer surface of the tank is also at 70°C. Room temperature is 20°C.

(a) If the rate of loss of energy from the tank may be analysed by assuming that there is a layer of still air 10 mm thick between the tank and the air in the room (with, therefore, a 50 K temperature difference across it) calculate the rate of loss of energy from the tank. Thermal conductivity of air $= 0.25\,\mathrm{W\,m^{-1}\,K^{-1}}$.

(b) An insulating jacket of glass wool (thermal conductivity $0.040\,\mathrm{W\,m^{-1}\,K^{-1}}$) of thickness 30 mm is then placed round the tank. The same layer of still air may be assumed to be next to the outside of the jacket. Calculate the temperature of the interface between the jacket and the layer of still air, and hence find the rate of loss of energy from the tank. Assume that the effective cross-sectional area of the jacket may be taken to be $1.6\,\mathrm{m^2}$.

11.16 *(a)* Why does the wire in a fuse nearly always melt at its centre?

(b) Why does water in a saucepan often start boiling at the edges and not at the centre?

11.17 The U–value (thermal conductance) U of a material is defined by $U = k/l$ where l is the thickness of the material.

(a) Deduce the units of U.

(b) Explain what U measures.

The thermal resistance R of a material is defined by $R = 1/U$. When two materials of thermal resistance R_1 and R_2 are placed in series (e.g. a layer of plasterboard fixed to a brick wall) the total thermal resistance R is given by $R = R_1 + R_2$, as with electrical resistances.

(c) Calculate U, and hence R, for each of the following:

(i) brick 120 mm thick ($k = 1.0\,\mathrm{W\,m^{-1}\,K^{-1}}$)

(ii) breeze block 120 mm thick ($k = 0.40\,\mathrm{W\,m^{-1}\,K^{-1}}$)

(iii) foamed plastic 80 mm thick ($k = 0.050\,\mathrm{W\,m^{-1}\,K^{-1}}$)

(iv) glass 4.0 mm thick ($k = 1.0\,\mathrm{W\,m^{-1}\,K^{-1}}$)

(v) air 25 mm thick ($k = 0.25\,\mathrm{W\,m^{-1}\,K^{-1}}$)

(d) What is the total thermal resistance of the following combinations of the above, when placed in series:

(i) air + brick + air

(ii) air + brick + foamed plastic + brick + air

(iii) air + glass + air

(e) What are the U–values for each of these combinations?

(f) What is the rate of transfer of energy through a wall which measures 5.0 m by 3.0 m, when the outside and inside temperatures are 20°C and 2°C, and it has a U–value of (i) $3.1\,\mathrm{W\,m^{-2}\,K^{-1}}$, (ii) $0.49\,\mathrm{W\,m^{-2}\,K^{-1}}$?

(g) What is the rate of transfer of energy through a window which measures 2.0 m by 1.0 m, when the outside and inside temperatures are 20°C and 2°C, and it has a U–value of $4.9\,\mathrm{W\,m^{-2}\,K^{-1}}$?

11.18 The Building Regulations in Great Britain state that for new houses the U–value for walls must be less than $1.0\,\mathrm{W\,m^{-2}\,K^{-1}}$. A typical cavity wall consists of two brick walls, each 120 mm thick, with a layer of air 50 mm thick between them. Assume that there is also a layer of still air, 25 mm thick, next to each of the outer brick surfaces; does this type of construction meet the regulations? Use the data from the previous question. (Hint: calculate U, and hence find R, for each material, and hence the total thermal resistance.)

11.19 Two of the walls in one room of a house are outside walls. The walls are 2.5 m high, and their total length is 9.0 m. Each wall has one window which measures 1.2 m by 2.0 m. The U–values for the materials of the wall and windows are $0.50\,\mathrm{W\,m^{-2}\,K^{-1}}$ and $5.3\,\mathrm{W\,m^{-2}\,K^{-1}}$ respectively (these values allow for the stationary layers of air next to the wall and the window). When the internal and external temperatures are 18°C and 3°C, what is the rate of transfer of energy by conduction through the walls?

11.20 The diagram shows a sectional view of a single pane of glass in a wall taking account of the existence of stationary layers of air near the glass, sketch a graph to show how the temperature varies with distance, starting at a point inside the room, and ending at a point in the air outside.

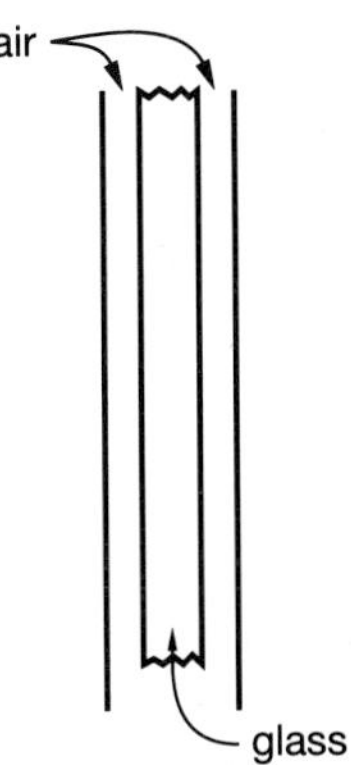

11.21 The thermal resistance R of material of thickness l is defined by $R = l/U = l/k$.

(a) Calculate the thermal resistance of window glass which is 4 mm thick.

(b) Typical values of thermal resistance for the almost stationary layers of air next to the glass are $0.13\,\mathrm{m^2\,K\,W^{-1}}$ (inside) and $0.060\,\mathrm{m^2\,K\,W^{-1}}$ (outside). Comment on your answer to *(a)* in the light of these values.

(c) Why is double glazing effective as a means of reducing energy transfer?

11.22 An office is heated by an electric heater which is switched on at 9 a.m. The temperature of the office begins to rise but by 11 a.m. it is found that the temperature has stopped rising, although the heater is still on.

(a) Why is this?

(b) Explain why, on a colder day, the maximum temperature reached is lower, and reached sooner.

11.3 Radiation

11.23 The intensity of the radiation arriving at the Earth from the Sun is about $1.4\,\mathrm{kW\,m^{-2}}$. If the distance of the Earth from the Sun is $1.5 \times 10^{11}\,\mathrm{m}$, what is the power output of the Sun?

11.24 Describe the changes in the radiation from an electric lamp filament when it is switched off and cools down to room temperature.

11.25 The diagram shows a heat sink which can be attached to a piece of high-power electrical apparatus so that it does not get too hot.

(a) Explain its shape, and why it is usually painted black.

(b) A quantity given for the heat sink is $4\,\mathrm{K\,W^{-1}}$ 'with fins vertical in free air'. By considering the unit $\mathrm{K\,W^{-1}}$, or otherwise, explain what the quantity means.

(c) What would happen if the heat sink were bolted to a device in which energy was being generated at a rate of 20 W?

(d) What might be the construction of a different heat sink which had a value of $8\,\mathrm{K\,W^{-1}}$?

(e) Explain whether the thermal resistance would be greater or smaller if the fins were not vertical.

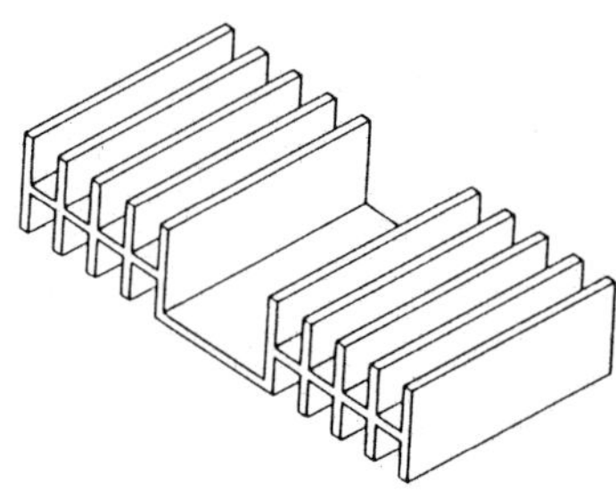

11.26 Explain why the inside of a car, or a greenhouse, becomes warm on a sunny day, even if the outside temperature is low.

11.27 Two solid copper spheres A and B hang in identical evacuated enclosures. They are initially at the same temperature, which is higher than that of the enclosure. If A's diameter is twice that of B, what are, initially, the ratios

(a) (rate of loss of energy of A)/(rate of loss of energy of B)

(b) (rate of fall of temperature of A)/(rate of fall of temperature of B)?

11.28 Use your answer to the previous question to explain why

(a) small mammals spend a lot of their time eating

(b) small birds are more likely than large birds to die in winter.

11.29 Give two reasons why you feel cold if you sit near a window when it is cold outside. [Hint: one explanation involves convection, and the other radiation.]

11.30 When an electric lamp is switched on it very quickly becomes white-hot but then does not become any hotter although energy continues to be supplied from the mains.

(a) Why does it reach a steady temperature?

(b) What factors determine the temperaure which is reduced?

11.31 Describe how you would demonstrate experimentally that a body with a dull black surface radiates better than a body with a shiny surface, if the two bodies are at the same temperature.

11.32 The rate of emission of energy from the surface of a particular body is proportional to the fourth power of the kelvin temperature, i.e. to T^4. If a body radiates at a rate of 2.0 W at 300 K, what is its rate of emission of energy by radiation at

(a) 600 K

(b) 2000 K

(c) 200 K?

12 The ideal gas

Data Molar gas constant $R = 8.31\,\mathrm{J\,mol^{-1}\,K^{-1}}$
Avogadro constant $L\ (= N_A) = 6.02 \times 10^{23}\,\mathrm{mol^{-1}}$
Boltzmann constant $k = 1.38 \times 10^{-23}\,\mathrm{J\,K^{-1}}$

12.1 The ideal gas law

12.1 At the start of a journey the pressure of the air in a car tyre is 276 kPa and the temperature is 12°C. After being driven the pressure is 303 kPa. Assuming that the volume of the air remains constant, what is now its temperature?

12.2 The volume of air in a bicycle tyre is 400 cm^3 and the pressure is 145 kPa.

(a) If the temperature did not change, what volume would the air occupy when the tyre bursts on a day when the atmospheric pressure is 102 kPa?
(b) In practice the temperature falls: if it falls from 30°C to 10°C, what volume would the air occupy?

12.3 A balloon is filled with air until its volume is 1.5 litres and the pressure is 110 kPa. The temperature is 290 K. Assuming that the volume and the temperature remain constant, how many more molecules must be blown into the balloon to increase its pressure to 115 kPa?

12.4 Some gas occupies a volume of $6.0 \times 10^{-3}\,\mathrm{m^3}$ and exerts a pressure of 80 kPa at a temperature of 20°C. What pressure does it exert if, separately

(a) the temperature is raised to 40°C
(b) the volume is halved
(c) the temperature is raised to 586 K
(d) the volume becomes $2.5 \times 10^{-3}\,\mathrm{m^3}$
(e) the volume becomes $7.7 \times 10^{-3}\,\mathrm{m^3}$ and the temperature becomes 57°C?

12.5 A faulty mercury barometer contains some air above the mercury in the tube. On a day when the atmospheric pressure is 785 mm of mercury, the height of the mercury in the tube is 725 mm and the length of the space above the mercury is 125 mm. When the barometer tube is raised vertically the space above the mercury becomes larger so the pressure of the air falls and the height of the mercury in the tube becomes 730 mm.

(a) In mm of mercury, what was the original air pressure in the tube?
(b) What is now the pressure?
(c) What is now the volume?
(d) How much was the tube raised?

12.6 The volume of one cylinder in a diesel engine is 360 cm^3 and the cylinder contains a mixture of fuel and air at a temperature of 320 K and a pressure of 101 kPa. The volume of the mixture is then reduced to 20 cm^3 and at the same time the temperature rises to 1000 K. What is the new pressure in the cylinder?

12.7 A cylinder of volume 0.20 m^3 contains gas at a pressure of 200 kPa and a temperature of 290 K.

(a) How many moles of gas are there in the cylinder?
(b) How many molecules of gas are there in the cylinder?
(c) What is the mass of gas if it is (i) hydrogen ($M_r = 2$), (ii) nitrogen ($M_r = 28$)?

12.8 In an experiment in which the pressure p of a gas and its volume V were measured at constant temperature, the following readings were obtained:

p/kPa	102	143	178	200	233
V/cm^3	40.5	28.7	23.4	20.7	17.8

Plot graphs of (a) p against V, and (b) p against $1/V$. Does the second graph enable you to say that these measurements show that pV = constant?

12.9 Show that the gradient of the second graph in question 12–8 is equal to nRT. If the temperature of the gas was 287 K, what was the number of moles of gas present?

12.10 If the following masses of gas, all at the same temperature, are placed successively in the same container, which will exert the greatest pressure, and which the least: (a) 20 g of hydrogen (b) 20 g of helium (c) 200 g of oxygen?

12.11 An air bubble of volume $3.0 \times 10^{-5}\,m^3$ escapes from a diver's equipment at a depth of 45 m where the water temperature is 5°C. What is its volume as it reaches the surface, where the temperature is 12°C? (Atmospheric pressure = 101 kPa, density of seawater = $1020\,kg\,m^{-3}$.)

12.12 A vessel of volume $0.20\,m^3$ contains a mixture of 2.0 g of hydrogen molecules and 8.0 g of helium molecules. The temperature is 320 K.

(a) Calculate the numbers of moles of each gas.
(b) What is the total amount of substance (i.e. the number of moles)?
(c) What is the pressure in the vessel?

12.13 Describe how you would perform an experiment to investigate how the volume of a gas depends on its temperature while its pressure remains constant. Draw a diagram of the apparatus, describe how you would make the measurements, explain what precautions you would need to take, and sketch a graph to show the sort of results you would expect.

12.2 The kinetic theory of gases

12.14 Consider a rectangular box with sides of 0.30 m, 0.40 m and 0.50 m respectively. Suppose it contains 1.5×10^{24} molecules, each of mass 5.0×10^{-26} kg. Suppose that each face of the box has one-third of the molecules moving at right angles to it, and that all the molecules have the same speed of $500\,m\,s^{-1}$. Consider the face which measures 0.40 m by 0.30 m. Calculate

(a) the time between successive impacts of a particular molecule on that face
(b) the size of the change of momentum when a molecule strikes this face
(c) using your two previous answers, the average rate of change of momentum when a molecule strikes this face
(d) the average force, caused by all the molecules, on this face
(e) the pressure on this face.

12.15 Referring to question *12.14*, explain what the pressure would be

(a) on one of the other faces
(b) if molecules of mass 8.0×10^{-26} kg were used instead.
(c) if molecules of speed $600\,m\,s^{-1}$ were used instead.

12.16 In questions *12.14* and *12.15* it was assumed that the molecules do not collide with each other: in practice they do. Considering the simple case of a collision between two molecules which are travelling parallel to one edge of the box, and which collide head-on, explain whether the collision makes any difference to the momentum changes on the opposite faces of the box.

12.17 The kinetic theory of gases predicts how the pressure of a gas depends on properties of the gas and its temperature. Two forms of this result are
$p = \frac{1}{3}\rho\langle c^2\rangle$ and $pV = \frac{1}{3}Nm\langle c^2\rangle$

(a) Explain what each of the quantities p, ρ, V, N, m and $\langle c^2\rangle$ represents.
(b) Give a unit for each of the quantities.

12.18 *(a)* Given that $pV = \frac{1}{3}Nm\langle c^2\rangle$ and $pV = nRT$ derive an expression for the mean translational k.e. $\frac{1}{2}m\langle c^2\rangle$ in terms of n, R, N and T.
(b) Write $k = nR/N$ to simplify this result.
(c) What is the significance of k, and what is it called?

12.19 List four assumptions of the kinetic theory of gases, and for each explain why it is necessary to make the assumption.

12.20 How does the kinetic theory of gases explain why the pressure of a fixed mass of gas at constant temperature is inversely proportional to its volume?

12.21 How does the kinetic theory of gases explain the following?

(a) the volume of a gas is proportional to its kelvin temperature, at constant pressure

(b) the pressure of a gas is proportional to its kelvin temperature, at constant volume.

12.22 The measured speeds of 10 vehicles on a motorway are, in $m\,s^{-1}$, 31, 32, 28, 40, 33, 32, 35, 34, 32, 25. Calculate

(a) their mean speed

(b) their r.m.s. speed.

12.23 The density of argon gas is $1.61\,kg\,m^{-3}$ at a pressure of 100 kPa.

(a) What is the r.m.s speed of argon molecules under these conditions?

(b) What would be the r.m.s. speed if the pressure were halved, the temperature remaining the same?

12.24 Consider some gas contained in a cylinder, as shown in the figure. The space in the cylinder is initially 400 mm long, and the piston is moving at $0.50\,m\,s^{-1}$. Consider a molecule moving parallel to the axis of the cylinder at a speed of $400\,m\,s^{-1}$. It can be shown that when it rebounds elastically from the moving piston its speed increases by double the speed of the piston, e.g. from $400\,m\,s^{-1}$ to $401\,m\,s^{-1}$. Suppose that the piston moves 5 mm inwards.

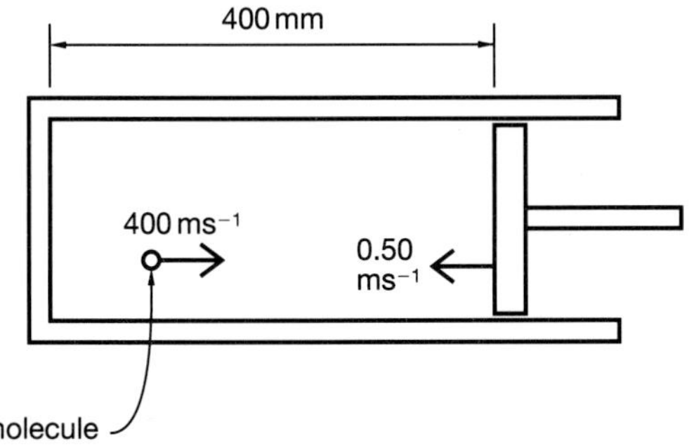

(a) How long does the piston take to do this?

(b) What is the time interval between the molecule making successive impacts on the piston (assume that the space remains 400 mm long)

(c) While the piston moves 5 mm, how many impacts does the molecule make on it?

(d) After these impacts what is the speed of the molecule?
(This is only an approximate answer because you were told to assume that the length of the space did not change, but it gives some idea of the reason why the molecule moves faster because the piston is being pushed in.)

(e) What would you say to a friend who said 'I don't see how pushing a piston slowly can make gas molecules, already moving hundreds of times faster than the piston, move even faster.'?

12.25 Air contains a mixture of different gases: nitrogen, oxygen, argon, etc. Explain whether the molecules of the different gases have different

(a) mean translational kinetic energies

(b) r.m.s. speeds.

12.26 Two cylinders have the same volume. One contains hydrogen, the other oxygen. The pressures and temperatures in the two cylinders are the same. Explain whether the numbers of molecules in each cylinder are the same.

12.3 Consequences of kinetic theory

12.27 What is the temperature of a gas if its molecules have a mean translational k.e. of *(a)* 5.65×10^{-21} J, *(b)* 1.24×10^{-20} J?

12.28 What is the mean translational k.e. at 290 K of the molecules of the following gases:

(a) hydrogen ($M_r = 2$),

(b) nitrogen ($M_r = 28$), bromine ($M_r = 160$)?

12.29 What is the r.m.s speed at 290 K of the molecules of each of the gases listed in question *12.28*?

12.30 The figure overleaf shows the distribution of molecular speeds v for 1 000 000 oxygen molecules at two temperatures 300 K and 600 K. At any particular whole-number speed the height of the curve represents the number of molecules which have speeds within $\pm 0.5\,\mathrm{m\,s^{-1}}$ of that speed (e.g. for the graph with the higher peak about 2000 molecules have speeds between $319.5\,\mathrm{m\,s^{-1}}$ and $320.5\,\mathrm{m\,s^{-1}}$).

(a) Explain which graph corresponds to 300 K and which to 600 K.

(b) Estimate the number of oxygen molecules which have speeds within $\pm 0.5\,\mathrm{m\,s^{-1}}$ of $750\,\mathrm{m\,s^{-1}}$ at (i) 300 K, (ii) 600 K.

(c) Is the area beneath the 300 K the same as the area beneath the 600 K curve? What does this area represent?

(d) Estimate the number of oxygen molecules which have speeds of less than $250\,\mathrm{m\,s^{-1}}$ at (i) 300 K, (ii) 600 K.

(e) What is the median speed (i.e., the speed of the greatest number of molecules) at (i) 300 K, (ii) 600 K, and (iii) the ratio of these speeds?

(f) What is the r.m.s. speed of oxygen molecules at (i) 300 K, (ii) 600 K, and (iii) the ratio of these speeds?

(g) Copy the axes, scales and the 300 K graph, and add a graph which shows the distribution of speeds at 1200 K.

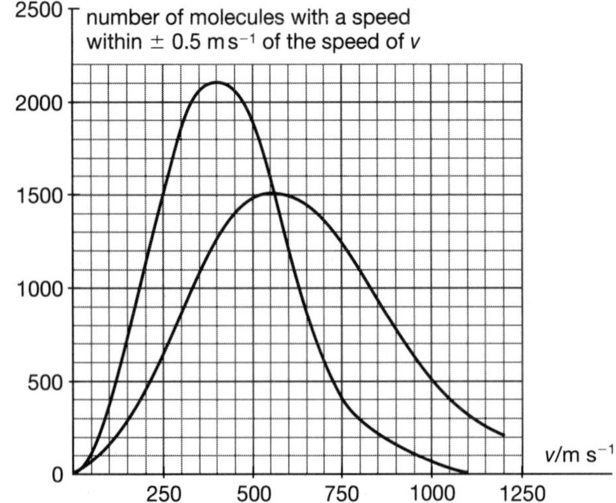

12.31 An early method of investigating the distribution of molecular speeds used apparatus like that shown in the figure. Atoms or molecules emerged from the oven and passed through the slit S and into a rotating drum. They crossed the drum and were deposited on a glass plate. The intensity of the deposition was measured optically.

(a) Draw a diagram of the glass plate, labelled AB as in the figure, and shade it to show what the distribution of atoms or molecules would be like.

(b) At which end were the fastest molecules? Explain.

(c) What is the r.m.s. speed of a bismuth atom, at 110 K? ($A_r = 209$, $m_u = 1.66 \times 10^{-27}\,\mathrm{kg}$)

(d) If the diameter of the drum is 200 mm, how fast must it be rotated if atoms with this r.m.s. speed are to strike the glass plate 45° around the circumference from A?

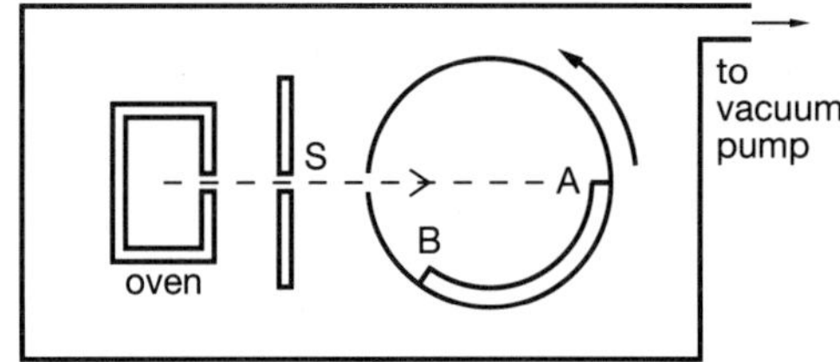

12.4 The internal energy of a gas

12.32 The internal energy U of a monatomic gas is given by $U = \frac{3}{2}nRT$. What is the internal energy at 290 K of ***(a)*** 40 g of helium gas, ***(b)*** 400 g of argon? ($M_r = 4$ for helium, $M_r = 40$ for argon)

12.33 How much internal energy is there in 5.0 mol of a monatomic gas (for which $C_V = \frac{3}{2}R$) at temperatures of ***(a)*** 300 K, ***(b)*** 600 K?

12.34 If 2.00 mol of a monatomic gas at 600 K are given 14.9 kJ of energy by heating at constant volume, what does the temperature become?

12.35 A monatomic gas has a molar heat capacity (at constant volume) of $\frac{3}{2}R$.

(a) How much energy is needed to raise the temperature of 10.0 mol of the gas from 273 K to 500 K at constant volume?

(b) If 2.5 kJ of energy are given to 5.0 mol of a monatomic gas at constant volume, what will be the rise in temperature?

12.36 Hydrogen and nitrogen have s.h.c.s. of $10.18\,\text{kJ}\,\text{kg}^{-1}\,\text{K}^{-1}$ and $0.7450\,\text{kJ}\,\text{kg}^{-1}\,\text{K}^{-1}$ respectively. Their molar masses M_m are $2.016 \times 10^{-3}\,\text{kg}\,\text{mol}^{-1}$ and $28.01 \times 10^{-3}\,\text{kg}\,\text{mol}^{-1}$ respectively. What are their molar heat capacities? Comment on your result.

12.37 A cylinder is fitted with a frictionless piston and contains gas at a constant pressure of 50 kPa. The area of the piston is $1.0 \times 10^{-2}\,\text{m}^2$.

(a) What force does the gas exert on the piston?

(b) What work does the gas do when the piston moves outwards 5.0 mm, the pressure inside the cylinder being kept constant (e.g. by heating)?

12.38 *(a)* Sketch graphs of p against V for a gas at two different temperatures T_1 and T_2 ($T_2 > T_1$).

(b) Draw lines to show the variation of p with V when (i) the temperature of the gas falls from T_2 to T_1 to constant pressure, the temperature of the gas then rises from T_1 to T_2 at constant volume, (iii) the gas then returns to its original state at constant temperature. Label the lines (i), (ii) and (iii).

(c) For each of the three processes explain whether the internal energy of the gas has risen, fallen or remained the same.

(d) How might these changes have been accomplished; e.g. if the internal energy fell, what happened to the energy?

12.39 The graph shows the variation of pressure with volume for a gas at two temperatures, 300 K and 400 K. Use information from the graph to calculate

(a) the number of moles of gas present

(b) the pressure of the gas at X

(c) the volume of the gas at Y.

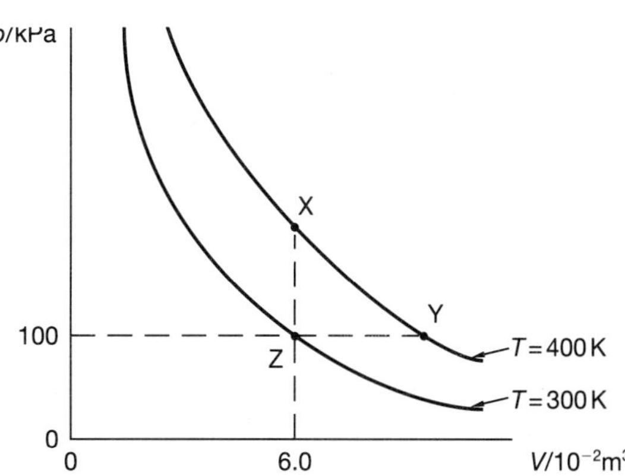

12.40 Refer to question *12.39*. For each answer attach the appropriate sign.

(a) How much work ΔW is done in compressing the gas from Y to Z?

(b) If the internal energy U of the gas is given by $U = \frac{3}{2}nRT$, what is the change ΔU in internal energy in this process?

(c) Work is done on the gas, but its internal energy decreases. How is this possible? Calculate the energy ΔQ transferred by heating.

12.41 *(a)* Sketch graphs of p against V for a gas at two different temperatures T_1 and T_2 ($T_2 > T_1$).

(b) Suppose for some gas contained in a cylinder the initial and final temperatures T_1 and T_2 are 280 K and 430 K respectively and that its initial pressure is 80 kPa and its initial volume is $12 \times 10^{-3}\,\text{m}^3$. If the gas is heated at constant volume from T_1 to T_2, use $U = \frac{3}{2}nRT$ to calculate the increase in internal energy. What are ΔQ and ΔW for this process?

(c) If, instead, the gas is heated at constant pressure from T_1 to T_2, what is ΔU? What are ΔQ and ΔW?

12.42 *(a)* 40 mol of a monatomic gas is contained in a cylinder at a constant temperature of 300 K. Calculate values of its pressure corresponding to volumes V given by $V/10^{-2}\,\text{m}^3 = 5.0, 6.0, 7.0, 8.0$ and 9.0, and plot a graph of p against V for this range of values of V. Hence find a rough value for the work done ΔW by the gas when it expands at constant temperature from a volume of $5.0 \times 10^{-2}\,\text{m}^3$ to a volume of $9.0 \times 10^{-2}\,\text{m}^3$.

(b) What are ΔU and ΔQ for this process?

12.43 ***(a)*** Sketch graphs of p against V for a gas at two different temperatures T_1 and T_2 ($T_2 > T_1$) and add a line to your diagram to help you explain what is meant by an adiabatic process.

(b) The table gives corresponding values of p and V for an adiabatic expansion:

$V/10^{-2}\,m^3$	5.0	6.0	7.0	8.0	9.0
p/kPa	200	155	125	104	88

Plot these values and hence find an approximate value for the work done by the gas when it expands.

(c) Explain whether your answer is greater or smaller than the work which would be done by the gas in an isothermal expansion with the same change of volume.

(d) For the adiabatic expansion what are ΔQ and ΔU?

12.44 Describe the type of process for which, with the notation of the first law of thermodynamics, (a) $\Delta Q = 0$, (b) $\Delta U = 0$, (c) $\Delta W = 0$, illustrating your answer by drawing lines on a p–V graph for a gas.

12.45 Assuming that the gas is not allowed to expand and do work, use the expression $U = \frac{3}{2}nRT$ to derive an expression for the molar heat capacity of a monatomic gas, i.e. the energy needed per mole and per degree rise in temperature.

12.46 Explain whether the internal energy of a gas always increases when

(a) its temperature rises

(b) it is compressed adiabatically

(c) its volume decreases.

12.5 Heat engines

12.47 A quantity of gas may be taken along the paths *abc* and *adc* in the figure.

(a) Describe what is happening to the gas when it is taken along each of these paths.
Along *abc* the work done by the gas is 40 kJ and the energy supplied by heating is 90 kJ. Along *adc* the work done by the gas is 20 kJ.

(b) Calculate the pressure ratio p_2/p_1.

(c) If $U_a = 45$ kJ, what is U_c?

(d) How much energy is supplied by heating along path *adc*?

(e) If $U_d = 70$ kJ, what is ΔQ for the paths (i) *ad*, (ii) *dc*?

(f) If the work done on the gas when it returns along the curved path *ca* is 35 kJ, what is ΔQ for the path?

(g) What does the area of the rectangle *abcd* represent?

(h) How much work would be done on the gas if it returned along a straight line joining *c* and *a*?

(i) Calculate the temperature ratio T_c/T_a.

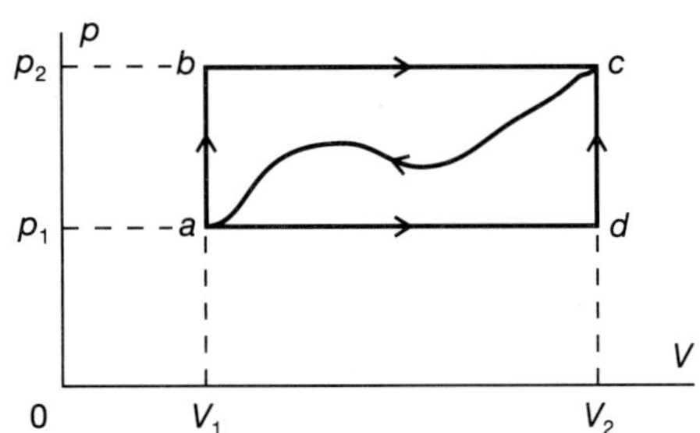

12.48 The figure shows a cycle *abcda* round which some gas may be taken, starting at *a*. The temperatures of the three isothermal curves are shown. The pressure and volume at *a* are 100 kPa and 1.0 m^3 respectively.

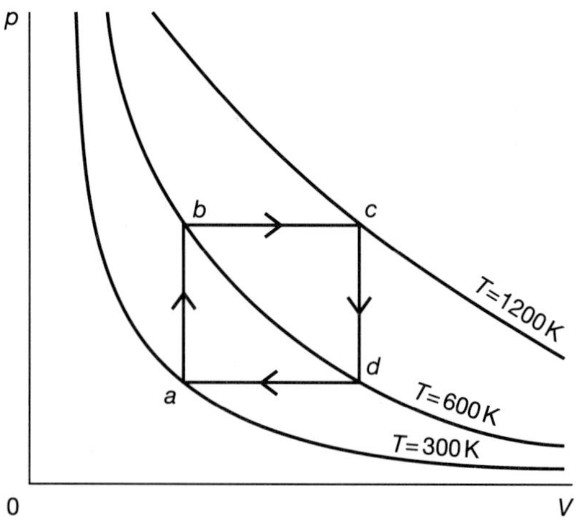

(a) What are the values of pressure and volume at *b*, *c* and *d*?

(b) Work is done by the gas along *bc*, and on the gas along *da*. On a copy of the graph shade areas which represent these two amounts of work done, and explain why the area *abcd* represents the net work done by the gas.

(c) Copy this table.

path	ΔQ	ΔW	ΔU
ab			
bc			
cd			
da			
abcda			

Complete the column headed ΔW, remembering to attach signs to the quantities.

(d) The energy supplied to the gas by heating along *ab* is 150 kJ. Enter this value in the table, and also the value of ΔU for *ab*.

(e) From *a* to *b* the temperature rose from 300 K to 600 K; from *b* to *c* it rose from 600 K to 1200 K. What was ΔU, and hence ΔQ for *bc*?

(f) Now complete the rest of the table.

(g) Why, for the complete cycle *abcd*, would you expect ΔU to be zero?

12.49 0.40 mol of a monatomic gas ($C_v = \frac{3}{2}R$) at an initial pressure of 100 kPa and an initial temperature of 300 K is taken round the following cycle: (i) it is cooled at constant pressure until it is at 150 K, (ii) it is heated at constant volume until its temperature is 450 K, (iii) it is heated at constant pressure until it regains its original volume, (iv) it is cooled at constant volume until it is in its original state.
Calculate the original volume of the gas, and sketch the cycle on a p–V graph, marking in the values of pressure, volume and temperature. Calculate

(a) the highest temperature reached

(b) ΔU, ΔW and hence ΔQ for each of the processes (i) to (iv)

(c) the net work done by the gas in the cycle

(d) the energy supplied by heating during processes (ii) and (iii)

(e) the fraction of the energy supplied to the gas which is converted to mechanical energy.

12.50 A gas is (i) allowed to expand isothermally so that its pressure p_1 falls to a pressure p_2 and its volume V_1 increases to a volume V_2, then (ii) compressed at constant pressure p_2 to its original volume V_1, then (iii) heated at constant volume V_1 until its pressure is again p_1. Sketch the cycle on a p–V graph.

(a) Draw up a table with headings ΔW, ΔU, ΔQ and ΔT and for each of the processes (i), (ii) and (iii) complete the table to show whether these quantities are positive, negative or zero.

(b) For the complete cycle, are the values of ΔW, ΔU, ΔQ and ΔT positive, negative or zero?

12.51 A gas is (i) compressed adiabatically from a pressure p_1 and volume V_1 to a pressure p_2 and volume V_2, then (ii) allowed to expand isothermally to a pressure p_3 and its original volume V_1. Its pressure then (iii) falls at constant volume until its pressure is again p_1. Sketch the cycle on a p–V graph.

(a) Draw a table with headings ΔW, ΔU, ΔQ and ΔT and for each of the processes (i), (ii) and (iii) complete the table to show whether these quantities are positive, negative or zero.

(b) For the complete cycle are the values of ΔW, ΔU, ΔQ and ΔT positive, negative or zero?

12.52 *(a)* Sketch two isothermals for temperatures T_1 and T_2 ($T_2 > T_1$) on a p–V graph.

(b) On your graph draw a cycle *abcda* for which (i) *ab* is an isothermal compression at temperature T_1, (ii) *bc* an adiabatic compression, (iii) *cd* an isothermal expansion at temperature T_2 and (iv) *da* an adiabatic expansion.

(c) Draw up a table with headings ΔW, ΔU, ΔQ and ΔT and for each of the processes (i), (ii) (iii) and (iv) complete the table to show whether these

quantities are positive, negative or zero.

(d) For the complete cycle are the values of ΔW, ΔU, ΔQ and ΔT positive, negative or zero?

12.53 ***(a)*** Sketch two isothermals, which need not be to scale, for temperatures of 300 K and 550 K on a *p–V* graph.

(b) On your graph draw a cycle *abcd* for which *ab* is an isothermal compression at 300 K, *bc* an adiabatic compression to 550 K, *cd* an isothermal expansion at 550 K and *da* an adiabatic expansion to 300 K.

(c) Draw up a table with headings ΔW, ΔU, ΔQ, with one line for each of the paths *ab*, *bc*, *cd* and *da*. Then write '0' in the four spaces for which you know the values must be zero.

(d) Given that $U = \frac{3}{2}nRT$ for the gas, and that on this occasion $nR = 40\,\mathrm{J\,K^{-1}}$, calculate ΔU for the paths *bc* and *da*, and enter these in the table. Also enter the values of ΔW for these paths.

(e) If along path *ab* 7.3 kJ of work is done on the gas, and along path *cd* 13.4 kJ of work is done by the gas, complete the rest of the table.

(f) What is the net work done by the gas, and the energy supplied by heating?

(g) Hence calculate the thermal efficiency of the process.

(h) On your graph shade the area which represents the net work done by the gas.

(i) Now imagine another cyclic process which follows the same path *abc*, but the adiabatic compression is continued until the temperature is 650 K at point c_1. The gas then expands isothermally to d_1, and then expands adiabatically, until it reaches the original point *a*. Sketch this new cycle on your original graph.

(j) Along path *ab* the amount of work done on the gas is still 7.3 kJ, but now the amount of work done by the gas along c_1d_1 is 15.8 kJ. Calculate the efficiency of this cycle.

(k) How could the thermal efficiency of this kind of cycle be increased still further?

12.54 What is the thermal efficiency of a heat engine working between temperatures of (a) 300 K and 550 K, (b) 300 K and 650 K, (c) 300 K amd 750 K?

12.55 ***(a)*** In 1992 one electricity company charged 7.35 p for each kWh of energy; in the same area British Gas charged 1.57 p. Assuming that the use of electrical energy for heating in the home is 100% efficient, but the use of gas for heating is only 75% efficient, how many times more expensive is it to use electrical energy rather than gas for heating water?

(b) What is the underlying cause of this difference?

13 Circular motion

Data $g = 9.81\,\text{N kg}^{-1}$
2π radians = 360°

13.1 Describing circular motion

13.1 An arc of a circle of radius 2.50 m subtends an angle of 60.0° at the centre. Find
(a) the angle in radians
(b) the length of the arc.

13.2 Draw a straight line graph to convert from angles measured in radians to angles measured in degrees up to 180°.
(a) Use the graph to write down to *two* significant figures (i) how many degrees are equivalent to 1.0 rad, $\pi/4$ rad, 2/3 rad, (ii) how many radians are equivalent to 90°, 5°, 120°.
(b) Calculate the percentage error in taking (i) 1.0 rad to equal 60°, (ii) 90° to be equal to 1.6 rad.

13.3 A motor car tyre of radius 0.270 m is punctured in close succession by two drawing pins on the road. The angle subtended at the centre of the wheel by the part of its circumference between the two tacks is 140°. What was the shortest possible distance on the road between the drawing pins?

13.4 A gardener pulls a rope to try to start a motor lawn mower. She pulls 35 cm of rope from a shaft of diameter 4.0 cm.
Calculate the angle through which she turns the shaft and hence the number of revolutions of the motor she produces in trying to start it.

13.5 A man pulls on a cord to try to start an outboard motor. Initially at rest, after 1.2 s it is rotating at 1200 r.p.m. (revolutions per minute). Assuming its speed increases uniformly what is
(a) its final angular velocity in rad s^{-1}
(b) the angle it has turned through
(c) the number of revolutions made by the motor?

13.6 What is the angular velocity, in rad s^{-1} of
(a) a flywheel rotating at 5000 r.p.m.
(b) the minute hand of a clock
(c) the Earth on its axis?
Consider the precision of the data you use and hence give your answers to an appropriate number of significant figures.

13.7 All points on the Earth's surface have an angular velocity of $7.3 \times 10^{-5}\,\text{rad s}^{-1}$. Calculate the distance travelled in 1.0 h by
(a) a point on the equator
(b) a point at latitude 56°N.
Take the radius of the Earth to be 6400 km.

13.8 A geosynchronous satellite makes a complete circular orbit once in 24 hours. The radius of the orbit is 4.2×10^7 m.
(a) What is its angular velocity?
(b) What is its speed?

13.9 A record rotates at 33⅓ r.p.m. and has a radius of 0.15 m. What is
(a) its angular velocity
(b) the speed of a point on its circumference
(c) the speed of a point midway between its centre and its circumference?

13.10 A line drawn on a rotating flywheel appears stationary when illuminated by a stroboscopic lamp whose rate of flashing is 50 Hz. When the rate of flashing is raised to 100 Hz, the line again appears stationary. When the rate of flashing is raised to 200 Hz, two stationary lines are seen, opposite each other. Explain these observations.

What is the least possible rate of rotation of the flywheel *(a)* in rev s^{-1} *(b)* in rad s^{-1}?

13.11 A girl at the seaside whirls a bucket of water in a vertical circle of radius 0.5 m. If the angular velocity is constant and she completes 3 revolutions in 2 s, calculate the centripetal acceleration of the water in the bucket. Comment on your answer.

13.12 A particle moving in a circular path with a centre O and radius r at constant speed v is at some time at a point P. At a time t later it is at Q, where angle POQ $= \theta$.
Draw a diagram to show the particle's velocity at P and at Q and prove that the size of the change of velocity (i.e. new velocity minus old velocity, by vector subtraction) is $2v\sin\frac{1}{2}\theta$. Show also that its direction bisects the angle POQ and is directed towards O.

13.13 Refer to the previous question. What is

(a) the length of the arc PQ

(b) the time taken for the particle to move from P to Q

(c) the average acceleration of the particle?

Calculate the average acceleration kv^2/r of the particle for the following values θ:

$$60°, 40°, 20°, 10°, 5°$$

giving k to 4 significant figures. As θ tends to zero, what will the average acceleration tend to?

13.14 The designer of an amusement park loop-the-loop roller-coaster wants a centripetal acceleration of $20\,\mathrm{m\,s^{-2}}$ at the top of a loop of radius 7.0 m.

(a) Calculate the minimum speed he must ensure the roller coaster has at the top of the loop.

(b) What is the minimum height h above the top of the loop from which a freewheeling roller coaster must accelerate from rest in order to reach this minimum speed?

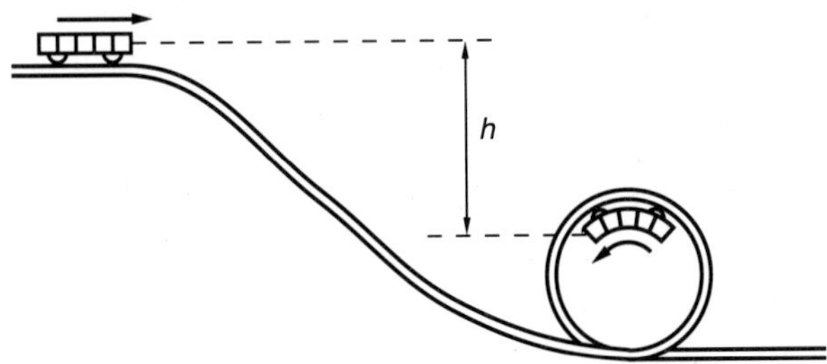

13.2 Centripetal forces

13.15 A particle moves in a circular path at a constant speed. Draw a diagram of the path, mark the position of the particle at some point on the path, and for that point show the direction of

(a) its velocity

(b) its acceleration

(c) the resultant force on it.

13.16 What is the acceleration of a car which has a constant speed of *(a)* $10\,\mathrm{m\,s^{-1}}$ *(b)* $20\,\mathrm{m\,s^{-1}}$, and is moving in a circle of radius 100 m?

13.17 Explain to a person who has not studied physics why he is accelerating when he is travelling round a corner in a car. What evidence might you offer to convince him?

13.18 A point on the Equator makes one revolution in 24 hours.

(a) What is the speed of the point?

(b) What is its acceleration?

Take the radius of the Earth to be 6.4×10^6 m.

13.19 Referring to the previous question, draw a free-body diagram for a man standing on a weighing machine at the Equator. Because he is on the Earth's surface he is moving in a circular path and therefore has a centripetal acceleration.

(a) Calculate his weight, if his mass is 75.00 kg and the value of g at the Equator is $9.780\,\mathrm{N\,kg^{-1}}$.

(b) Calculate the push of the weighing machine on him. Take $r_E = 6.4 \times 10^6$ m.

13.20 The bob of a simple pendulum of length 1.2 m is pulled to one side so that it is a vertical height of 35 mm above its lowest point and is then released. Calculate

(a) its speed at its lowest point

(b) its acceleration there.

Show the direction of its velocity and acceleration (at its lowest point) on a diagram.

13.21 A child of mass 30 kg is playing on a swing. Her centre of mass is 3.2 m below the supports when she moves through the bottom of her swing at $6.0\,\mathrm{m\,s^{-1}}$.

(a) Draw a free-body force diagram of the child at this moment.

(b) Calculate (i) her centripetal acceleration and (ii) the push of the seat of the swing on her.

13.22 A cyclist turns a corner at a constant speed of $5.0\,\mathrm{m\,s^{-1}}$ in a circular arc of radius 8.0 m. Draw a free-body force diagram to show the forces acting on him.

(a) What is his acceleration?

(b) Calculate the resultant force on him and his bicycle, if together they have a mass of 90 kg?

13.23 A car of mass 900 kg is driven over a hump-backed bridge at a speed of $18\,\mathrm{m\,s^{-1}}$. The road surface of the bridge forms part of a circular arc of radius 50 m.

(a) Draw a free-body force diagram for the car when it is at the top of the bridge.

(b) Calculate the push of the road on the car then.

(c) What is the greatest speed at which the car may be driven over the bridge if its wheels are not to lose contact with the road?

13.24 A golfer strikes a ball with a club which at the moment of contact is travelling at $40\,\mathrm{m\,s^{-1}}$. The club may be considered to be a mass of 250 g travelling in a circle of radius 1.6 m.

(a) Calculate the centripetal force on the club.

(b) What is the centrifugal force on the golfer?

Comment on the size of the centrifugal force.

13.25 In throwing the hammer an athlete whirls a steel ball of mass 7.3 kg in a circle at up to $2.4\,\mathrm{rev\,s^{-1}}$. If the effective radius of the circle is 1.9 m calculate the pull of the ball on the wire, assuming that the weight of the sphere is negligible.

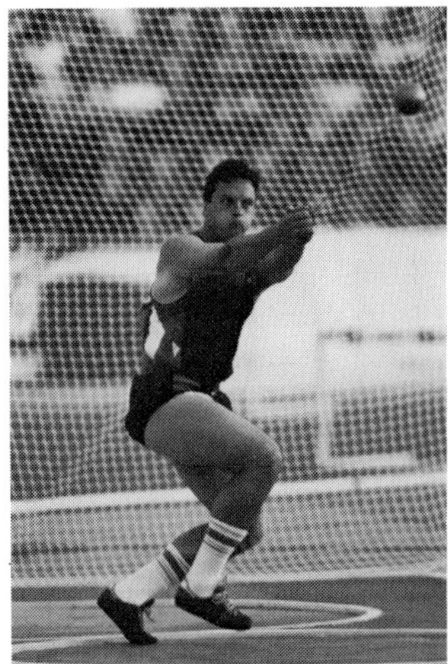

13.26 The figure shows a free-body force diagram for a car of mass m on a banked motor race track (P and F represent the *total* perpendicular and frictional push of the track on the car respectively). It moves at speed v in a horizontal circle of radius r.

(a) Apply $ma = F_{res}$ in (i) the horizontal direction (ii) the vertical direction.

(b) If $\theta = 26°$, and $r = 300\,\mathrm{m}$, what value should v have if the frictional force is to be zero?

(c) If a car drives round the turn at speed of $30\,\mathrm{m\,s^{-1}}$, explain whether the frictional force on the car will act in the direction shown, or in the opposite direction.

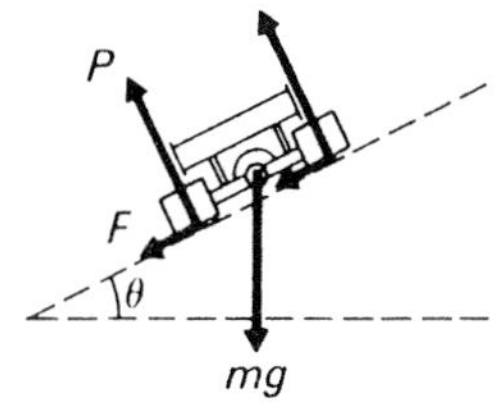

13.27 *(a)* When you stand on a weighing machine, what force is it which pushes on the weighing machine and makes it record a force? [It is *not* your weight.]

(b) Is this force always the same size (while you have the same mass)?

(c) Suggest a situation in which it could momentarily be zero.

(d) If it was zero the weighing machine would record that at that moment you were 'weightless': would you then have no weight?

(e) Can you directly feel your own weight?

13.28 In which of the following situations would a person *feel* weightless:

(a) falling freely near the Earth

(b) falling, with an open parachute, from an aircraft

(c) on board a space module on its way to the Moon with (i) motors running (ii) motors switched off
(d) in a satellite orbiting the Earth?

13.3 Couples and torques

13.29 When steering a car the driver pulls and pushes the steering wheel with parallel forces of 8.0 N. If the wheel is of radius 0.20 m, calculate the torque exerted. What would be the effect of having a much smaller steering wheel?

13.30 The figure shows a rod of weight $W = 1.2$ N which also has forces P, Q, R exerted on it.
(a) Taking moments about A, calculate the moment of each of the forces W, P, Q, R, using clockwise to be positive. What is the sum of the moments? Is the bar in equilibrium?
(b) What is the moment of the couple caused by (i) P and Q (ii) W and R? What is the sum of these moments?
(c) Suppose the couple consisting of the forces P and Q were moved to the other half of the bar, keeping their separation at 0.30 m, but placing P at 0.10 m from the centre. Would the bar still be in equilibrium? Explain.

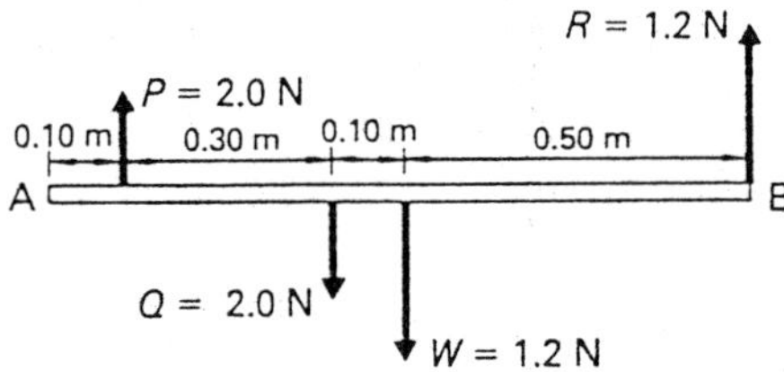

13.31 Find a paperback book and either measure its mass (using kitchen scales if you are at home) or estimate it. Grip it between your thumb and first finger and lift it, keeping the book upright with its longer edges horizontal.
How far from the centre line of the book can you grip it, keeping the longer edges horizontal, using just your thumb and finger? Measure this distance. (If you can manage this with your thumb and finger at the very edge of the book, find a more massive book and try again.)
(a) Draw a free-body force diagram for the book, marking (i) the pull of the Earth on the book (ii) the upward pull of your hand on the book (iii) the torque exerted by your hand on the book.
(b) Calculate the torque.

13.32 An inn sign consists of a uniform rectangular wooden board, which normally hangs in a vertical plane, hinged along its upper edge. When the hinges are rusty it is found to hang in equilibrium making an angle of 10° with the vertical.
(a) Draw a free-body force diagram for the sign to show the forces acting on it, and the torque which the rusty hinge exerts on it.
The mass of the sign is 9.0 kg, and its height is 1.2 m.
(b) Find the upward pull of the hinge on the sign.
(c) What is the frictional torque which the hinge exerts on the sign?

13.33 A man pulls open a door fitted with an automatic door closing mechanism. The width of the door is 1.2 m, and the handle is at the edge of the door.
Draw a free-body force diagram for the door when he is holding it open at an angle of 30° to its original position, assuming that he is pulling at right angles to the original position of the door.
(a) If he exerts a force of 9.0 N and the door is then in equilibrium, what torque is exerted by the door closer?
(b) What force would he have to exert to do the same thing if the handle had been 0.20 m from the line of the hinges?

13.34 A motor car road test report states that the maximum torque is 160 N m at 3400 r.p.m. and the maximum power is 70 kW at 4900 r.p.m. Find
(a) the power at 3400 r.p.m.
(b) the torque at 4900 r.p.m.

13.35 The power of a motor is being measured using a band brake. When the motor is rotating at 3000 r.p.m. the readings on the spring balances attached to the two ends of the belt are 140 N and 30 N, and the diameter of the pulley round which the belt passes is 0.32 m. Calculate

(a) the torque exerted by the motor
(b) the power of the motor.

13.36 A cyclist can maintain a rate of working of 200 W.

(a) If she pushes the pedals round 5 times in 2.0 s, what average torque does she exert?
(b) If she pushes on the pedals at a distance of 0.18 m from the axis of rotation, what is the average force which she exerts?

13.37 The current supplied by a car battery when it is turning the starter motor of a car is 170 A; the p.d. across the battery terminals is then 9.2 V.
Assuming that the motor is 80% efficient, calculate the torque exerted by the starter motor on the engine if it rotates it at 700 r.p.m.

14 Gravitational fields

Data $g = 9.81\,\text{N kg}^{-1}$
$G = 6.67 \times 10^{-11}\,\text{N m}^2\,\text{kg}^{-2}$
mass of Earth $= 5.97 \times 10^{24}$ kg
radius of Earth $= 6.37 \times 10^{6}$ m
mass of Moon $= 7.34 \times 10^{22}$ kg
radius of Moon $= 1.64 \times 10^{6}$ m

14.1 Newton's law of gravitation

14.1 What is the size of the gravitational pull of a sphere of mass 10 kg on a sphere of mass 2.0 kg, when their centres are 200 mm apart? What is the gravitational pull of the 2.0 kg sphere on the 10 kg sphere?

14.2 Calculate (i) the gravitational pull of the Earth on each of the following bodies (ii) their acceleration where they are (see data above):

(a) the Moon, distance from centre of Earth 3.8×10^{8} m
(b) a geosynchronous satellite, mass 100 kg, distance from centre of Earth 4.2×10^{7} m
(c) a satellite near the Earth, mass 80 kg, distance from centre of Earth 8.0×10^{6} m.

14.3 Show that the unit for G, the gravitational constant, can be expressed as $\text{m}^3\,\text{s}^{-2}\,\text{kg}^{-1}$.

14.4 *(a)* Calculate the gravitational force of attraction between (i) two touching lead spheres of radius 50 mm (ii) two touching lead spheres of radius 100 mm. Density of lead $= 1.1 \times 10^{4}\,\text{kg m}^{-3}$.
(b) When Cavendish (1798) performed his experiment to measure G his large lead spheres had a diameter of 152 mm and a mass of 168 kg and his small lead spheres had a diameter of 51.0 mm and a mass of 6.22 kg. What was the maximum force with which each sphere could have pulled on the other?

14.5 An astronaut stands on the surface of the Moon. He is carrying a life-support pack of mass 62 kg. Calculate the push of the pack on him. (See the data at the start of this section.)

14.6 The electrical force of repulsion between two protons (mass 1.7×10^{-27} kg) whose centres are 1.0×10^{-10} m apart is 2.3×10^{-8} N.

(a) What is the gravitational force of attraction between the protons?

(b) What is the ratio (electrical force/gravitational force)?

14.7 If the pull of the Moon on a space vehicle is the same size as (but opposite in direction to) the pull of the Earth on the space vehicle when its distance from the centre of the Earth is 9.0 times its distance from the centre of the Moon what fraction of m_E, the mass of the Earth, is the mass of the Moon? [Hint: write the Earth-Moon distance as 10*d*.]

14.8 *(a)* Use $W = mg$ to find the weight of a mass of 5.00 kg at the surface of the Earth.

(b) Hence use $F = Gm_1m_2/r^2$ to calculate the mass of the Earth.

(c) Deduce the mean density of the Earth.

(d) When the scientists first measured the value of G they said they were 'weighing the Earth'. Explain what they meant.

14.9 *(a)* Show that the gravitational pull of the Sun on the Moon is 179 times that of the Earth on the Moon. (See the data at the start of this section.) Take the mass of the Sun = 2.0×10^{30} kg, the Earth–Sun distance = 1.5×10^8 km, the Earth–Moon distance = 3.8×10^5 km.

(b) Suggest why, despite this, the Moon is more influential than the Sun in producing the tides.

(c) What are spring tides and neap tides? Explain why each occurs approximately twice during each month?

14.10 *(a)* Plot a suitable graph from the following data about four of Uranus' moons to check Kepler's third law of planetary motion: $T^2 \propto r^3$.

Moon	*mean distance from Uranus/km*	*period of revolution/h*
Ariel	192 000	60.5
Umbriel	266 000	99.5
Titania	436 000	209
Oberon	582 000	323

(b) If a further moon of Uranus were discovered with a period of 170 h, what would be its mean distance from Uranus?

(c) Write down an equation connecting the gravitational force on a moon in a circular orbit of radius *r* with the centripetal acceleration and mass of the moon, expressed in terms of the moon's orbital period *T*.
Hence, using your graph, estimate the mass of Uranus.

14.2 Uniform gravitational fields

14.11 A mass of 3.0 kg is lifted 1.6 m from the surface of the Earth.

(a) What is its change of potential energy?

(b) What is the change of potential?

14.12 If the Earth were flat, or uniform thickness *d*, and 'went on' for ever, the uniform gravitational field above its surface would be given by

$$g = \tfrac{1}{2}G\rho d$$

Show that this expression gives the correct unit for g and calculate the thickness *d* needed to give g = 9.8 N kg^{-1} assuming a value for ρ of 5500 kg m^{-3}.

14.13 Describe the motion of a projectile fired horizontally in a uniform gravitational field by drawing a scaled diagram showing its position at uniform time intervals.

14.14 It is suggested that a simple way of measuring g is to use a spring balance to measure the weight *W* of a known mass *m*. Do you regard this as a sensible experiment? [How might the spring balance be calibrated?]

14.15 The figure shows part of the gravitational field near the surface of the Earth. On this scale the field is approximately uniform.

(a) What is the distance apart of the equipotential surfaces?

(b) What is the gravitational force on a mass of 2.0 kg (i) at A (ii) at B?

(c) What is the gravitational p.e. of a mass of 2.0 kg (i) at A (ii) at B?

(d) How much work must be done to move the mass from B to A?

(e) Suppose a stone of mass 2.0 kg has been thrown so that it passes (on a curved path) through A and B: its speed when it passes through A is $3.0\,\mathrm{m\,s^{-1}}$. What is its speed (i) when it is at B (ii) when it hits the ground?

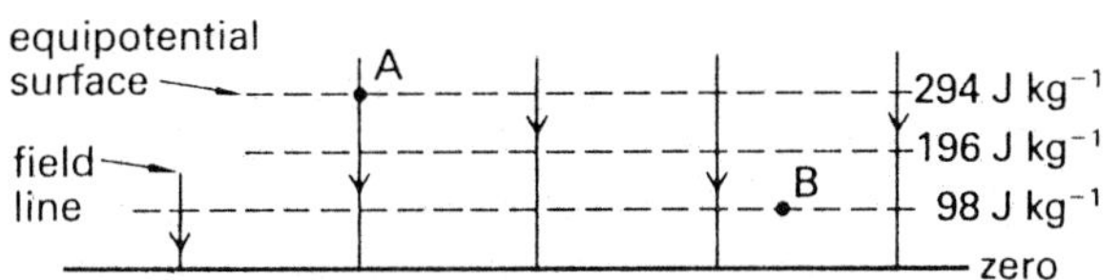

14.16 Copy the diagram used in the previous question and draw *three* possible paths for a freely falling object which is thrown to pass through both A and B. What feature of the motions is common to each of the paths you have drawn?

14.17 Draw and label a set of equipotential surfaces separated by 10 m at the moon's surface. Take the gravitational field strength at the surface of the moon to be $1.7\,\mathrm{N\,kg^{-1}}$.

14.3 Radial gravitational fields

14.18 How far above the surface of the Earth is the gravitational field strength

(a) half

(b) a quarter,

of its value at the surface?

14.19 The figure shows a region near the surface of the Earth.

(a) Taking the zero of gravitational potential to be at infinity, calculate the gravitational potential (i) at A (ii) at B. [Use the data on page 77]

(b) What is the change in g.p.e. of a space capsule of mass 1500 kg when it moves from A to B?

(c) If it later returns through B at a speed of $4.0\,\mathrm{km\,s^{-1}}$, how fast will it be moving at C?

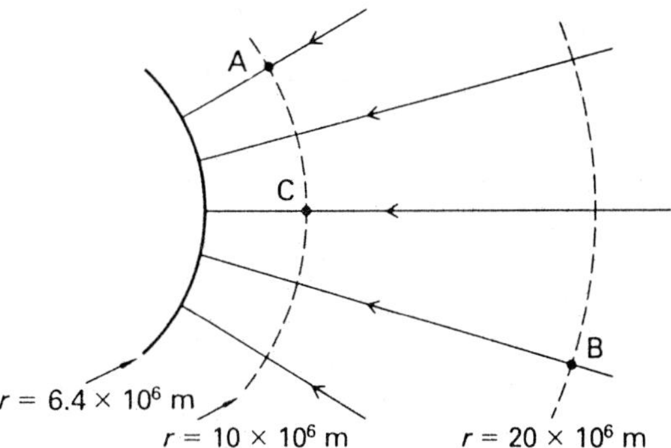

14.20 Show that big gee, G, and little gee at the Earth's surface, g_0, are related by the equation

$$g_0 = \tfrac{4}{3}\pi G \rho r_E$$

where ρ and r_E are the density and radius of the Earth. Use this expression, together with the data on page 77, to calculate a value for ρ.

14.21 The Voyager space probe, launched on September 5th, 1977, approached the outer planet Jupiter about 18 months later. Its distance from the centre of Jupiter and its speed directly towards it, v, were recorded at weekly intervals.

date (1977)	$r/10^9\,\mathrm{m}$	$v/\mathrm{km\,s^{-1}}$
Jan 30	35.10	10.90
Feb 6	28.08	11.00
Feb 13	21.06	11.14
Feb 20	14.04	11.40
Feb 27	7.02	12.17

(a) Plot a graph of v^2 against $1/r$ for these data. Use the graph to find the speed of Voyager 1 when it was a very long way from Jupiter.

(b) Explain how the graph confirms that the space probe's engines were not used during this period. [Hint k.e. $= \tfrac{1}{2}mv^2$ and g.p.e. $= -Gmm_J/r$.]

(c) The gradient of the graph is equal to $2Gm_J$. Deduce a value for the mass of Jupiter.

14.22 Calculate the gravitational pull F of the Earth on a body of mass 10 kg at distance r from the centre of the Earth given by $r/10^6\,\text{m} = 6.4, 8, 10, 15, 20, 30$, and plot a graph of F against r.
The area between the graph and the r–axis represents the work done by the force F. Estimate the change of gravitational potential energy of the body when it moves from $r = 15 \times 10^6\,\text{m}$ to $r = 25 \times 10^6\,\text{m}$.

14.23 *(a)* Use the equation $V_g = -Gm_E/r$ (where $Gm_E = 4.0 \times 10^{14}\,\text{N m}^2\,\text{kg}^{-1}$) to calculate values of gravitational potential V_g for the following values: $r/10^6\,\text{m} = 6.4, 10, 20, 40, 100$. Plot a graph of V_g (on the y–axis) against r (on the x–axis).

(b) Using $dV_g/d = -g$, draw tangents to your curve to estimate the gravitational field strength g at (i) $r = 30 \times 10^6\,\text{m}$ (ii) $r = 60 \times 10^6\,\text{m}$.

14.24 *(a)* What is the gravitational potential energy of a body of mass 100 kg at the Earth's surface, taking the zero of potential to be at infinity?

(b) How much k.e. must it be given at the Earth's surface to just escape from the Earth's gravitational field?

(c) What speed would it then have (its escape speed)?

(d) Does this speed depend on the mass of the body? Explain.

14.25 Suppose that the Sun shrank to become a neutron star of radius 1.5 km yet retained its present mass of $2.0 \times 10^{80}\,\text{kg}$. Calculate the gravitational field at its surface.
(In fact, the Sun would undergo changes before it became a neutron star which would involve it losing a considerable proportion of its present mass.)

14.26 *(a)* Show that the Earth's gravitational field reduces by 1% of its value at sea level, $r = 6370\,\text{km}$, at a height of 32 km.

(b) Without further calculation explain at what height it will reduce by a further 1%.

14.27 Calculate the escape speed for the Moon. (See data on page 77). The temperature of the Moon's surface rises to about 400 K, when sunlight falls on it. At this temperature the r.m.s speed of oxygen molecules is $560\,\text{m s}^{-1}$. Why has the Moon no atmosphere?

14.28 The Universe is expanding. The speed of recession v of a galaxy a distance r from us is given by

$$v = Hr$$

where H is the Hubble constant and is at the moment equal to $1.6 \times 10^{-18}\,\text{s}^{-1}$.

(a) Show that the often-quoted value $H = 15\,\text{km s}^{-1}$ per million light years is equivalent to that given above. Take the speed of light to be $3.0 \times 10^8\,\text{m s}^{-1}$.

(b) Explain why v will decrease with time and discuss how the total mass of the Universe will affect whether galaxies continue to recede for ever or reach a maximum separation and then begin to contract.

(c) It can be shown that for a Universe which *just* continues to expand for ever, the age of the Universe is given by $2/3H$. Calculate the present age of the Universe in this case.

14.4 Satellites

14.29 What is the period of a satellite which is moving a few thousand metres above the Earth's surface? Take $g = 9.8\,\text{N kg}^{-1}$ at this height.

14.30 *(a)* Calculate the orbital radius of a synchronous satellite, i.e. one which has a period of 24 hours so that it appears to remain stationary above one point on the Earth's surface. Roughly how many Earth radii is this orbital radius? Why must the satellite be in the plane of the Equator?

(b) Draw a scale diagram to estimate the angle above the horizontal that a receiving aerial in latitude 45° must point in order to receive signals from the satellite.

14.31 The period of Io, the most prominent of Jupiter's satellites, is $1.53 \times 10^5\,\text{s}$, and the radius of its orbit is $4.20 \times 10^8\,\text{m}$. Calculate the mass of Jupiter.

14.32 The *Apollo* 11 spacecraft was orbiting the Moon at a speed of $1.65\,km\,s^{-1}$ before the first lunar module landed.

(a) How far was it above the Moon's surface? (See the data on page 77).

(b) What would be the speed of a satellite moving in orbit just above the surface of the Moon?

14.33 The *Apollo* 11 space capsule was placed in a parking orbit (around the Earth) of radius $6.56 \times 10^6\,m$ before moving onwards to the Moon.

(a) Calculate the value of the gravitational field strength at this radius.

(b) What was the acceleration of the capsule then?

(c) Use $W = mg$ to find the weight of a 70 kg astronaut in the capsule.

(d) What was his acceleration?

(e) Use $ma = F_{res}$ to find the resultant force on him.

(f) Did any force other than his own weight act on him?

(g) What would a weighing machine in the capsule have recorded if he had stood on it?

15 Storing electric charge

Data $g = 9.81\,N\,kg^{-1}$

15.1 Capacitors

15.1 In the arrangement shown in the figure the meter is a sensitive light-spot type with its zero set in the centre of its scale. The two-way switch is initially in position Y. Describe what you would observe, and account for it in terms of the movement of charge in the circuit,

(a) when the switch is moved to position X

(b) when the switch is then lifted off contact X and held mid-way between X and Y without touching either

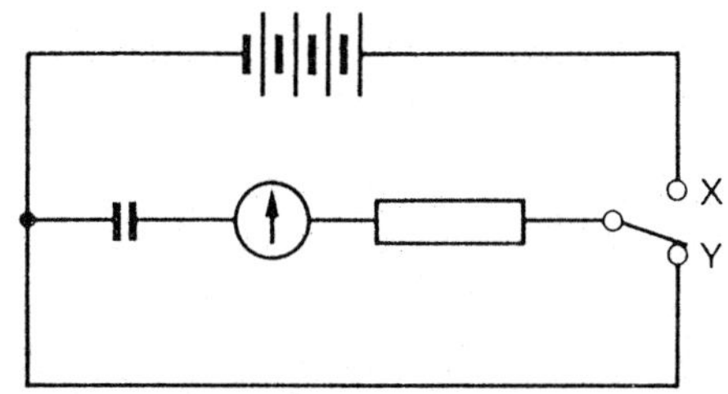

(c) when the switch is moved again to position Y.

15.2 In the previous question an oscilloscope may be used to observe what is happening in the circuit. Describe what traces you would expect to see on the screen in each of the three stages *(a)*, *(b)* and *(c)* of that question, (i) if the oscilloscope is joined across the resistor, (ii) if the oscilloscope is joined across the capacitor.

15.3 What is meant by *ripple* in a smoothed 12 V laboratory a.c. power supply unit? Explain, with the aid of a diagram, how this ripple can be further smoothed by using a capacitor.

15.4 A certain type of microphone consists of a strip of metal foil separated from a metal plate by a narrow air gap and insulated from it. The plate and the foil are connected to a suitable d.c. supply. Sound waves arriving at the foil cause it to vibrate to and fro varying the width of the air gap. Describe what changes you would expect to occur in the charges on the foil and on the plate as the foil vibrates. At what point in the vibration of the foil would

(a) the charge on the foil be a maximum
(b) the current in the connecting leads be a maximum?

15.5 The figure shows a water circuit which can be used as an analogy for an electrical circuit. The tank contains a rubber membrane through which the water cannot pass but which stretches further and further the harder the pump works.
Sketch the water circuit and add alongside it the analogous electrical circuit using standard symbols. Write a few words explaining the way in which each component in the water circuit acts like its partner in the electrical circuit.

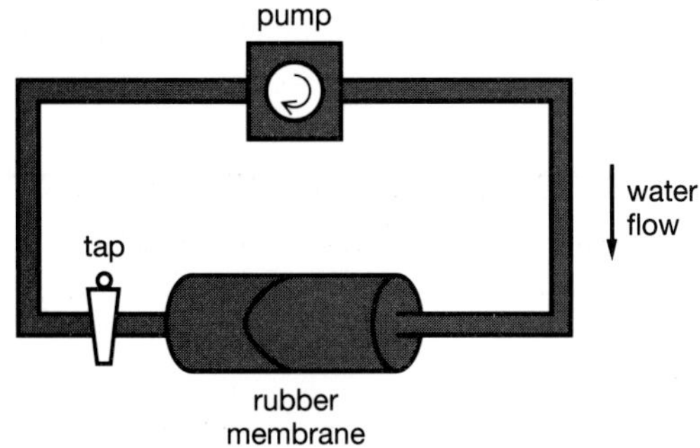

15.2 Capacitance

15.6 A capacitor of capacitance 10 μF is connected to a battery of e.m.f. 12 V. What are the charges on its plates?

15.7 What potential difference must be applied between the plates of a 100 pF capacitor for the charges on them to be ±0.025 μC?

15.8 Copy and complete the following table which gives the charge Q on capacitors of capacitance C when there is a p.d. *V* across them. Express your answers using prefixes (not in standard form).

V	C	Q
12.0 V	2.2 μF	
	5000 μF	10 mC
1.5 V	4.7 μF	
	220 μF	66 nc
100 V		1.0 nC
600 mV		280 μC

15.9 *(a)* What charge is carried on each of the plates of a 100 μF capacitor when there is a potential difference between the plates of 200 V?
(b) If this capacitor is charged through a large resistance in 4.0 s, what is the average charging current? Will the charging current at the start of this time be greater or less than the average current?

15.10 A 33 μF capacitor is charged and then insulated. During the next minute the potential difference between the plates falls by 4.0 V. What is the average leakage current between the plates?

15.11 A steady charging current of 50 μA is supplied to the plates of a capacitor and causes the potential difference between them to rise from 0 to 5.0 V in 20 s. What is its capacitance?

15.12 Show that the unit of capacitance, the farad, is equivalent to $A^2 s^4 kg^{-1} m^{-2}$.

15.13 Draw a circuit, using a constant current source, which could be used to measure the capacitance C of a capacitor. If C is known to be about 50 μF, suggest values for any electrical components you use, including the current source, and also the range of any meters.

15.14 A capacitor of capacitance 0.47 μF is connected across the Y–input terminals of an oscilloscope. The horizontal (time-base) control is set at 100 ms div^{-1}, and the Y–input control at 5.0 V div^{-1}. A battery is then connected across the capacitor for a short period of time *t*, and the trace shown in the figure is observed.
(a) Estimate the time *t*.
(b) Estimate the change of p.d. across the capacitor.
(c) What is the rate of change of p.d. (dV/dt)?

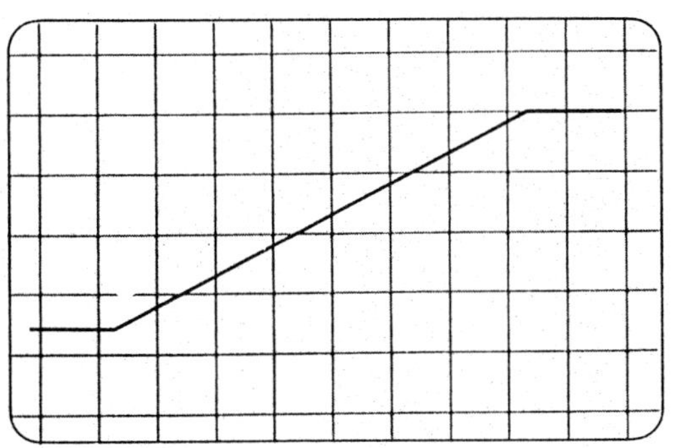

(d) What can you say about the charging current?

15.15 A capacitor is joined in series with a resistor, a low resistance microammeter, a switch and a 12 V battery as shown in the circuit diagram.

(a) When the switch is first closed, what is (i) the p.d. across the capacitor (ii) the p.d. across the resistor (iii) the current (iv) the charge on each of the capacitor plates?

(b) Calculate also the same quantities when the switch has been closed for some time so that steady conditions have been reached.

(c) If the capacitor had continued to charge at its initial rate, how long would it have taken to become fully charged?

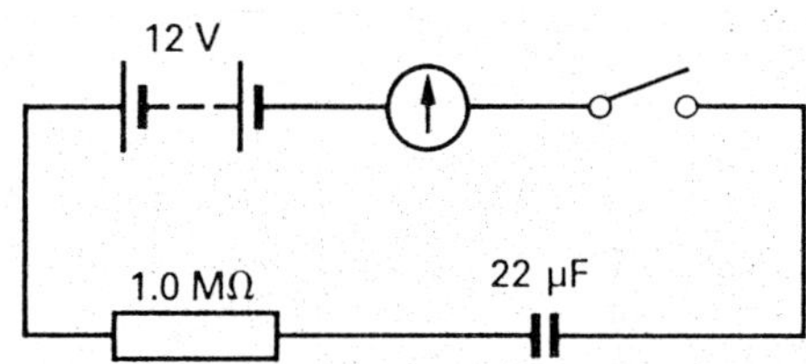

15.16 In the previous question, at a certain instant after the switch has been closed the microammeter reads 9.5 μA. Calculate, for this instant

(a) the p.d. across the resistor

(b) the p.d. across the capacitor

(c) the charge on each of the capacitor plates.

15.17 A capacitor of capacitance 180 pF is charged to a potential difference of 12 V and then discharged through a sensitive meter, and this sequence of operations is repeated by means of a reed-switch 250 times per second. What is the average current in the meter?

15.18 A vibrating reed is used to connect a capacitor alternately to a battery and to a meter. In this way the capacitor is fully charged by the battery and fully discharged through the meter 50 times per second.

(a) Draw a circuit diagram showing how this arrangement is set up. Explain the purpose of the diode joined in series with the reed-switch coil in your arrangement.

(b) If the e.m.f. of the battery is 12 V and the meter records an average current of 2.4 mA, what is the capacitance of the capacitor?

15.19 If in the circuit shown for question *15.15* the 1.0 MΩ resistor was a variable resistor, explain how you could use the circuit to charge the capacitor at a steady rate.

If the capacitance was not known, what measurements would you take and what addition(s) to the circuit would be required in order to measure the capacitance of the capacitor?

15.20 Two capacitors are arranged in series as in the figure. A charge of 60 μC is pushed onto the left plate w of the 30 μF capacitor and the same charge is removed from plate z of the 60 μF capacitor.

(a) What will happen to the charge on the pair of plates x and y?

(b) Calculate the p.d. across each capacitor.

(c) What is the p.d. *V* between P and Q?

(d) Calculate the capacitance of a single capacitor connected between P and Q which would store 60 μC of charge when connected to this same p.d. *V*.

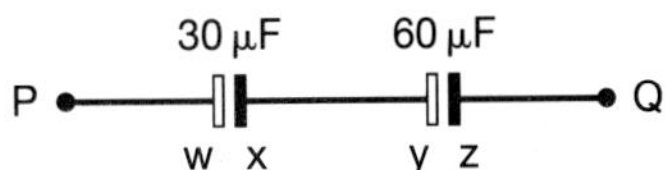

15.21 Plot a graph showing how the charge Q in a 1.5 μF capacitor varies with the potential difference V across it for values of p.d. from 0 up to 30 V.
On the same axes draw a further two lines to show the relation between Q and V for a pair of such capacitors

(a) in parallel
(b) in series.

15.22 Three capacitors of capacitances 2.0 μF, 3.0 μF and 6.0 μF are joined ***(a)*** in parallel ***(b)*** in series. What is the combined capacitance in each case?

15.23 In the arrangement shown the battery has an e.m.f. of 9.0 V, and the capacitors A, B and C have capacitances of 3.0 μF, 1.5 μF and 4.5 μF respectively. Work out the charge stored in each capacitor and the p.d. between its plates.

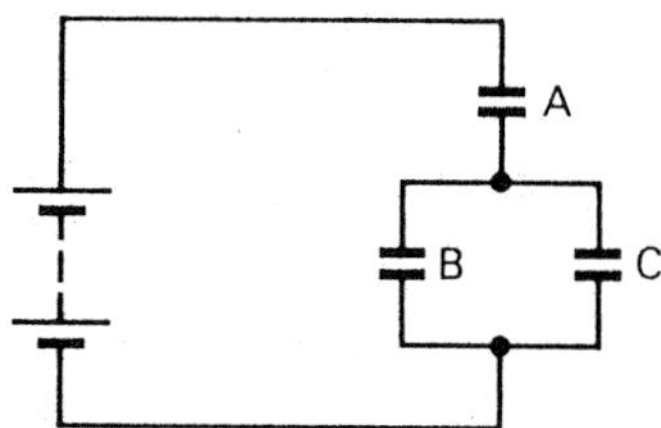

15.24 A capacitor of capacitance 22 μF is charged by connecting it to a 400 V supply, and is then discharged.

(a) Calculate the energy converted during the discharge.
(b) If the discharge takes 10 μs, what is the average power of the discharge?

15.25 To what p.d. must a 1500 μF capacitor be charged to enable it, when it is discharged through a small electric motor, to lift a 10 g mass through a vertical height of 1.0 m? (Assume that 10% of the electrical energy is converted to gravitational potential energy in this process.)

15.26 ***(a)*** A capacitor of capacitance 16 μF is connected for a short time across a 150 V d.c. supply. What is the charge on the capacitor plates, and what is the energy stored?
(b) A second (initially uncharged) capacitor of capacitance 8.0 μF is now joined in parallel with the first. (i) Calculate the new potential difference across the capacitors. (ii) How much energy is now stored in the system?
(c) How do you account for the change of energy?

15.27 An 8.0 μF capacitor is charged by joining it to a 500 V supply through a resistor.

(a) What charge flows through the supply and the resistor?
(b) How much electrical energy is taken from the supply?
(c) How much electrical energy is stored in the capacitor?
(d) How do you account for the difference between these two amounts?

15.28 Discuss the analogy between the behaviour of a capacitor $V = Q/C$ and the behaviour of a spring $F = kx$. (These two equations are often referred to as mathematical models for a capacitor and a spring respectively.)

15.29 After a capacitor of capacitance 4.7 μF has been charged to a p.d. of 500 V it is disconnected from the supply and joined across a neon bulb which conducts only so long as the potential difference across it is more than 100 V.

(a) What electric charge passes through the bulb?
(b) How much electrical energy does the capacitor transfer?

15.30 Two capacitors, one of capacitance 8.0 μF charged to a potential difference of 50 V, and the other of capacitance 4.0 μF charged to a potential difference of 200 V, are joined in parallel (positive terminals together). Calculate

(a) the charge on each capacitor before they are joined together
(b) the potential difference across them after they are joined together [Hint: the p.d. must be the same across each and charge is conserved.]
(c) the charge that flows from one capacitor to the other (and indicate on a diagram exactly where this charge flows)

(d) the decrease in the energy stored as the result of joining the capacitors together.

15.31 A steady p.d. of 200 V is maintained across a combination of two capacitors in series, one of capacitance 2.0 μF and the other of capacitance 0.50 μF. What is

(a) the combined capacitance
(b) the charge stored in each capacitor
(c) the potential difference across each capacitor
(d) the energy stored in each capacitor?

15.32 Two capacitors of capacitance 5.0 μF and 3.0 μF are joined in series.

(a) What is their combined capacitance?
(b) What capacitor joined in parallel with this combination will produce a combined capacitance of 4.0 μF?
(c) What energy will be stored in this system when it is connected to a d.c. supply of 12 V?

15.33 A capacitor of capacitance 6000 μF is charged to a potential difference of 50 V. It is then discharged through a compact tangle of copper wire of total mass 2.5 g.

(a) If the s.h.c. of copper is 380 J K^{-1} kg^{-1}, calculate the rise in temperature produced.
(b) What problems would you have in measuring this rise in temperature?

15.34 If you have three capacitors of capacitances 3.0 μF, 6.0 μF and 8.0 μF, how could you produce a combination of capacitance 10 μF?

15.35 In a certain piece of equipment you need to replace a 1 μF capacitor which is used with potential differences up to 500 V. All you have available is a stock of 1 μF capacitors tested to work up to 200 V. What combination of these would you use?

15.36 It takes 6.0 J of energy to transfer 10 mC of charge from one plate of a charged 50 μF capacitor to the other. How much charge was there initially on each plate? [Hint: call the initial charge Q.]

15.3 Meters

15.37 A digital voltmeter is designed to measure p.d.s of up to 2.0 V and has an input resistance of $1.0 \times 10^{-13}\,\Omega$. Explain how such an instrument may be adapted to measure *(a)* currents up to 20 pA *(b)* charges up to 200 nC.

15.38 Describe how you would use a coulombmeter to check the sign of the frictional charges produced when rods made of various *conducting* materials are rubbed. [Hint: you will need to grip the rods with insulating gloves.]

15.39 A coulombmeter has ranges up to 20 nC, 200 nC and 2000 nC. If the range is changed by switching in different capacitors across the input terminals and the 2000 nC range uses a 4.7 μF capacitor, what values are used for the other ranges?
Is this a sensible method for altering the range? What other method might be used?

15.40 A capacitor of unknown capacitance is charged by connecting it momentarily across a 30 V d.c. supply. It is then touched across the input terminals of a digital voltmeter which is being operated with an input capacitance between its terminals of 0.010 μF. The instrument reads 0.25 V.

(a) Calculate (i) the charge delivered to the digital voltmeter (and capacitor) (ii) the unknown capacitance.
(b) What is the charge on the unknown capacitor when the p.d. across it is 0.25 V?
(c) Calculate the percentage of the charge on the unknown capacitor that remains on it after it has been touched across the digital voltmeter terminals.

15.41 A leaf electrometer has a capacitance of 15 pF. When a potential difference of 800 V is applied between cap and case the leaf deflects through 8 divisions of the scale. In this position, owing to imperfect insulation, the deflection is found to decrease slowly at the rate of one division in 5 minutes. Assuming that the deflection is proportional to the applied p.d., estimate

(a) the leakage current

(b) the resistance of the insulation.

15.42 The graph in the figure shows how the deflection θ of a leaf electrometer varies with the p.d. V between cap and case. The capacitance of the instrument is 12 pF.

(a) What is the p.d. indicated by a deflection (i) of 60° (ii) of 30°?

(b) If it takes 12 hours for the deflection of the instrument to fall from 60° to 30°, estimate the average leakage current during this time.

(c) Estimate the resistance of the insulation between cap and case.

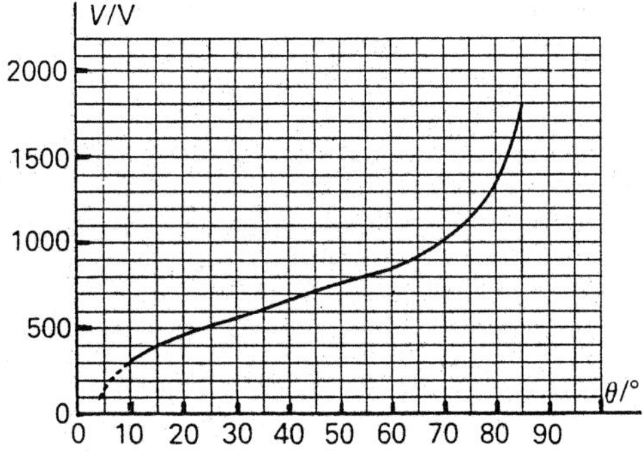

15.43 Refer to the graph in the previous question showing how the deflection of a leaf electrometer varies with the p.d. V applied across it.

(a) Is there any range of p.d.s over which the variation could be described as linear?

(b) Is there any range of p.d.s. over which θ could be described as directly proportional to V?

(c) If the uncertainty in estimating θ is in practice about 5°, what is the uncertainty in the p.d. recorded by the instrument (i) at 500 V (ii) at 1500 V?

(d) If an alternating p.d. of 1000 V (r.m.s.) is connected across the electrometer, what deflection would you expect?

15.4 Charging and discharging

15.44 A capacitor of capacitance 10 μF is charged to a potential difference of 20 V and then isolated. If its leakage resistance is 10 MΩ how long will it take approximately for the potential difference across it to fall to 19 V?

15.45 The capacitor in the figure has an initial charge of 10 000 μC. At time $t = 0$ the switch is closed so that the capacitor gradually discharges through the resistor.

(a) Calculate (i) the initial p.d. across C and (ii) the current in R when the switch is closed. (The p.d. across R = the p.d. across C.)

(b) Assuming this current was constant from $t = 0$ to $t = 10$ s, calculate (iii) the charge flowing in this 10 s interval and (iv) the new charge on C.

(c) Now repeat calculations (i)–(iv) for the next 10 s interval.

(d) Set up a table to show successive values of the quantities calculated in steps (i)–(iv) for up to 10 intervals, i.e. until $t = 100$ s.

(e) Plot a graph of the charge on the capacitor against time.

(f) Plot a graph of the current in the resistor against time.

(g) Write a computer program which would plot values of Q or I and t using this iterative method.

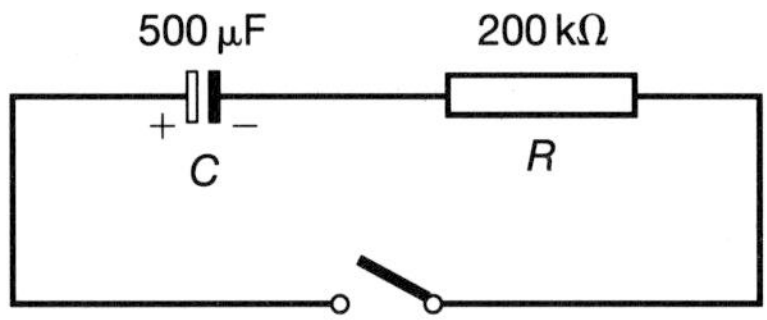

15.46 A capacitor is joined across a digital voltmeter and charged to a potential difference of 1.00 V. The potential difference V is then measured at 20 s intervals, as tabulated below. When time $t = 30$ s, a resistance R of 1.5 MΩ is joined across the capacitor.

t/s	0	20	40	60	80	100	120
V/V	1.00	1.00	0.81	0.54	0.35	0.23	0.15

(a) What is the current in the resistor at $t = 30$ s?

(b) Plot a graph of V against t, and measure the rate of decrease of V immediately after $t = 30$ s.

(c) Hence calculate the capacitance C of the capacitor.

(d) Plot also a graph of ln (V/V) against t to demonstrate the exponential fall of p.d., and measure the time constant (RC) of the decay process.

(e) From the time constant calculate the capacitance C. Explain which method of finding C gives the better value of C, and why.

15.47 A capacitor is joined in series with a 150 kΩ resistor, a microammeter and a switch to a d.c. supply. At time $t = 10$ s, the switch is closed, and readings of the current are taken until $t = 80$ s. A graph of I against t is shown in the figure.

(a) Calculate the p.d. of the supply.

(b) At what moment does the p.d. across the resistor fall to exactly half its initial value?

(c) The area under the graph represents the charge that flows through the resistor. By estimating the area of strips of the graph representing successive time intervals of 10 s, calculate and tabulate the total charge Q in the capacitor at 10 s intervals from $t = 10$ s to $t = 80$ s.

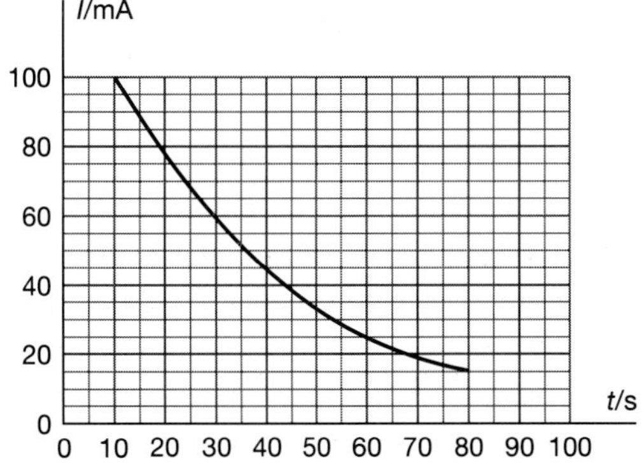

(d) Plot a graph of Q against t.

(e) What is the total charge in the capacitor at the moment given by *(b)* above?

(f) What is the p.d. across the capacitor at this moment?

(g) Calculate the capacitance of the capacitor.

15.48 *(a)* Suggest values of R and C which would produce circuits with time constants of 1.0 s, 25 s, 5.0 minutes.

(b) You have four 1.0 μF capacitors and four 100 kΩ resistors but no other components. Draw a diagram to show how you could produce a circuit with a time constant of 0.50 s.

15.49 A poor-quality 100 μF capacitor is charged and connected to a digital voltmeter (of very high resistance). It is found that the p.d. across the capacitor falls to half its initial value in 300 s. What is

(a) the time constant of the discharge process

(b) the resistance of the insulation of the capacitor?

15.50 A reed-switch kept vibrating at a rate of $50\,s^{-1}$ is used to connect a capacitor of capacitance 1.0 μF alternately to a 10 V supply and a 1.0 kΩ resistor. The time during which the capacitor is not connected either to the supply nor to the resistor can be taken as negligible.

(a) If an oscilloscope is joined across the resistor, indicate the type of trace you would expect to observe.

(b) What is the peak p.d. across the resistor?

(c) What is the peak current in the resistor?

(d) What is the average current in the resistor?

15.51 In one method for measuring the speed of a rifle bullet v, the bullet is made to break strips of conducting foil first at A and then at B, where the distance AB is d. See the diagram overleaf.

(a) Design an RC circuit in which opening a switch at A starts the discharge of a charged capacitor and opening a switch at B stops the discharge. Add a voltmeter which would enable you, if R and C are known, to find the time taken by the bullet to get from A to B.

(b) If v is about 300 m s^{-1}, suggest suitable values for d, R and C which would enable v to be measured. [Hint: you would wish C to lose about half its charge during the experiment.]

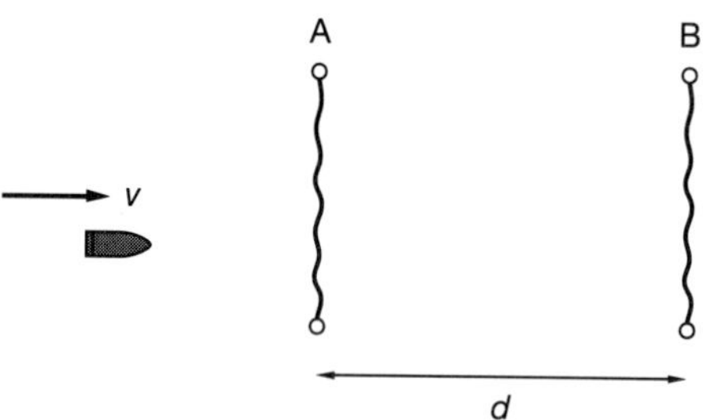

15.52 A 400 μF capacitor is charged to a p.d. of 100 V. It is then joined across a resistor of resistance 250 kΩ, which is of heat capacity 0.050 J K^{-1} and is initially at a temperature of 290 K. Assuming that the resistor is thermally isolated, calculate

(a) the initial current

(b) the initial rate of conversion of electrical energy to internal energy

(c) the initial rate of rise of temperature

(d) the temperature of the resistor after it has been connected across the capacitor for 50 s.

15.53 A 47 μF capacitor is charged to 6.0 V and then discharged through a 1.0 MΩ resistor.

(a) What is the initial charge stored in the capacitor?

(b) Calculate the initial current I_0 and hence find the time t_d the capacitor would take to discharge fully if this discharging current were to remain constant.

(c) Calculate the product RC for this circuit.

(d) Show that, in general, $RC = I_0 t_d$.

16 Electric fields

Data $g = 9.81\,\mathrm{N\,kg^{-1}}$

$e = 1.60 \times 10^{-19}\,\mathrm{C}$

$\varepsilon_0 = 8.85 \times 10^{-12}\,\mathrm{F\,m^{-1}}$

mass of an electron $m_e = 9.11 \times 10^{-31}\,\mathrm{kg}$

16.1 Electrical forces

16.1 Some small fragments of paper are scattered on a wooden bench top. When a polythene strip that has been rubbed with a woollen duster is moved across the bench top a few centimetres above it the paper fragments leap up and stick to it; a few seconds later some of the paper fragments suddenly leave the surface of the polythene strip, dive down to the bench top and jump quickly up again to the strip. Explain what is going on in terms of the electric charges involved.

Another experimenter does the same test, but has left a small gas burner alight at the back of his bench. He observes no movement of paper fragments at all. Explain why this is so. (You can try both these experiments on a table at home. Use a plastic ballpoint pen instead of the polythene strip.)

16.2 *(a)* What electrical force acts on a small polystyrene ball carrying a charge of 5.0 nC in a horizontal electric field of strength 0.50 MN C^{-1}?

(b) If this polystyrene ball is of mass 0.30 g, what gravitational force acts on it in the Earth's gravitational field?

(c) If the polystyrene ball is suspended by a fine insulating thread in both the above fields, draw a free-body diagram for the ball, and calculate the angle to the vertical at which the thread will come to rest in the above two fields.

16.3 By considering the defining equations of the quantities involved show that $1\,\text{V}\,\text{m}^{-1} = 1\,\text{N}\,\text{C}^{-1}$.

16.4 A charged polystyrene ball of mass 0.14 g is suspended by a nylon thread from a fine glass spring. In the absence of any electric field the spring extends by 30 mm. The polystyrene ball is then placed in an electric field that acts vertically upwards, of strength $2.0 \times 10^5\,\text{V}\,\text{m}^{-1}$, and the spring extends by a further 6.0 mm. What is the electric charge on the polystyrene ball?

16.5 What radius of water drop carrying a surplus charge of 1 electron would remain stationary under the combined action of the Earth's electric and gravitational fields? Show on a diagram the direction of the lines of force of the electric field near the ground. Take the Earth's electric field strength as $300\,\text{V}\,\text{m}^{-1}$, and the density of water as $1000\,\text{kg}\,\text{m}^{-3}$. (See data opposite.)

16.2 Electric potential

16.6 A small metal object in contact with an earthed plate carries a charge of $8.0 \times 10^{-9}\,\text{C}$. How much work is done on it by the electric field if it is moved to another plate at a potential of $-3.5\,\text{kV}$?

16.7 An electron is emitted with negligible energy from an earthed electrode in a vacuum tube. It is then accelerated towards another electrode maintained at a potential of 60 V.

(a) Calculate the kinetic energy gained by the electron.

(b) What speed does it reach? (See data opposite.)

16.8 Two parallel metal plates are fixed 20 mm apart and are maintained at a potential difference of 1000 V.

(a) What is the potential gradient in the gap?

(b) What force would act on a particle in the gap carrying a charge on $2.0 \times 10^{-11}\,\text{C}$ when its distance from the negative plate is (i) 10 mm (ii) 2.0 mm?

16.9 A vacuum tube contains two parallel electrodes 7.5 mm apart. A p.d. of 150 V is maintained between them.

(a) What is the electric field strength in the gap?

(b) What is the force acting on an electron in the gap?

(c) If an electron is emitted at negligible speed from the negative electrode, how long does it take to cross the gap? (See data opposite.)

16.10 Four flat metal plates A, B, C and D are arranged parallel to one another, as in the figure. The plates are each 1.0 mm thick, and the distance between adjacent plates is 25 mm. The two outer plates A and D are earthed, while B and C are maintained at potentials of +150 V and +450 V respectively.

(a) Draw a graph to show how the potential varies along a line perpendicular to the plates from plate A through to plate D.

(b) What is the electric field strength at different positions along this line, both between the plates and inside the metal. (You should give both the direction and magnitude of the field.)

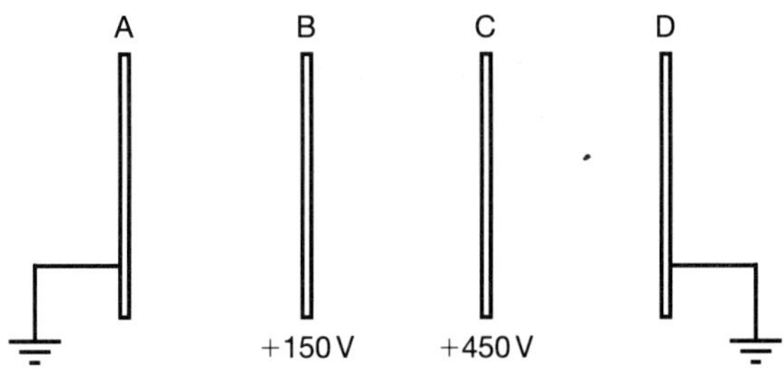

16.11 *(a)* The figure overleaf shows a small charged particle at a point A in a *uniform* electric field. The particle experiences an electrical force *F* as shown of $5.00 \times 10^{-7}\,\text{N}$. The grid lines in the figure are at intervals of 2.5 mm. Calculate the work done by the electrical force if the particle is moved (i) from A to B (ii) from A to C (iii) from A to D.

(b) If the particle carries a charge of $-2.50 \times 10^{-11}\,\text{C}$, and the point A is at a potential of 200 V, what are the potentials of B, C and D? Which of the grid lines in the figure coincide with lines of force and which coincide with equipotential surfaces?

(c) If the field described in this question is in fact produced by a pair of flat metal plates, one of which is earthed and the other of which is at a potential of 1000 V, copy the diagram and draw the positions of the two plates on it.

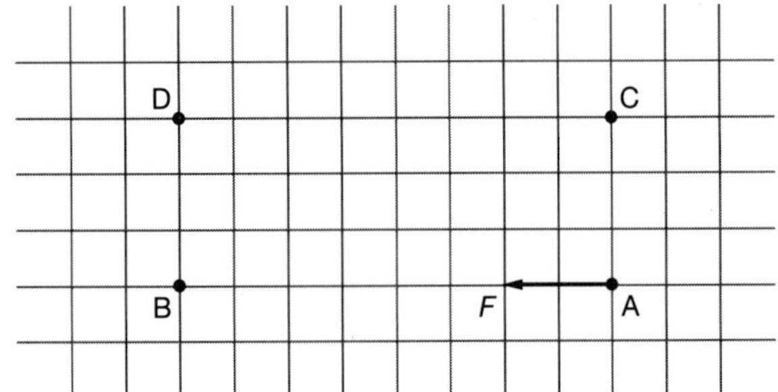

16.3 The electronic charge

16.12 In Millikan's oil drop experiment we observe the drops to move with constant *speed* owing to the viscous drag of the air on the oil drops. Draw free-body force diagrams for an oil drop both when the electric field is switched on and when there is no electric field. Explain why the speed rather than the acceleration of the oil drop is constant.

16.13 A charged oil drop of mass 2.0×10^{-15} kg is observed to remain stationary in the space between two horizontal metal plates when the p.d. between them is 245 V and their separation is 8.0 mm. What is the charge on the drop?

16.14 What potential difference would you need to maintain between two horizontal metal plates 6.00 mm apart so that a particle of mass 4.00×10^{-15} kg with three surplus electrons attached to it would remain in equilibrium between them? Which plate would be the positive one?

16.15 Refer to the previous question. When the potential difference between the plates is 480 V, the particle moves slowly downwards in the space between them. When it has fallen 4.00 mm, what is the work done

(a) by the gravitational force acting on it

(b) the electrical force acting on it?

(c) What is the change in its potential energy (gravitational + electrical)? Explain fully the energy conversions involved in this movement.

16.4 Permittivity

16.16 The fair weather electric field strength at the Earth's surface is 300 V m^{-1} directed vertically downwards.

(a) What is the density of charge on the Earth's surface and of what sign is it?

(b) If the surface area of the British Isles is 3.0×10^{-11} m^2, what is the total surface charge carried in fair weather on this part of the Earth's surface?

16.17 The surface density of charge on a certain region of a metal object is 1.6×10^{-5} C m^{-2}. What is the strength of the electric field close to this surface?

16.18 A capacitor consists of two parallel metal plates 12 mm apart in air, each of area 0.040 m^2. If the potential difference between the plates is 4.0 kV, calculate

(a) the electric field strength in the gap

(b) the surface charge density on each plate

(c) the total charge on each of the plates.

What would the total charge on the plates be if the gap between them was filled with an oil of relative permittivity 2.5?

16.19 A capacitor is made by coating a strip of plastic on both sides with metal foil. The plastic strip is 10 m long, 40 mm wide and 2.0×10^{-5} m thick, and is of relative permittivity 2.8. What is its capacitance, and what is the energy stored in it when the potential difference between the layers of metal foil is 500 V?

16.20 A mica capacitor consists of nine rectangular metal plates, measuring 30 mm by 20 mm, interleaved with sheets of mica of thickness 0.15 mm and relative permittivity 6.0. Calculate its capacitance.

16.21 Polythene has a relative permittivity of 3.0 and breaks down for electric field strengths in excess of $60\,\mathrm{MV\,m^{-1}}$. If it is desired to construct a capacitor with polythene insulation of capacitance $1.0\,\mu\mathrm{F}$ and able to withstand p.d.s. up to 1500V, work out

(a) the thickness of insulation required

(b) the area of each plate

(c) the energy per unit volume of polythene at the maximum design p.d. of 1500V.

Draw a diagram to show the form of construction you would employ for this capacitor, and suggest values for the length and width of the sheet of polythene you would use.

16.22 Two square metal plates (0.10m by 0.10m) are arranged horizontally one above the other 2.5mm apart. The lower plate is earthed, and the upper one is raised to a potential of 5.0kV and then insulated. Calculate

(a) the capacitance of the arrangement

(b) the charge carried on each plate

(c) the energy stored in the arrangement.

If the upper plate is now raised (keeping it insulated) until the gap between the plates is 5.0mm, calculate

(d) the potential of the upper plate

(e) the energy stored. By what means has the extra energy been supplied to the apparatus?

16.23 A capacitor consists of two parallel circular metal plates of diameter 250mm placed 1.0mm apart in air. These plates are connected to the cap and case of a leaf electrometer, and the system is charged by connecting it momentarily across a d.c. supply of 200V. When the separation of the plate is increased to 4.0mm, the deflection of the leaf increases until it indicates a p.d. of 700V. Explain this observation, and calculate the capacitance of the leaf electrometer.

16.24 Two metal plates are arranged parallel to one another 1.50mm apart; the capacitance of the capacitor so formed is 400pF. The plates are permanently connected to the terminals of a storage battery of e.m.f. 24.0V.

(a) Calculate the charge on each plate.

(b) What is the energy stored in the capacitor?

The separation of the plates is now increased to 4.50mm. Calculate

(c) the new charge on each plate

(d) the charge that flows through the battery, and state whether this charges or discharges the battery

(e) the change in the energy stored in the *battery*

(f) the change in the energy stored in the *capacitor*

(g) the mechanical work done in increasing the plate separation

(h) the average force with which one plate attracts the other.

16.25 A capacitor is filled with a poor quality insulator of resistivity $1.5 \times 10^{-12}\,\Omega\,\mathrm{m}$ and relative permittivity 4.0. This capacitor is charged by joining it to a 100V supply and then isolated.

(a) What is the time constant (RC) of the discharge process?

(b) What is the p.d. across the capacitor 60s after being isolated from the supply?

16.26 A reed-switch capacitance meter is used to measure how the capacitance of a pair of parallel metal plates 0.25m square varies with their separation d. The reed-switch connects the capacitor first to a supply of 25.0V and then to a meter through which the capacitor is discharged. The frequency of the a.c. supply which drives the reed-switch is 300Hz. The following values of the average current I through the meter are obtained for values of d shown:

d/mm	1.5	3.0	4.5	6.0
$I/\mu\mathrm{A}$	3.6	2.3	1.7	1.5

(a) Plot a graph of I against $1/d$.

(b) Do you consider these results justify the assumption that the capacitance is inversely proportional to d? Explain why your graph does not pass through the origin.

(c) Measure the gradient of your graph, and use it to calculate a value for ε_o the permittivity of air.

16.27 The insulation of dry air breaks down in an electric field of strength $3.0\,\mathrm{MV\,m^{-1}}$. What is the surface density of charge on a metal object that would produce such a field?

16.5 Fields near conductors

16.28 Normally the air gap between a pair of parallel plates connected to a high-voltage supply is an almost perfect insulator, and a meter joined in series registers zero. Explain *two* ways in which you could introduce ions into the gap so that a current passes between them.

16.29 In order to discharge the surface of a plastic rod an experimenter moves it near a metal comb with very sharp teeth. Explain what is happening in this situation. Explain also why the method is not completely effective, being bound to leave some charge on the rod.

16.30 Some of the parts of a piece of electronic equipment are enclosed in aluminium cans. Explain why this is done.

16.6 Radial fields

16.31 Two rain drops A and B falling side by side 10 mm apart carry charges of +4.0 pC and −5.0 pC respectively, as in figure *(a)* in the diagram. What is the force with which one rain drop acts on the other? What is the electric field strength at a point X half-way between them?

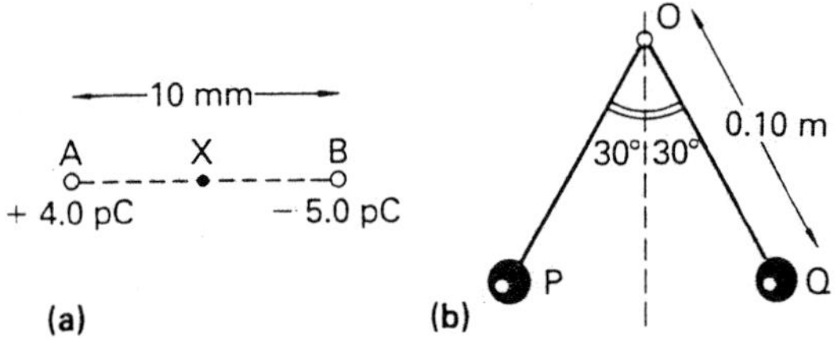

16.32 Two small conducting spheres P and Q, each of mass 1.5×10^{-5} kg are suspended from the same point O by insulating threads 0.10 m long. When the spheres are charged (with equal charges) they come to rest with both threads inclined at 30° to the vertical, as shown in figure *(b)* above. Calculate the charges on the spheres. If the charges on the two spheres were of the same sign but of *different* sizes, would the two threads now come to rest at *equal* angles to the vertical? Draw a diagram to show what you would expect.

16.33 A uranium nucleus can be regarded as a spherical object of radius 2×10^{-14} m containing 92 protons (as well as neutrons).

(a) Estimate (i) the electric field strength (ii) the electric potential at the surface of the nucleus.

(b) If an α-particle (charge $2e$) is close to the surface of the uranium nucleus, estimate (i) the electric force acting on it (ii) the electrical potential energy it has in this position.

16.34 A small sphere bearing a charge of + 1.0 nC is situated at a distance of 180 mm from another small sphere carrying a charge of + 4.0 nC.

(a) Calculate the work that must be done in moving the first sphere to a point 60 mm from the second.

(b) What is the electrical force with which one sphere acts on the other in the latter position?

16.35 In a small van de Graaff generator the sphere at the top is of diameter 0.30 m; it is mounted on a plastic column whose resistance is $5.0 \times 10^{10}\,\Omega$. If the current carried into the sphere by the belt is 3.0 μA, calculate

(a) the final steady potential of the sphere

(b) the final steady charge on the sphere

(c) the electric field strength close to its surface.

16.36 In a small van de Graaff machine the sphere at the top is of diameter 0.20 m and reaches a potential of 3.0×10^{5} V before discharging to an earthed object nearby.

(a) At what rate is charge being carried by the moving belt up into the sphere if there are 20 discharges per minute?

(b) If now a microammeter is permanently connected between the sphere and Earth, what current would you expect it to register?

17 Magnetic fields and forces

Data electronic charge $e = 1.60 \times 10^{-19}$ C
mass of electron $m_e = 9.11 \times 10^{-31}$ kg
mass of proton = mass of neutron = 1.66×10^{-27} kg
permeability of free space $\mu_0 = 4\pi \times 10^{-7}$ N A^{-2}

17.1 Magnetic fields

17.1 Two bar magnets are identical in size and appearance. Explain how, by observing their behaviour when suspended in the Earth's magnetic field, you would find

(a) the N (or North-seeking) pole of each magnet
(b) which magnet is the stronger.

17.2 A student is plotting the magnetic field pattern around a magnet. The three parts of the figure show features to be found in different parts of his diagram.
In (a) he has two lines of force crossing: explain why this cannot be correct.
In (b) he has two adjacent lines of force running in opposite directions; what can you say about the field between them?
In (c) he has two lines of force which are converging: what can you say about the field between them?

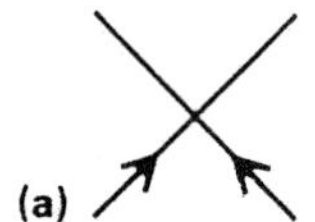

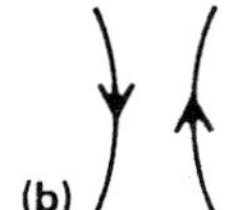

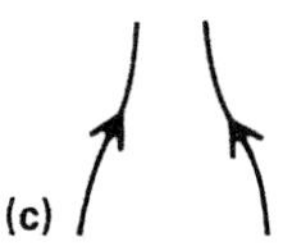

17.3 A bar magnet is placed on a table top with its axis in the magnetic meridian. Draw a graph to show how you would expect the strength of the magnetic field to vary along the axis of the magnet, starting from a point far to the north of the magnet and ending at a point far to the south of the magnet, if

(a) the N pole of the magnet is pointing north
(b) the S pole of the magnet is pointing north.

17.4 A bar magnet is placed, with its axis in the magnetic meridian, on a large sheet of paper on a laboratory bench with its N pole pointing north, as shown in the figure. Assume that along the line XX the strength of the magnet's field is the same size as the Earth's field at the points labelled P.

(a) Draw a diagram of the magnet on the sheet of paper, and draw
  (i) the magnetic field pattern caused by the Earth
  (ii) the magnetic field pattern caused by the magnet
  (iii) the resultant magnetic field pattern.
(b) Describe how you would use a plotting compass to plot the resultant magnetic field around the magnet in this situation.

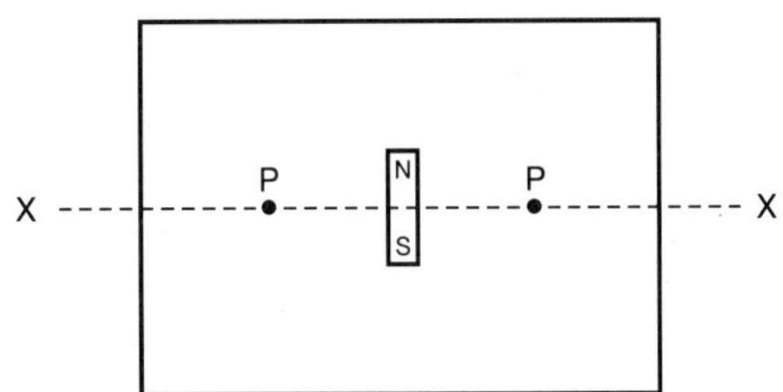

17.5 Sketch the magnetic field pattern around two bar magnets when they are placed as shown in the figure. For each arrangement consider the cases when like poles are near each other, and unlike poles are near each other.

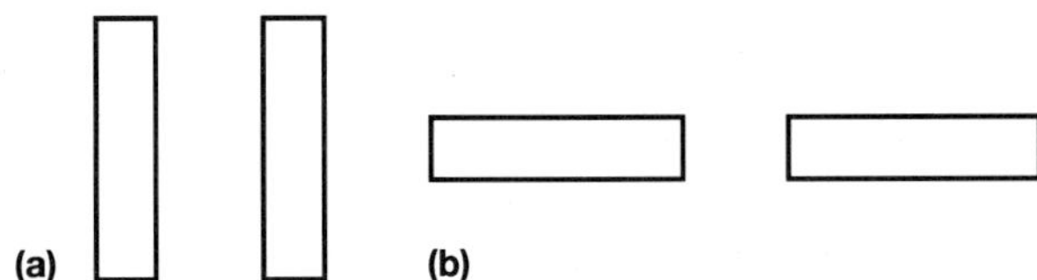

17.6 Two ceramic (slab) magnets are placed on a table, and have unlike pole faces facing each other. Sketch the magnetic field pattern around them, in the plane of the table, when they are about 30 mm apart. Indicate the region where the field is approximately uniform.

17.7 A straight wire carrying a steady current is placed on a laboratory bench. How would you use a plotting compass to find the direction of the current if the wire is laid

(a) north to south

(b) east to west?

17.8 *(a)* Copy the figure, which shows wires carrying currents into and out of the paper, and sketch the separate magnetic field patterns, in the plane of the paper, caused by the two wires.

(b) On a second copy of the figure sketch the resultant magnetic field pattern. As is usual, the lines should be closer together where the field is stronger.

(c) Sketch the magnetic field pattern in and around a solenoid.

17.2 The force on a current-carrying conductor

17.9 *(a)* Draw a diagram to show the relative directions of the current I in a wire of length l, a magnetic flux density B at right angles to the current, and the force F on the wire.

(b) Write down an equation which defines the size of B.

(c) What is the unit of B in terms of (i) N, A, m and (ii) the base units of the SI?

17.10 A horizontal conductor of length 50 mm carrying a current of 3.0 A lies at right angles to a horizontal magnetic field of flux density 0.50 T.

(a) What is the size of the magnetic force on it?

(b) Draw a diagram to show the direction of the force.

17.11 Currents of 5.0 A flow in each of the conductors OA, OB, OC and OD shown in the figure. The conductors are in a magnetic field of flux density 0.15 T parallel to the plane of the diagram. What is the size and direction of the force on each conductor?

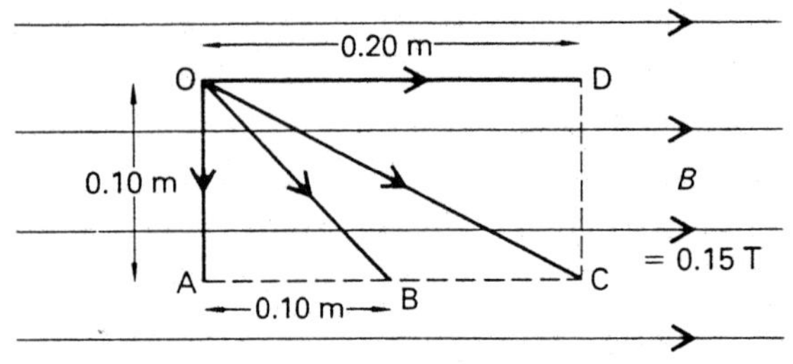

17.12 The figure shows a simple wire-frame current balance, one end of which is placed inside a solenoid. The wire rests on two knife edges at A and B; AB = CD = 0.15 m, and CB = DA = 0.20 m. There is a current of 6.0 A which enters the left-hand side of the frame by means of these knife edges (the insulator X prevents current flowing round the right-hand side). A separate current is supplied to the solenoid; the field which has a flux density of 3.5 mT caused by this current inside the solenoid may be considered to be uniform and everywhere parallel to its axis. The directions of the two currents are shown in the figure.

(a) Why is there no magnetic force on AD and CB? On a copy of the figure show the direction of the force on CD.

(b) What is the size of the force on CD?

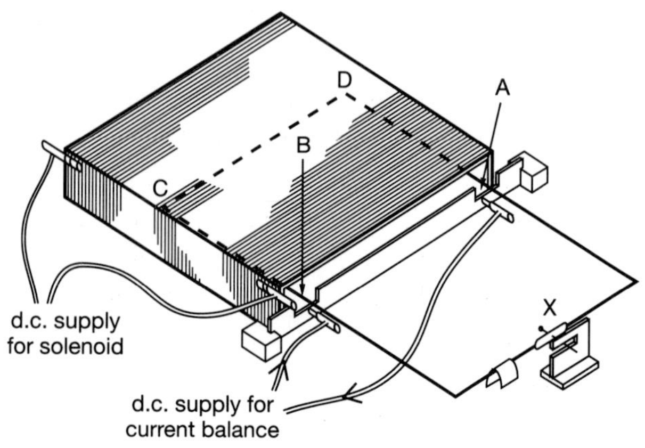

(c) What mass would need to be placed on the wire at the other end of the frame in order to restore equilibrium?

17.13 Explain how you would use the wire-frame current balance described in question *17.12* to show that the force on a current-carrying wire is proportional to the current, the length of the wire and the magnetic flux density. You should say what measurements you would take, how you would use them, and discuss how any systematic errors could be avoided or allowed for.

17.14 A rectangular coil ABCD of 20 turns of wire carrying a current of 5.0 A is placed with its plane horizontal and AB and CD at right angles to a uniform magnetic field of flux density 0.20 T. AB = CD = 60 mm; BC = DA = 40 mm.

(a) Draw a diagram of this arrangement and mark on the diagram the direction of the magnetic forces on the coil.

(b) What is the size of each force?

(c) What torque would be needed to keep the coil in equilibrium in its present position?

(d) What torque would be needed when the coil has turned, from its original position, through an angle of (i) 60°, (ii) 90°?

17.15 *(a)* Draw a diagram to show two shaped magnetic pole pieces, and an iron cylinder placed between them so that a radial magnetic field is created.

(b) Draw the direction of the magnetic field lines in the gaps between the pole pieces and the cylinder.

(c) Explain why using a radial field is an advantage in the construction of a moving-coil meter, illustrating your answer with diagrams.

(d) In a moving-coil meter with a radial magnetic field the rectangular coil measures 20 mm by 15 mm and has 100 turns. The magnetic flux density in the gap is 0.40 T. Why do you not need to know which side of the coils are perpendicular to the field in order to work out the torque which a current would produce?

(e) What torque is caused by a current of 100 μA?

(f) If the hair springs which resist the turning of the coil exert a torque per degree of $0.035\,\mu\text{N}\,\text{m}\,\text{deg}^{-1}$, through what angle will the meter needle turn when the current is 100 μA?

17.16 A freely suspended bar magnet oscillates in a magnetic field of flux density B with a period T which is inversely proportional to $\sqrt{B}$. Describe in detail how you would use this idea to investigate the variation of magnetic field along the axis of a bar magnet.

17.17 The strength of a magnetic field between two pole pieces may be measured by lowering into the gap a U–shaped wire frame, as shown in the figure.

(a) Copy the part of the figure which shows the frame and mark on your diagram suitable directions for the current and the field so that the vertical wires of the frame are pressed on to it (rather than being pulled away from it).

(b) If the flux density is 0.50 T, the width of the frame is 45 mm and the current in the wire is 25 mA, what is the magnetic force on the frame?

(c) The frame is now rotated through 20° about a vertical axis, so that the bottom edge remains horizontal, but still wholly within the uniform field. What now is the magnetic force on the wire?

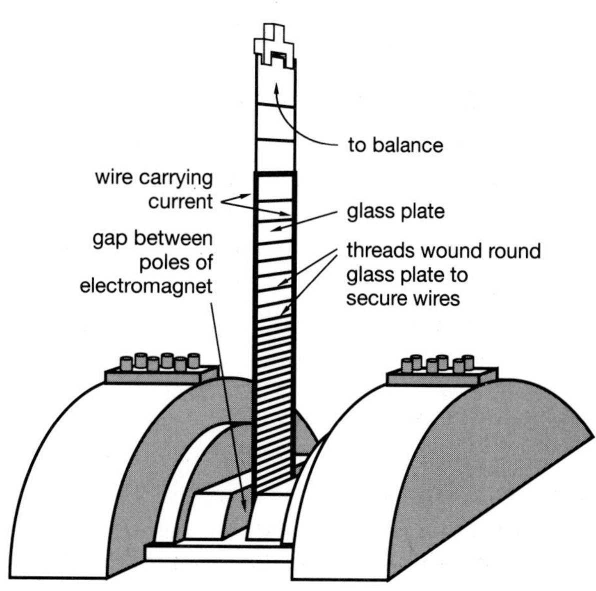

17.18 A moving-coil loudspeaker contains a magnet which creates a radial magnetic field in the circular gap as shown in the figure. The coil, which is placed in this gap, is connected to the speaker diaphragm.

(a) When the current in the coil is clockwise, what is the direction of the magnetic force on the coil?

(b) Explain what happens when the coil is supplied with alternating current.

(c) If the flux density in the gap is 1.1 T, and the coil has 500 turns of diameter 30 mm, what is the force on the coil when the current is 150 mA?

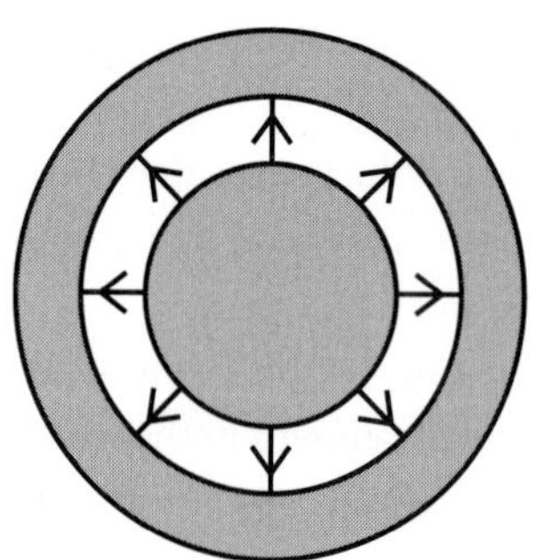

17.3 The force on a moving charge

17.19 Use the equations $F = BIl$ and $I = QnvA$ to show that the force on a moving charge is given by $F = BQv$.

17.20 ***(a)*** What is the size of the magnetic force on an electron moving with a velocity of $2.0 \times 10^7\,\mathrm{m\,s^{-1}}$ at right angles to a uniform magnetic field of flux density 15 mT?

(b) Show on a diagram the directions of the field, the velocity and the force.

17.21 Explain why there is no magnetic force on an electron which is moving inside a solenoid, parallel to the axis of the solenoid.

17.22 What is the magnetic force, and what is the direction of the force, on an electron of speed $8.0 \times 10^6\,\mathrm{m\,s^{-1}}$ in a uniform magnetic field of 1.5 mT as shown in the figure, if it is moving in the direction ***(a)*** OA, ***(b)*** OB, ***(c)*** OC?

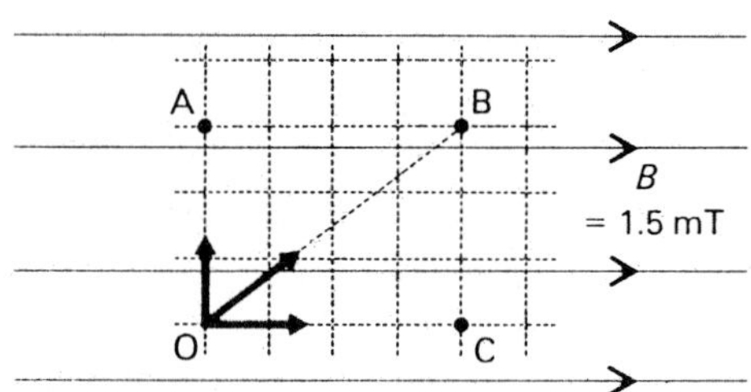

17.23 The size and direction of the Earth's magnetic field vary with time and from place to place; a typical value for the United Kingdom is 47 μT at an angle of 67° to the horizontal.

(a) What are the horizontal and vertical components of this field?

(b) Which component does an ordinary plotting compass measure?

(c) Describe how you would construct a device for measuring the angle which the Earth's magnetic field makes with the horizontal, and how you would use it.

17.24 Laboratories use evacuated tubes in which streams of electrons are fired from an electron gun to strike a fluorescent screen. Suppose such a tube is designed so that when there is no magnetic field the stream of electrons produces a sharp spot at the centre of the screen.

(a) The tube is used in a laboratory so that the electrons are travelling north. Draw a diagram of the face of the tube, as seen from the front, to show how the electrons will be deflected by the Earth's magnetic field, which is inclined to the horizontal at 67°.

(b) If the electrons are accelerated by a p.d. of 3.0 kV, how fast will they emerge from the electron gun?

(c) If the size of the Earth's magnetic flux density is 47 μT what is the magnetic force on an electron, and its acceleration?

(d) If the distance from the electron gun to the screen is 0.25 m, for what time are the electrons in flight?

(e) Assuming that the sideways acceleration is constant in size and direction, how far will the spot be deflected on the screen?

17.25 A stream of electrons is spreading out from the electron gun at one end of an evacuated Maltese Cross tube. The electrons which miss the Maltese Cross (a thin cross-shaped sheet placed in the tube as an obstacle) strike the fluorescent screen at the end of the tube and there the screen fluoresces with a green colour. The electrons which strike the Maltese Cross flow back to the electron gun, and the Maltese Cross therefore casts a cross-shaped shadow on the screen. As seen from the front of the tube, what happens to the shadow on the screen when a bar magnet is brought up to the tube

(a) from the side, with its axis horizontal, and its N pole nearest the tube

(b) from above, with its axis vertical, and its S pole nearest the tube

(c) from the front, with its axis coincident with the axis of the tube, and its N pole nearest the tube?

17.26 A stream of electrons is moving along the axis of an evacuated tube at a speed of $2.0 \times 10^6 \, \mathrm{m\,s^{-1}}$. The beam enters a region where there is a horizontal magnetic field of flux density 30 mT at right angles to the beam.

(a) Draw a diagram to show the directions of the velocity, the field and the magnetic force.

(b) Calculate the size of the magnetic force.

(c) An electric field in the same region is then switched on. Mark on your diagram the direction of the field if the resultant force on the electrons is to be zero.

(d) What should be the electric field strength?

(e) If the strengths of the two fields are B and E, and the velocity of the electrons is v, derive a relationship between B, E and v.

(f) Suppose the fields have been adjusted so that together they create zero resultant force on the electrons: if the electrons were then made to move a little faster, show on your diagram the direction in which they would be deflected.

(g) This arrangement of crossed fields is sometimes said to be a velocity selector. Why do you think it is given this name?

17.27 A velocity selector (as described in question 17.26) consists of a magnetic field of flux density 0.500 T which is perpendicular to an electric field of strength $3.00 \times 10^5 \, \mathrm{N\,C^{-1}}$. Singly-charged magnesium ions, with mass numbers of 24, 25 and 26, are passed through the velocity selector and enter a region where the magnetic flux density has the same value as before, but there is no electric field: in this region the ions move in circular arcs.

(a) What is the velocity of the ions which pass through the velocity selector?

(b) What are the radii of the circular arcs in which the ions move after they have passed through the velocity selector?

17.28 An electric current of 1.5 A is passing along a horizontal strip of copper which is 10 mm wide and 0.10 mm thick.

(a) If the number density of the free electrons in the copper is $1.0 \times 10^{29} \, \mathrm{m^{-3}}$, calculate their drift speed.

(b) If the strip is placed in a vertical magnetic field of flux density 1.5 T, what is the magnetic force on each electron?

(c) Show on a diagram the directions of the velocity of the electrons, the magnetic field, the magnetic force and show what edges of the strip will have excess negative and positive charge.

(d) This redistribution of charge will create an electric field; mark on the diagram the direction of this field.

(e) As more electrons are pushed to one side, the electric field will increase until the electric force balances the magnetic force. What will be the strength of this electric field?

(f) Assuming that the electric field is uniform, what p.d. would there be between opposite edges of the strip?

17.29 Suppose a strip of copper and a strip of germanium, of the same dimensions, are placed in series in a circuit. If the number densities of the charge carriers in the two materials are $1.0 \times 10^{29}\,\text{m}^{-3}$ and $6.0 \times 10^{20}\,\text{m}^{-3}$ respectively, calculate the ratios

(a) (drift speed of charge carriers in germanium)/(drift speed of charge carriers in copper)

(b) (Hall p.d. in germanium)/(Hall p.d. in copper).

17.30 A current is flowing from left to right in the strip of conducting material shown in the figure. There is a uniform magnetic field whose direction is into the paper. A voltmeter is connected as shown.

(a) In which direction will the charge carriers be pushed by the Hall effect – towards AB or towards DC – if the charge carriers are (i) positive, (ii) negative?

(b) Will the voltmeter give a positive or a negative reading if the charge carriers are (i) positive, (ii) negative?

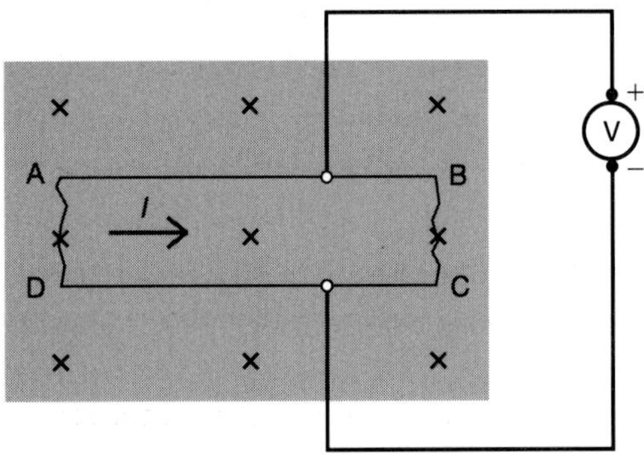

17.31 The figure below shows a uniform magnetic field: its direction is into the paper and its strength is 0.25 T. An electron at P is fired in the direction shown with a speed of $2.0 \times 10^{6}\,\text{m}\,\text{s}^{-1}$.

(a) On a copy of the diagram mark the direction of the magnetic force on the electron and calculate the size of the force.

(b) Explain why the electron will move in a circular path.

(c) Using the fact that the centripetal acceleration a is given by $a = v^2/r$, where v is the speed of the electron and r the radius of its path, find the radius of the electron's circular path.

(d) How long will the electron take to make one complete circular orbit?

(e) A second electron is fired from P in the same direction with twice the speed. Calculate the radius of its path.

(f) How long will it take the second electron to complete one orbit?

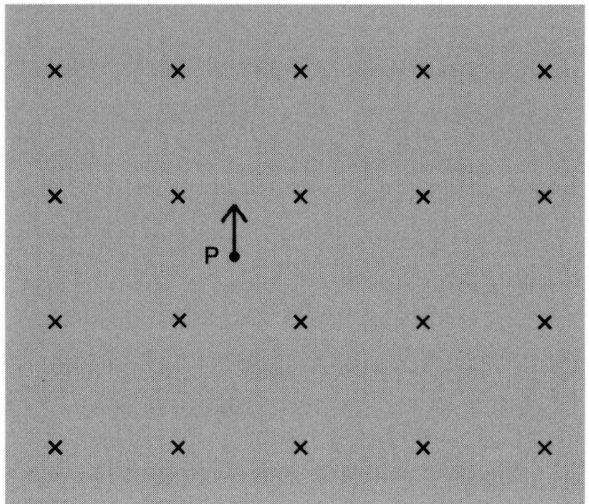

17.32 If a particle with charge Q and mass m is moving with speed v at right angles to a magnetic field of flux density B, and moves in a circular path of radius r, derive an expression

(a) for r in terms of Q, m, v and B

(b) for the period T in terms of B, Q and m.

17.33 In a fine-beam tube electrons are accelerated through a p.d. of 250 V.

(a) How fast are they then moving?

(b) If they move in a circle of radius 90 mm, what is the strength of the magnetic field?

17.34 In a fine-beam tube

(a) what can you deduce about the magnetic field from the fact that the path of the electron is circular?

(b) explain what would be the effect on the radius of (i) decreasing the accelerating p.d., (ii) increasing the strength of the magnetic field.

(c) what causes the colour of the beam?

17.35 A cyclotron is a machine which uses the same p.d. many times to accelerate charged particles. The figure shows the principle: the ions are generated at S and are accelerated through a p.d. between the two hollow metal dees. In the dees they are moving at right angles to a magnetic field, so they move in a semicircle. When they return to the edge of the dee, the p.d. is in the opposite direction and accelerates them again across the gap to the other dee, where they again move in a semicircle. The process is repeated many more times than can be indicated in the figure.

(a) The p.d. between the dees might be 150 kV, and the ions might make 100 crossings of the dees. What difficulty might there be in trying to accelerate ions in a straight line through a single p.d. of 100 × 150 kV?

(b) Use $QV = \frac{1}{2}mv^2$ to find the speed reached by a singly charged ion which has a mass of 1.7×10^{-27} kg if it starts from rest and is accelerated once through the p.d. of 150 kV.

(c) How long will it then take the ion to travel round the semicircular dee at this speed, if the magnetic flux density is 1.6 T?

(d) It will then again be accelerated through 150 kV. How long will it take to travel through the next semicircle: a shorter time, or the same time as before?

(e) The p.d. between the dees has to change direction so that it always accelerates the ions, from whichever direction they are coming. For this cyclotron, what would need to be the frequency of this alternation?

(f) Why would it be more difficult to construct a machine like this if the time for an ion to traverse each dee was not always the same?

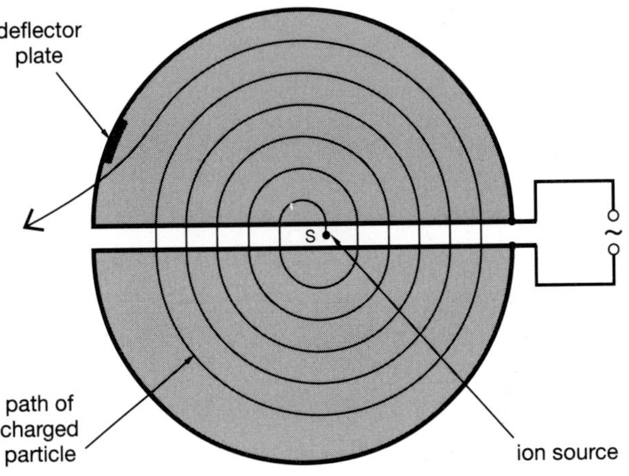

17.36 What difficulty might arise if the cyclotron in question *17.35* were used to accelerate electrons?

17.37 CERN is building an electron-positron accelerator which includes an evacuated tube which runs around a circle of radius 4.3 km. The magnets at the circumference of this circle create a vertical magnetic flux density of 1.0 T.

(a) What is the momentum of an electron which moves round this circular path?

(b) If the mass of one of the electrons was equal to its rest mass, what would be its velocity?

(c) Why is your answer to *(b)* totally impossible? Estimate the mass of the electron. (Hint: assume the electron's speed is approximately equal to the speed of light, i.e. $3 \times 10^8\,\mathrm{m\,s^{-1}}$.)

17.38 A magnetron is a device for producing high-frequency power. It consists of a cylindrical evacuated tube which contains a cathode, which is a straight wire from which electrons are emitted when it is heated. Surrounding the wire, as shown, in sectional view in the figure, is a cylindrical anode of radius 10 mm. The current caused by the flow of electrons when a p.d. is applied may be measured by an ammeter connected between the cathode and the anode.

(a) On a copy of the diagram draw lines to show the direction of the electric field between the cathode and the anode.

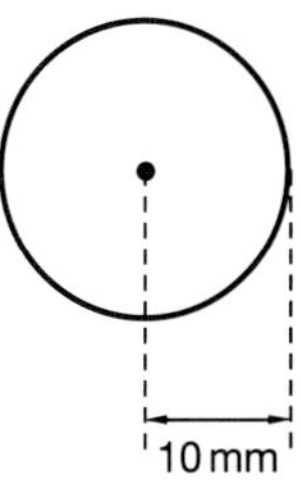

(b) You may assume that the electrons are emitted from the cathode with zero velocity. If the p.d. between anode and cathode is 60.0 V what is the speed of the electrons when they reach the anode?

(c) Explain why the acceleration is greatest at the cathode.

(d) The tube may be placed inside a solenoid. If this creates a magnetic field into the paper, sketch the path of an emitted electron if there is a small current in the solenoid.

(e) At some point, if the current in the solenoid is further increased, it is found that the current in the tube falls to zero. Explain why this happens, and on a second copy of the diagram sketch the path which an electron takes.

(f) Assuming that the electrons gain almost all their velocity within a very short distance of the cathode, what current in the solenoid would cause the current in the tube to fall to zero, if the solenoid has 3600 turns per metre?

(g) It is found that high-frequency electromagnetic waves can then be extracted from this device at the frequency of rotation of the electrons. What is that frequency for this magnetron?

17.39 A stream of helium nuclei moving with a velocity of $1.5 \times 10^{7}\,\mathrm{m\,s^{-1}}$ enters a magnetic field of 2.0 T. Initially the nuclei are moving at right angles to the field.

(a) What is the charge on each nucleus?

(b) What is the magnetic force on one nucleus?

(c) If the mass of the nucleus is $6.6 \times 10^{-27}\,\mathrm{kg}$, what is the acceleration of the nucleus?

(d) Draw a diagram which shows the magnetic field (into the paper) and the circular motion of the helium nucleus after it has entered the field.

(e) Explain why the speed of the nuclei does not change after it has entered the field.

(f) Explain why the motion is circular.

(g) Calculate the radius of the circular path in which the nuclei move.

17.40 The figure shows three mutually perpendicular axes Ox, Oy and Oz. There is a uniform magnetic field of strength 0.20 T in the direction Ox.

(a) What is the path of an electron which starts from O in the direction (i) Ox, (ii) Oy? Show these paths on a copy of the figure.

(b) An electron starts from O in the plane yOx, making an angle of 30° with Oy, as shown in the figure, and moving with speed $8.0 \times 10^{5}\,\mathrm{m\,s^{-1}}$. What are the resolved parts of its velocity in the directions (i) Ox and (ii) Oy?

(c) Explain why the electron will move in a helical path.

(d) How long will the electron take to travel 0.50 m in the direction Ox?

(e) How long will it take the electron to return the fifth time to the line Ox?

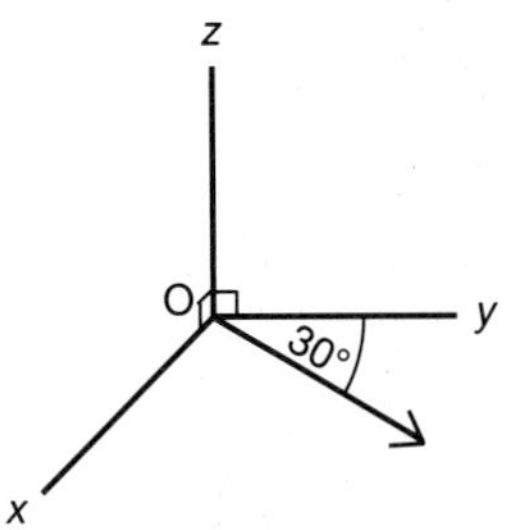

17.41 The Van Allan radiation belts contain charged particles which move along helical paths between the Earth's north and south magnetic poles, as shown in the figure.

(a) Explain why they move in helical paths, and why the radius of the path is smallest near the Earth.

(b) The particles shuttle backwards and forwards between the poles. Explain why they reverse their direction when they approach the poles.

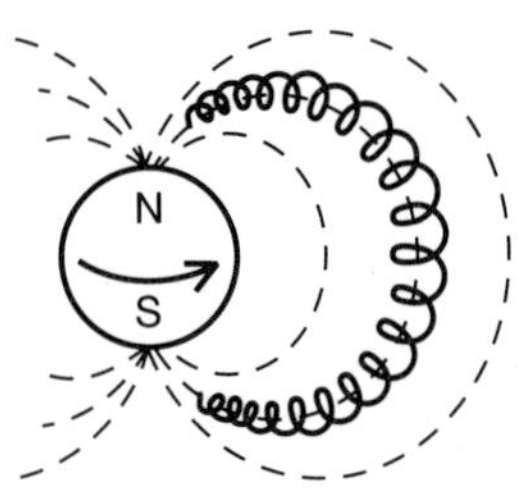

17.42 The figure is a photograph of the track of a charged particle in a bubble chamber. The track is curved because the particle is moving at right angles to a magnetic field.

(a) If the particle carries a positive charge and is travelling in an anti-clockwise direction, what is the direction of the magnetic field?

(b) What is happening to the radius of the path?

(c) What is happening to the speed of the particle?

(d) Derive an expression for the momentum mv of the particle in terms of the magnetic flux density B, the charge Q on the particle and r, the radius of its path.

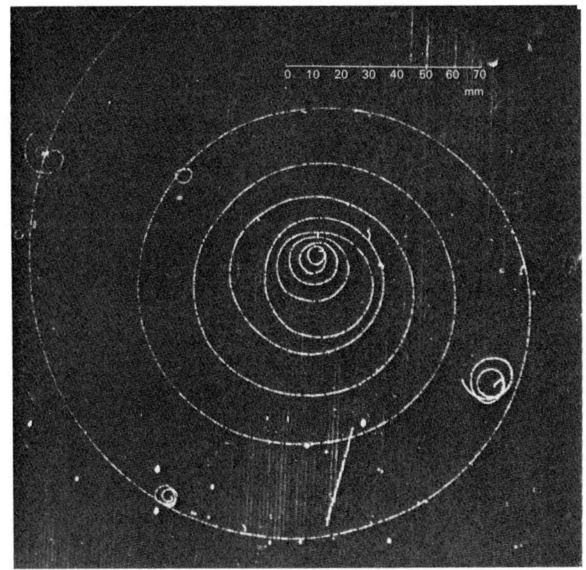

17.4 Magnetic flux densities around wires and coils

17.43 What is the magnetic flux density near the centre of a long solenoid which has 1200 turns, is 0.50 m long and carries a current of 3.0 A?

17.44 *(a)* Why must the flux density at the end of a solenoid be *exactly* half its size at the centre?

(b) If the flux density at the ends is half that at the centre, half of the field lines at the centre do not get to the end. Where do they go?

17.45 Sketch graphs to show how the magnetic flux density varies along the axis of a solenoid if

(a) the solenoid is infinitely long,

(b) it is long compared with its width,

(c) it is short compared with its width.

17.46 Two long solenoids A and B each have 1200 turns per unit length and carry the same current of 2.0 A. A's diameter is twice that of B, and B is placed inside A. At the mid-point of the solenoids, what is the magnetic flux density

(a) if viewed from one end, the current in both solenoids is in a clockwise direction, (i) inside B, (ii) in the gap between A and B

(b) if viewed from one end, the current in A is clockwise and the current in B is anticlockwise, (i) inside B, (ii) in the gap between A and B?

17.47 Part (i) of the figure shows the end view of two square-section solenoids, carrying the same current, in the same sense, placed next to each other. Part (ii) shows a rectangular solenoid with the same current and the same total area. All the solenoids have the same number of turns per unit length.

(a) How would you argue that the field strength throughout the rectangular solenoid is the same as the field strength in either square solenoid?

(b) Part (iii) of the figure shows two solenoids with a triangular cross-section. Use a similar argument to show that the field strength in each is the same as that in the square-section solenoid, and extend the argument to show that the field strength in a solenoid does not depend on the shape of its cross-section.

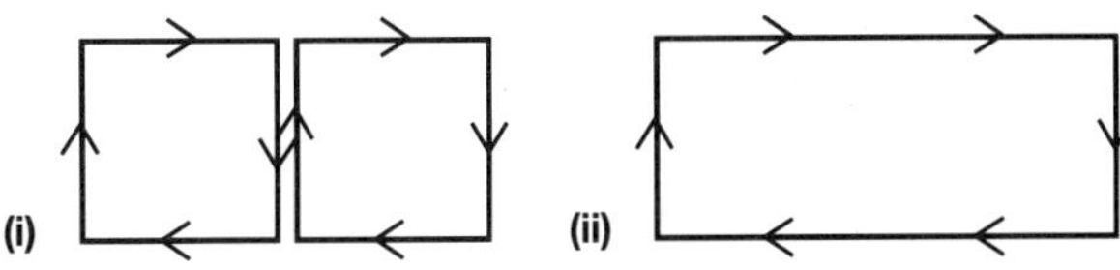

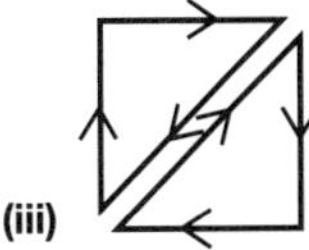

17.48 Show that the units of the equations $B = \mu_0 nI$ and $B = \mu_0 NI/2r$ are consistent.

17.49 Calculate the magnetic flux density at the centre of a circular coil which has 100 turns of diameter 40 mm carrying a current of 1.5 A.

17.50 The magnetic flux density at the centre of a circular coil of 50 turns of radius 15 mm is 1.68 mT. What is the flux density at the centre of another coil which carries the same current and has

(a) radius 25 mm and the same number of turns

(b) radius 10 mm and half the number of turns?

17.51 *(a)* What is the magnetic flux density at the centre of a circular coil which has 50 turns of radius 70 mm carrying a current of 2.0 A?

(b) If, looking at one face of the coil, the current flows clockwise, do the field lines emerge from that face or enter it? What is the polarity of that face?

(c) Sketch a graph to show how the magnetic flux density varies along the axis of the coil.

17.52 A coil has N turns of radius a and carries a current I. The magnetic flux density B at a point which is on the axis of a coil and a distance x from its centre is given by the equation

$$B = \frac{\mu_0 a^2 NI}{2(x^2 + a^2)^{3/2}}$$

(a) If $x = 0$, the value of B should be the same as that given by the equation $B = \mu_0 NI/2a$ for the flux density at the centre of a circular coil. Check that this is so.

(b) If $a = 70$ mm, $N = 320$ and $I = 0.80$ A, calculate B for values of x at 10 mm intervals from -100 mm to $+100$ mm, and plot a graph of B against x. If you have access to either a programmable calculator or computer, use it for the calculation and the plotting.

(c) A second identical coil, carrying the same current, is now placed 70 mm from the first coil with their axes coinciding (this arrangement is called a pair of Helmholtz coils). Calculate the total magnetic flux density caused by the two coils for values of x (measured from the first coil) from -100 mm to $+170$ mm, and plot a graph of B against x.

(d) What do you notice about the magnetic flux density on the axis between the coils?

17.53 The photograph shows a coil fitted to an aircraft during the Second World War. The purpose was to detonate magnetic mines. A change in the vertical magnetic field of 5 μT was necessary to detonate the mine. If the radius of the single-turn coil was 10 m, and the aircraft was flying 10 m above the sea level, what current would be needed in the coil to detonate a mine which was 30 m below the surface? (Use the equation given in question *17.52*.)

17.54 Sketch a graph to show the reading you would expect a Hall probe to record if you moved it, with its plane parallel to the plane of the coil, along the line AOA' in the figure below.

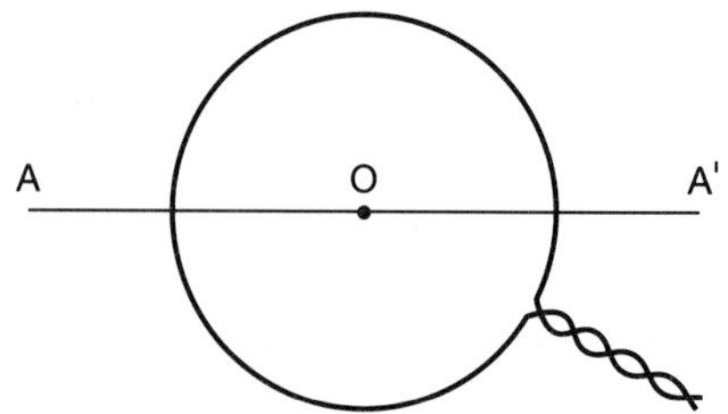

17.55 Suppose you were given a sheet of peg board (hardboard with small holes on a grid pattern into which pegs like golf tees can be pushed), a power supply, several metres of plastic-covered wire and Hall probe with the necessary voltmeter to record the Hall p.d.s. Describe what experiments you would carry out to investigate the magnetic field in and around a flat circular coil.

17.56 A long straight wire carries a current of 15 A.

(a) Calculate the magnetic flux density at a distance of 60 mm from the wire.

(b) Is this much greater than, similar to, or much less than the vertical component of the Earth's magnetic flux density?

(c) Explain why the flux density would be less if the wire were shorter (e.g. only 10 cm long).

17.57 A long straight wire carries a current of 10 A. Draw a graph with labelled axes to show how the magnetic flux density varies with distance r from the wire for values of r from 5 mm to 50 mm.

17.58 The magnetic flux density at a distance of 10 mm from a long straight wire carrying a current of 10 A is 0.20 mT. What is the magnetic flux density

(a) at a distance of 6.0 mm, with the current still 10 A

(b) at a distance of 10 mm, if the current is 3.0 A?

17.59 Draw two diagrams to show two parallel straight wires which are at right angles to the page; in one diagram use two crosses to show that the current is entering the page, and in the other use a cross and a dot to show that one current is entering and the other is leaving the page. If the currents have the same size, draw the magnetic field pattern around the wires, marking with a letter N any point where the field is zero.

17.60 Two parallel straight wires A and B carry currents in opposite directions: the currents are, respectively, 2.0 A and 3.0 A. They are 0.10 m apart. At what distance from wire A will the resultant magnetic field be zero?

17.61 The cross-channel direct current cable between the United Kingdom and France may carry a maximum current of 14.8 kA. A typical depth below the surface is 50 m.

(a) What magnetic flux density is created at the surface of the sea by the maximum current?

(b) Your answer to *(a)* is a significant fraction of the strength of the Earth's magnetic field but in practice ships need make no allowance for it. Why not?

17.62 A single cable in the grid system carries alternating current with a peak value of up to 2000 A. If the cable is aligned east-west, what is the size of the peak magnetic force on one metre of it caused by the Earth's magnetic field.

17.63 When a current is switched on in a solenoid, do the coils attract or repel each other?
Describe how, given any apparatus you might reasonably expect to find in your laboratory, you might investigate this effect quantitiatively.

17.64 A wire-frame current balance (like the one described in question *17.12*) is balanced, and then a long straight wire is brought up to it and placed directly beneath the wire at one end of the frame. The *same* current I is arranged to flow in the frame and the long straight wire, and the currents have the same direction.

(a) If the length of the wire in the frame is l, and when the two wires have a distance d between them, a mass m is needed to balance the frame, derive an expression giving l in terms of μ_0, l, d, m and g.

(b) This is known as an *absolute* method of measuring current since no electrical meters are used (the value of μ_0 follows from the definition of the ampere). What practical difficulties do you think there would be in using the apparatus to make a measurement of current?

17.65 Two parallel straight wires A and B carry currents in the same direction. Draw a diagram to show the wires, and their magnetic fields, making it clear which wire causes each field. Hence explain why A attracts B and why B attracts A.

17.66 Imagine a loop of very thin, flexible wire carrying a current. There is no gravitational or magnetic field. Explain what shape the loop would take up.

17.5 Magnetic materials

17.67 Explain what is meant by a magnetic domain, and describe what happens to the domains when a piece of magnetic material is placed in a magnetic field of increasing strength.

17.68 Use the idea of domains to explain why

(a) there is a limit to the magnetisation of a piece of magnetic material

(b) magnetisation can be destroyed by heating or hammering the material

(c) bar magnets are fitted with soft iron keepers when they are not being used.

17.69 A magnetised iron bar may be demagnetised by placing it in a solenoid which is supplied with alternating current, and then pulling it out of the solenoid along the axis, with the current switched on in the solenoid. Explain the principle of this method.

17.70 The figure shows hysteresis loops for two different specimens of iron: they are graphs which show how the magnetic flux density in the iron varies with the current applied to a solenoid wrapped round the iron.

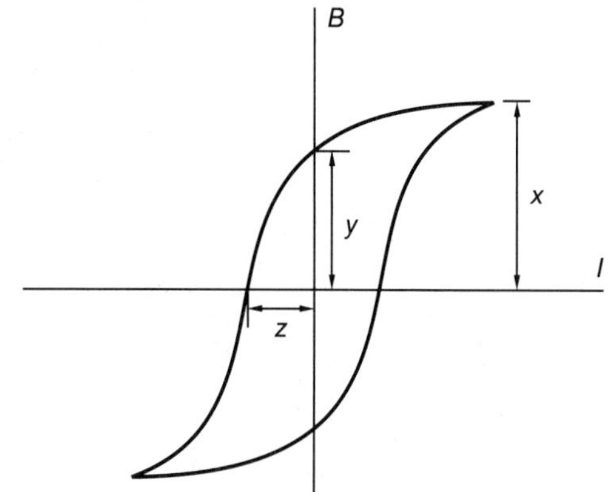

iron sample (A)

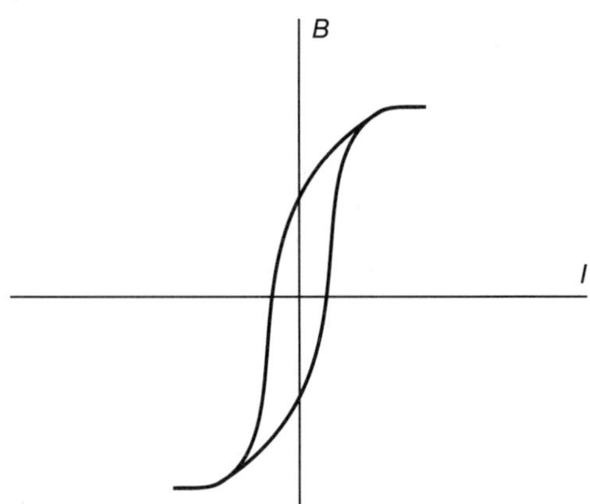

(a) What is the significance of (i) the measurements x, y and z on the figure, and (ii) area of the loop?

(b) Which material would be suitable for a transformer core, and which for a permanent magnet?

17.71 A toroidal iron ring, shown in the figure, has a mean circumferential length of 0.60 m. 1200 turns of wire, carrying a current of 0.50 A, are wrapped uniformly round it. If the relative permeability of the iron is 300, what is the magnetic flux density in the iron?

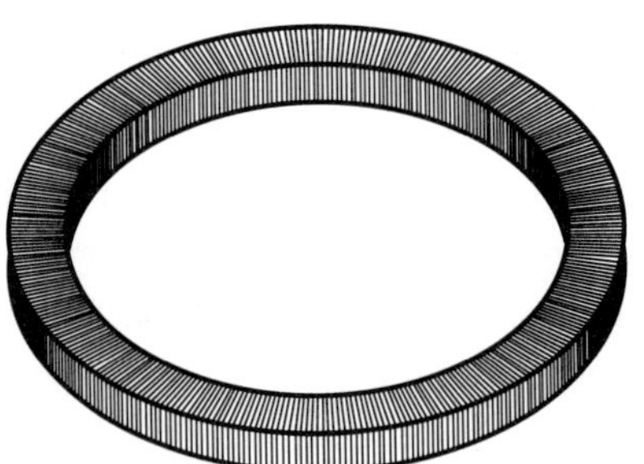

17.72 In question *17.71* you calculated the flux density inside a uniformly wound iron ring. In practice it does not matter much if the ring is not circular, or if the wire is not wrapped uniformly; it is just the number of turns which matters, so we can calculate the magnetic flux density in the situation shown in (i) of the figure.

(a) Suppose the mean length of iron is 420 mm. If the

coil has 300 turns carrying a current of 5.0 A, and the relative permeability of the iron is 500, what is the flux density in the iron?

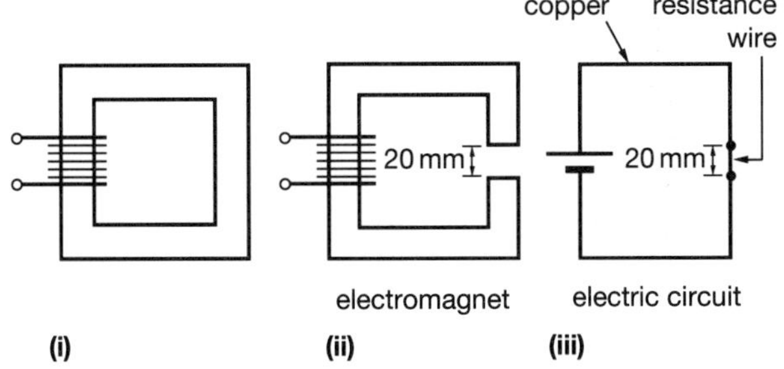

It is more difficult, but also more important, to be able calculate the flux density in (ii) since this shows an electromagnet; a 20 mm air gap has been cut out of the closed iron core shown in (i). To calculate the effect of this we make use of an analogy between the iron core and an electric circuit, as shown in (iii).

(b) In the circuit there is originally 420 mm of copper wire (resistance $1.0\,\Omega\,m^{-1}$). Then 20 mm of copper is replaced by a 20 mm length of resistance wire (resistance $500\,\Omega\,m^{-1}$). Show that the resistance is increased, and the current decreased, by a factor of (nearly) 25.

(c) In the 'magnetic circuit' the insertion of the air gap has a similar effect in reducing the flux density: the length of the iron is analogous to the length of wire, and the relative permeability is analogous to the resistance per unit length. So, without further calculation, by what factor is the flux density reduced?

(d) The width of the air gap is a compromise. Why can it not be made very much smaller or very much larger?

18 Electromagnetic induction

Data magnetic permeability of free space
$\mu_0 = 4\pi \times 10^{-7}\,N\,A^{-2}$

18.1 E.m.f.s induced by moving conductors

18.1 A teacher demonstrates that an e.m.f. is induced when a wire is moving between the poles of a U–magnet: the figure shows the directions of the field and the movement of the wire, and the inset shows an enlargement of part of the wire. On a copy of the inset mark

(a) the directions of the magnetic forces on the proton and the electron

(b) the positive and negative ends of this part of the wire

(c) the direction of the current if the ends of the wire were connected by wire which did not pass through the magnetic field.

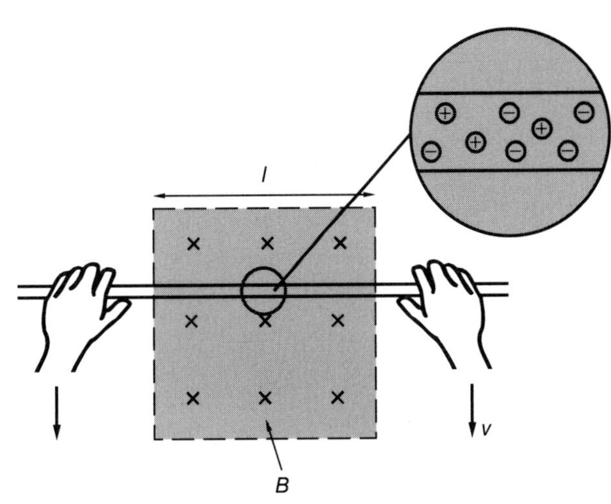

18.2 *(a)* If, in question *18.1*, there is an induced current in the wire, in which direction is the magnetic force caused by this current?

(b) Is this direction the same as, or opposite to, the direction in which the wire was being moved? Comment on your answer.

18.3 A large U–magnet is placed on a bench so that the magnetic field between its poles is horizontal. A long wire is connected to the terminals of a sensitive voltmeter placed on the bench.

(a) Describe and explain the reading on the voltmeter when the wire is moved at the same steady speed (i) vertically downwards between the poles of the magnet, (ii) horizontally from one pole to the other, (iii) in a direction inclined to the horizontal between the poles.

(b) The wire is then bent back on itself and the doubled wire is moved vertically between the poles. Explain the reading on the voltmeter.

18.4 *(a)* If, in question *18.1*, $B = 0.12\,T$, the length of wire between the poles is 25 mm, and the teacher moves the wire at a maximum speed of $1.5\,m\,s^{-1}$, what maximum e.m.f. will be induced?

(b) The teacher uses a moving coil voltmeter (of the correct sensitivity) to indicate the e.m.f. What features of the meter's construction means that it is unlikely to record the expected e.m.f.?

(c) What instrument could you use if you wanted a precise measurement of the maximum e.m.f. induced?

18.5 The wingspan of a Concorde aircraft is 25.6 m.

(a) If the vertical component of the Earth's magnetic field is $50\,\mu T$, and the aircraft is flying horizontally at $550\,m\,s^{-1}$, what e.m.f. is induced in the wing?

(b) Explain whether the direction of this e.m.f depends on where the aircraft is, and on which direction it is flying in.

(c) Discuss whether there would be a current in a wire connected between the wingtips.

18.6 A railway train is travelling due north at $160\,km\,h^{-1}$.

(a) Calculate the e.m.f. induced in an axle of length 1.8 m at a place whether the Earth's magnetic field is $50\,\mu T$ inclined at 65° to the horizontal.

(b) Explain whether the size and direction of the e.m.f depends on the direction in which the train is travelling.

(c) Discuss whether it is possible to make use of this e.m.f.

18.7 Show that the units on the two sides of the equation $\mathscr{E} = Blv$ are consistent.

18.8 A wire of length 0.60 m moves at a speed of $1.8\,m\,s^{-1}$ at right angles to a uniform magnetic field of flux density 0.50 T.

(a) What is the rate of sweeping out area?

(b) Hence calculate the e.m.f. induced in the wire.

18.9 A rod OA of length 1.5 m is pivoted at O about a horizontal axis and rotates in a vertical plane at a constant angular velocity of $24\,rad\,s^{-1}$. There is a uniform magnetic field of flux density 65 mT perpendicular to the plane of rotation.

(a) What is the rate at which the rod sweeps out area?

(b) What is the e.m.f. induced in the rod?

(c) On a diagram show the direction of the e.m.f for one position of the rod, showing also the direction of the field and the direction of movement of the rod when it is in that position.

18.10 The figure opposite shows a wheel of radius 0.20 m with metal spokes which is spinning clockwise about its axle O at 4.0 revolutions per second. There is a uniform magnetic field of flux density 30 mT at right angles to the plane of the wheel, as shown.

(a) What is the rate of sweeping out area by one spoke?

(b) What is the e.m.f. induced in one spoke?

(c) If the axle is earthed, what is the potential at (i) A, a point on the rim, (ii) B, a point 0.10 m from the axle, (iii) A', another point on the rim?

(d) Explain whether, if the rim is made of metal, any

current would flow in it.

(e) If, instead, the wheel were a solid disc, would there by any difference in the p.d. between O and A?

(f) How could the p.d. between the axle and the rim be made to send a current through a circuit?

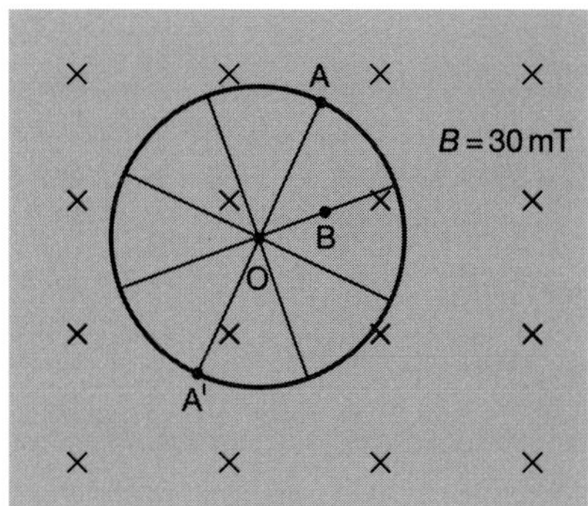

18.11 An electric fan has four blades each 150 mm long; it turns about a horizontal axle which points magnetic north. If the horizontal component of the Earth's magnetic field is 18 μT, and the speed of rotation of the fan is 2400 revolutions per minute, calculate the e.m.f. induced between

(a) the axle and the tip of any one blade

(b) the tips of two blades directly opposite each other

(c) the tips of two adjacent blades.

18.12 A rectangular coil is placed in a uniform magnetic field; it rotates about an axle which is at right angles to the field. One end O of the axle can be seen in the figure below.

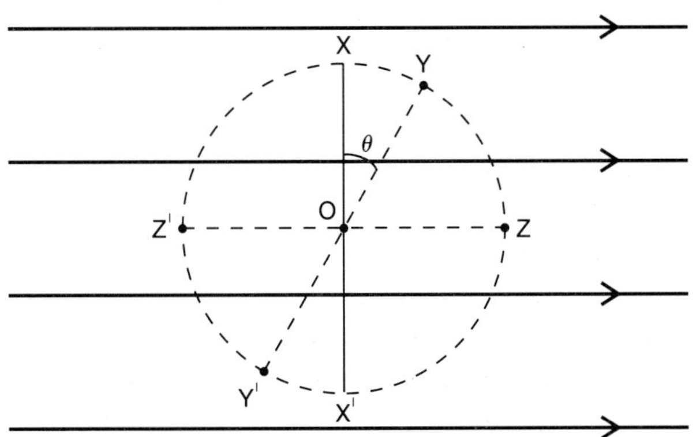

(a) In which position, XOX' or ZOZ', is the maximum e.m.f. induced?

(b) if the coil has 100 turns, its width XOX' is 40 mm, its breadth is 70 mm, the flux density is 80 mT and the rate of rotation is 1500 revolutions per minute, what is the maximum e.m.f. induced?

18.13 *(a)* On a copy of the figure for question 18.12 mark the direction of the velocity of Y.

(b) If angle XOY is θ, what is the resolved part, at right angles to the field, of Y's velocity?

(c) If the flux density is B, and the length of the conductor which is cutting the lines of force is l, what is the e.m.f. $\mathscr{E}$ induced in the coil when it is in position YOY'?

(d) Sketch a graph, with labelled axes, to show how the e.m.f. $\mathscr{E}$ varies with angle θ for angles from 0° to 360°.

18.14 Refer to the figure for question *18.12*. The coil has N turns of mean area A and rotates at angular velocity ω.

(a) Derive an expression for the e.m.f. $\mathscr{E}$ induced at angle θ.

(b) Write down a value for the peak e.m.f.

(c) State two angles θ at which the peak e.m.f. occurs.

(d) If the output of the coil is connected to a resistor of resistance R, what is the peak power output of the generator?

(e) What then is the peak torque needed to rotate the generator at angular velocity?

18.15 A rectangular coil is placed in a uniform magnetic field and rotates about an axle which is at right angles to the field (as in question *18.11*).

(a) Explain why the e.m.f. induced is alternating (i.e. changes direction).

(b) Explain how a split-ring commutator may be used to provide a d.c. output from such a generator.

18.16 The figure overleaf shows a horizontal cross-section through a cylindrical magnet which produces a radial field. A closed circular coil of mass m, radius r and resistance R is placed in horizontal position in the field, as shown in the figure: at radius r, the flux density is B. The coil is then released from rest so that it falls vertically.

(a) Use the equation $\mathscr{E} = Blv$ to derive an expression for the e.m.f induced in the coil when its speed is v.

(b) Hence deduce the current in the coil, in terms of r, B, v and R.

(c) When there is a current in the coil, there is a magnetic force on the coil caused by this current. In which direction does this force act? Why will the coil reach a terminal speed, even if air resistance is negligible?

(d) Calculate the terminal speed in terms of B, m, the gravitational field strength g, r and R.

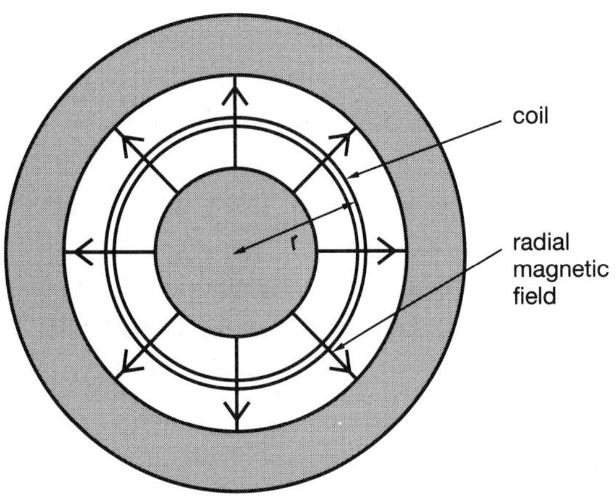

18.17 A bar magnet is moved towards a circular coil, as shown in the figure, and an e.m.f. is induced in the coil.

(a) Which of the magnet's field lines are being cut?

(b) Use Lenz's law to explain the direction of the e.m.f.

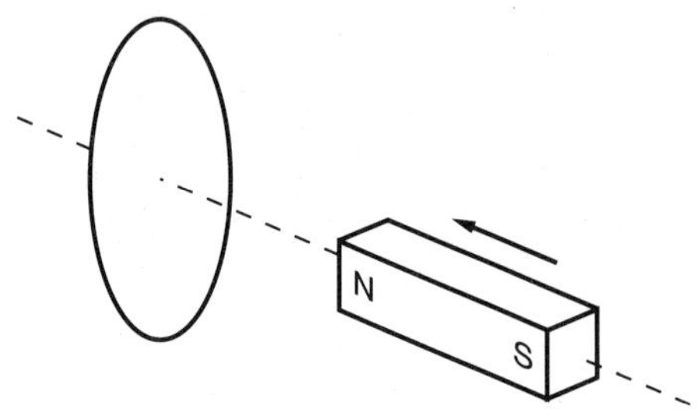

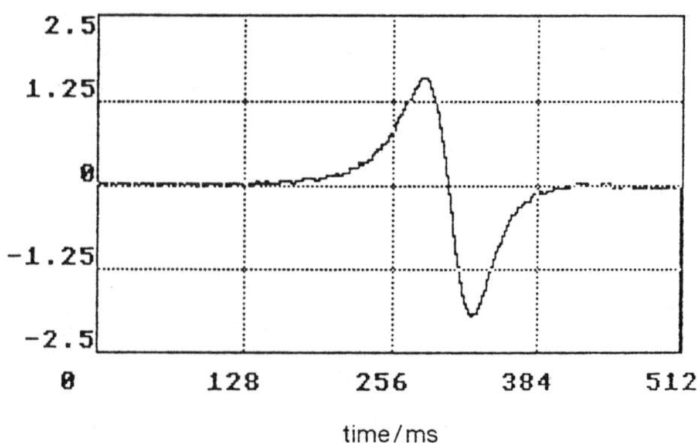

18.18 A circular coil is placed with its axis vertical and a bar magnet, with its axis aligned with the axis of the coil, is held above the coil and then dropped. A data logger is connected to the coil, records the e.m.f. induced in the coil at short time intervals and later draws a graph to show how the e.m.f. varies with time.

(a) The figure above shows the graph obtained as the magnet falls through the coil. Explain the shape of the graph.

(b) Give two arguments, one based on forces and the other based on energy, to explain why the magnet would take longer to fall if the data logger were removed and, instead, the ends of the coil were connected together.

(c) Copy the graph, and on the same axes sketch the graphs which would have been obtained if, separately (with the data logger again connected) (i) the coil had been replaced with one with twice the number of turns, (ii) the magnet had been dropped from about twice the height.

18.19 A bar magnet is pushed so that its N pole approaches a slab of copper. Use Lenz's law to predict the direction of the eddy currents in the copper, and sketch a diagram to show this direction.

18.20 A common demonstration of the effect of eddy currents uses a thick rectangular copper plate which swings like a pendulum bob through the gap between the poles of an electromagnet. The area of the plate is roughly the same as the area of the pole faces.

(a) Draw a diagram to show the direction of the field and the directions of the eddy currents when the copper plate is in its lowest position.

(b) What change, or changes, could you make in the design of the copper plate to reduce the eddy currents?

18.21 A bar magnet is suspended so that it can swing freely in a horizontal plane. It is set oscillating, and a sheet of copper is placed beneath it. Describe what happens, including a discussion of the energy changes involved.

18.22 A bar magnet is allowed to fall vertically down the insides of three lengths of tubing which have the same dimensions. One length is made of a plastic material, the second is made of copper and the third is made of (unmagnetised) iron. In which tube will the magnet take the longest time to fall, and in which tube will it take the shortest time to fall? Explain.

18.23 A gamma camera (used for the analysis of the gamma radiation from patients) has a magnetic field along its axis of 1.5 T. Suppose an aluminium plate is placed upright on a platform in this field, with its plane at right angles to the field. When it topples over it does so very slowly (taking 2 or 3 seconds to fall). Explain this.

18.24 A copper disc is placed between the poles of an electromagnet which is supplied with alternating current. The plane of the disc is perpendicular to the field of the electromagnet.

(a) Why does the disc become hot?

(b) Explain two methods by which the rate of production of energy could be increased, without disturbing or replacing the disc.

(c) Aluminium does not conduct as well as copper. Explain whether the production of energy in an aluminium disc of the same dimensions would be greater.

18.2 Magnetic flux

18.25 The average value of the Earth's magnetic field over the British Isles is 53 μT inclined downwards at an angle of 70° to the horizontal. Calculate the total flux through the British Isles if their area is $3.0 \times 10^{11}\,\mathrm{m}^2$.

18.26 A large electromagnet has circular pole pieces of diameter 0.20 m. The total flux produced by the magnet is 0.050 Wb. Calculate the average flux density between the pole pieces.

18.27 The figure shows a wire loop ABCD whose centre is O. It is placed at right angles to a uniform magnetic field of flux density 0.50 T. The dimensions of the loop and the field are shown in the figure.

(a) What is the flux through the loop?

(b) What is the size of the change in flux through the loop when the loop

(i) is moved, in its own plane, 0.20 m to the right

(ii) is moved, in its own plane, 0.30 m to the right

(iii) is rotated, in its own plane, through 90°, about its centre O

(iv) is rotated, about the line BC, through 90°

(v) is rotated, about the line BC, through 180°

(vi) is raised 0.10 m, parallel to the field (i.e. out of the paper)?

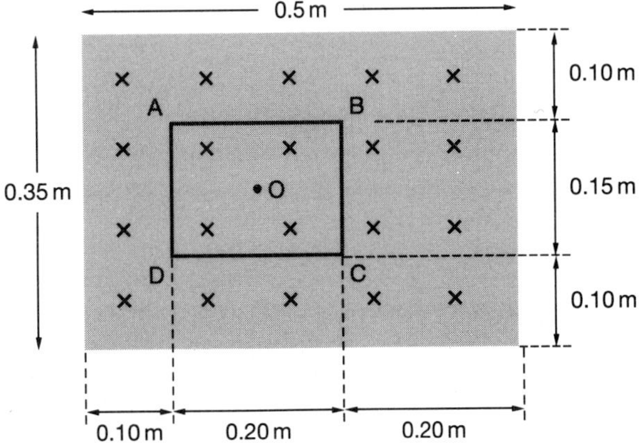

18.28 A circular coil of diameter 8 mm is placed near one end of a bar magnet: the axis of the coil and the magnet coincide. The flux densities, at distances of d/mm = 10, 15, 25 are B/mT = 300, 90, 20 respectively. What is the flux through the coil at each of these distance?

18.29 A metal-framed window which measures 0.80 m by 1.2 m, pivots about a horizontal axis and faces south. When closed, its plane is vertical and at right angles to the magnetic meridian. The Earth's field has a flux density of 50 μT at an angle of 67° with the horizontal. What is the size of the flux through the window when

(a) it is vertical

(b) it is horizontal

(c) it has been opened through an angle of 45°?

18.30 Two square-section solenoids each have 1200 turns per unit length and carry a current of 2.5 A. One measures 40 mm by 40 mm, the other 30 mm by 30 mm.

(a) What is the flux density in (i) the larger solenoid, (ii) the smaller solenoid?

(b) What is the flux in (i) the larger solenoid, (ii) the smaller solenoid?

18.3 Another way of inducing e.m.f.s

18.31 In question *18.17* you used the idea of cutting field lines to explain why an e.m.f. was induced. Now explain, using the idea of flux change, why an e.m.f. is induced.

18.32 A solenoid has a circular cross-section of diameter 30 mm, 1000 turns per metre and carries a current of 3.0 A. A coil of 10 turns is wrapped round the solenoid.

(a) What e.m.f. is induced in the coil, when the current in the solenoid is reduced to zero at a steady rate in 5.0 s, if the coil is placed (i) at the centre of the solenoid, (ii) at (precisely) one end of the solenoid?

(b) Explain whether it matters if the coil is wound tightly or loosely round the centre of the solenoid.

18.33 Two solenoids are mounted coaxially one inside the other. One of them is connected to a sensitive centre-zero voltmeter, and the second is connected through an ammeter to a variable d.c. supply. When the current in the second solenoid is increased from zero to 0.50 A in 5.0 s, the voltmeter reads +5.0 μV. What would you expect the voltmeter to read if

(a) the current is increased from zero to 0.50 A in 10 s

(b) the current is decreased from 0.50 A to zero in 2.5 s

(c) with the current steady at 0.50 A, the inner solenoid is completely removed from the other one in 10 s, at such a speed as to keep the voltmeter reading steady?

18.34 Two coils of insulated wire are wound one on top of the other on a cardboard tube. The outer coil is connected to a supply which provides a current which varies with time as shown in the figure; the inner coil is connected to a resistor.

(a) Copy the graph and add to it a graph which shows how the current varies in the inner coil.

(b) On a new set of axes draw a graph to show how the supply current would vary with time if its peak value was the same, but the frequency was doubled. Then add a graph which shows how the current now varies in the inner coil.

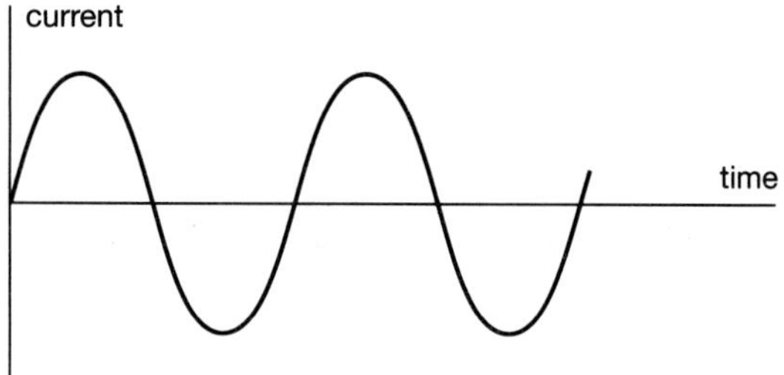

18.35 A circular coil and a copper ring are placed, as in the figure below, flat on a horizontal table.

(a) What is the direction of the current in the ring if the current in the coil is (i) clockwise and increasing, (ii) clockwise and decreasing,

(iii) anticlockwise and increasing,
(iv) anticlockwise and decreasing?

(b) The current in the coil is increased from zero to 4.0 A in 2.0 s. How will the current in the ring be affected if the current in the coil is increased from zero (i) to 2.0 A in 2.0 s, (ii) to 2.0 A in 1.0 s, (iii) to 4.0 A in 1.0 s?

(c) How will the energy converted in the ring be affected if these three processes occur?

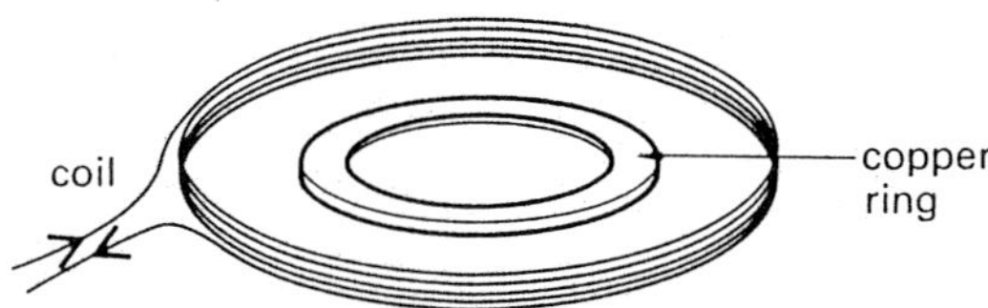

18.36 A circular copper ring of diameter 0.20 m and resistance 0.010 Ω is placed with its plane at right angles to a uniform magnetic field. If the field is changing at a rate of 2.0 mT s^{-1}, calculate

(a) the e.m.f.

(b) the current in the ring.

18.37 A solenoid is supplied with alternating current. Describe what happens if the following, each with the same smaller cross-sectional area, are placed, in succession, inside the solenoid:

(a) a solenoid whose ends are not connected together

(b) the same solenoid with its ends connected

(c) a solid copper bar

(d) a solid iron bar.

18.4 Magnetically linked circuits

18.38 The photograph shows a metal ring supported by a magnetic force from the coil at the base of the stand.

(a) Why must the current in the coil be alternating?

(b) Why must the retort stand rod be made from iron or steel?

(c) Why is aluminium a good choice of metal for the ring?

(d) What can you deduce about the directions of the current in the coil and the ring at any moment?

(e) Why does the ring move upwards if the current in the coil is increased?

(f) Is there any current in the retort stand rod? If so, what is its direction?

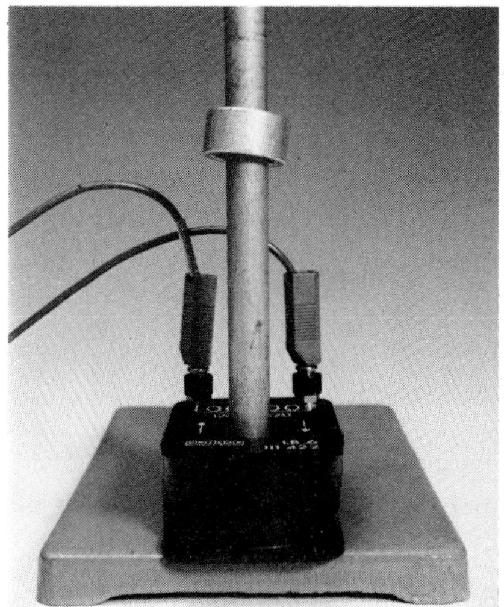

18.39 Two solenoids are placed coaxially one inside the other. The outer one is supplied with sinusoidally alternating current at a frequency of 50 Hz; the inner one is connected to a cathode ray oscilloscope.

(a) Draw a graph to show the variation with time of the current in the outer solenoid.

(b) Beneath this draw a graph to show the variation with time of the e.m.f. induced in the inner solenoid.

(c) Describe in words how the time-variation of the induced e.m.f. is related to the time-variation of the current supplied.

18.40 An alternating current of 3.0 A at a frequency of 50 Hz is passed through 50 turns of a helical spring stretched to a length of 0.80 m. A search coil with its axis parallel to that of the spring is placed inside the spring near its centre. It is connected to an oscilloscope. With suitable settings the vertical height of the trace showing the e.m.f. in the search coil is 40 mm. What height of trace would be obtained if, instead

(a) the frequency of the current in the spring was 100 Hz

(b) the 50 turns of the spring were stretched to 1.60 m

(c) current is supplied to only 25 turns of the coil, which are stretched to 0.80 m

(d) the axis of the search coil makes an angle of 60° with the axis of the spring

(e) the search coil is moved to one end of the spring, in the same plane as the end turn, but still coaxial.

18.41 A search coil with 5000 turns of mean area $1.0\,\text{cm}^2$ is placed in a magnetic field of peak value 3.5 mT oscillating sinusoidally at a frequency of 200 Hz.

(a) Explain at which moments the induced e.m.f. in the search coil has its maximum value.

(b) If the maximum rate of change of a magnetic field of peak value B and frequency f is $2\pi fB$, find the maximum e.m.f. induced in the search coil.

18.42 Describe how you would use a search coil to investigate how the strength of the magnetic field varies near a long straight wire carrying a current. You should describe how you would process the measurements you take, and include details of precautions taken to obtain a reliable result.

18.43 A search coil with N turns of mean area A is placed in a solenoid which has n turns per unit length and carries a sinusoidally varying current of peak value I_0 oscillating sinusoidally at a frequency f. The axes of the solenoid and the search coil coincide.

(a) If the variation with time t of the current I in the solenoid may be shown as $I = I_0 \sin 2\pi ft$, write down an expression for the flux ϕ in the search coil at time t.

(b) Use calculus to find the value of $d\phi/dt$.

(c) What is the peak value of the e.m.f. induced in the solenoid?

18.44 One solenoid is placed inside another. When the current in the outer one is raised from zero to 3.0 A in 2.0 s, the induced e.m.f. in the other is 5.0 mV.

(a) What is the mutual inductance of the solenoids?

(b) With the current held steady at 3.0 A the inner solenoid is now removed from the outer solenoid in such a way that the induced e.m.f. is again 5.0 mV. Explain whether the e.m.f. is in the same direction as before.

(c) How long does it take to remove the solenoid?

(d) Describe how the solenoid must be removed: e.g., at a steady speed, slowly then more quickly, or in some other way.

18.45 The figure shows a power supply which provides a sinusoidally alternating p.d. across a circuit which consists of an inductor and a resistor in series. Channel 1 of a double-beam oscilloscope is connected across the resistor which has a precisely known value of $10.0\,\Omega$. By measuring the p.d. across the resistance, the current in the circuit can be calculated from $I = V/R$. (That is the only reason why the resistor is there: its resistance is negligible compared with the impedance of the inductor.) The sensitivity of channel 1 is $50\,\text{mV div}^{-1}$. Channel 2 is connected across the terminals of a second inductor which is linked to the first by an iron core. Its sensitivity is $2\,\text{V div}^{-1}$. The timebase speed is $1\,\text{ms div}^{-1}$. The two oscilloscope traces obtained are as shown in the figure.

(a) From the trace for channel 1, show that the maximum rate of change of current is about $10\,\text{A s}^{-1}$.

(b) What is the induced e.m.f. when the rate of change of current is a maximum?

(c) What is the mutual inductance of the two inductors?

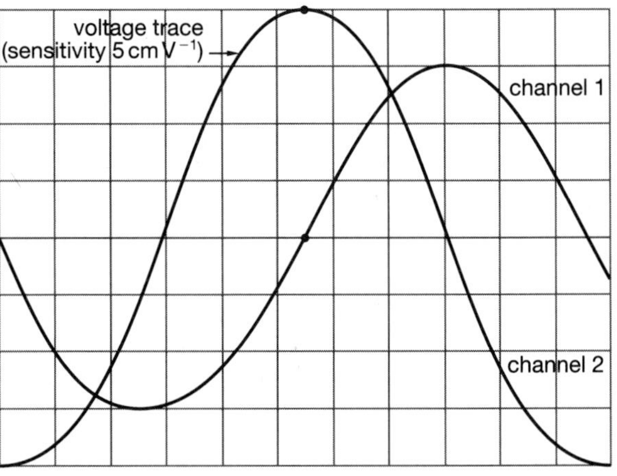

18.5 Inductance

18.46 ***(a)*** Explain why a coil of wire consisting of a single turn has some self-inductance.

(b) By what factor, approximately, is the self-inductance of a coil increased if its number of turns increases by a factor of 10?

(c) Why can your answer to *(b)* be only approximate?

18.47 Express the henry in terms of the base units of the SI.

18.48 An alternating supply was connected to a coil consisting of 600 turns of wire. When the frequency of the supply was 50 Hz the current in the coil was 2.4 A. Explain why the current

(a) fell to 1.2 A when the frequency was raised to 100 Hz

(b) fell to almost zero when an iron bar was placed in the coil.

18.49 An iron-cored inductor has a resistance of 1.4 Ω and an inductance of 2.0 H.

(a) What is the current after it has been connected to a direct supply of e.m.f. 6.0 V and negligible internal resistance?

(b) When an a.c. supply of peak value 6.0 V is used instead, the current falls to a few mA. Explain.

(c) What, approximately, is the peak value of the e.m.f. induced in the coil?

18.50 An electronic device called a ramp generator causes the current to grow at a rate of 50 mA s^{-1} in a coil of inductance 0.80 H. What e.m.f. is induced in the coil?

18.51 A battery of e.m.f. 6.0 V is connected through a switch, which is initially open, to an inductor and a resistor in series. Their inductance and resistance are 2.0 H and 10 Ω respectively.

(a) What is the initial rate of change of current?

(b) What is the final current?

(c) What is the rate of rise of current when the current is 0.10 A?

18.52 For the circuit shown in the figure

(a) what are the initial rates of rise of current shown on (i) ammeter A_1 (ii) ammeter A_2?

(b) what is the final current shown by (i) ammeter A_1 (ii) ammeter A_2?

(c) sketch graphs to show how the current on the two ammeters varies with time.

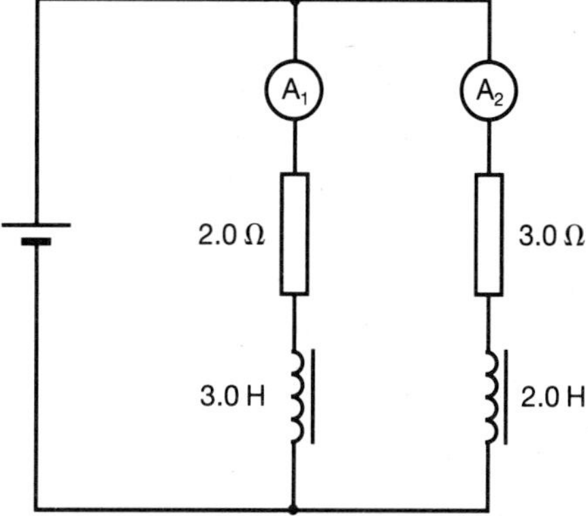

18.53 A battery of e.m.f. $\mathscr{E}$ is connected through a switch, which is initially open, to an inductance L and a resistance R in series. The switch is then closed: at some later time the current, before it has reached its final value, is I.

(a) Write down an equation connecting $\mathscr{E}$, L, R, I and t.

(b) Multiply both sides of this equation by I.

(c) What does each of the three terms now represent?

18.54 A battery of e.m.f. $\mathscr{E}$ is connected through a switch, which is initially open, to an inductance L and a resistance R in series. The switch is then closed: the current eventually reaches a value I.

(a) Draw a graph, labelled (a), to show how the current varies with time.

(b) On the same axes draw a second graph, labelled (b), to show how the current would vary if the inductor was replaced with an inductor of inductance $\frac{1}{2}L$.

(c) On the same axes draw a third graph, labelled (c), to show how the current would vary if, with the original inductor L, the resistor was replaced with a resistor of resistance $2R$.

18.55 In the circuit in question *18.51* the switch is later opened.

(a) Assuming that it takes 2.0 ms for the current to fall to zero, what is the average value of the e.m.f. induced in the inductor?

(b) What apparatus could you use to demonstrate the existence of this large e.m.f.?

18.56 A signal generator is set to produce a square wave output of amplitude 2.0 V and frequency 500 Hz: i.e. for 1.0 ms the e.m.f. is 2.0 V, and for 1.0 ms the output is zero, this cycle repeating itself indefinitely.

(a) Draw a graph to show this variation of e.m.f. for three cycles.

(b) The terminals of the signal generator were connected to a resistance R and inductance L in series. If the values of R and L are such that the current reaches 99% of its final value in 0.50 ms, draw a second graph beneath the first, with the same time axes, to show how the current in the circuit varies with time for three complete cycles.

18.57 An induction coil is used to provide the spark to explode the petrol-air mixture in petrol engines. In the conditions inside the cylinder a p.d. of about 10 kV is needed. The power supply for the induction coil is a 12 V battery: how does the coil produce the very high p.d. which is needed?

18.6 Energy conversions

18.58 The figure shows two straight wires AB and DC, each of length l, linked by fine flexible wires. The wires lie in a plane which is at right angles to a magnetic field B which passes into the page.

(a) Suppose that wire AB is fixed in position, and you move the wire DC away from it at a speed v. A current will be induced in the wire: call this I. What is the magnetic force on this wire?

(b) What is the force F which you must use to pull the wire at a steady speed v?

(c) What is your rate of working P_m?

(d) You are inducing an e.m.f. $\mathcal{E}$ which is delivering a current I. What is the rate of working P_e of the e.m.f.?

(e) Why must your rate P_m of mechanical working be equal to the rate P_e of electrical working?

(f) Hence derive an expression for $\mathcal{E}$ in terms of B, l and v.

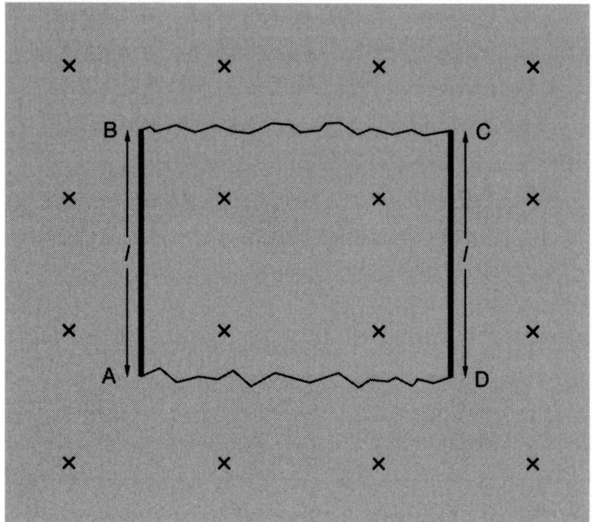

18.59 An electric motor takes a power of 200 W from the mains when it is running at a steady speed of 3000 r.p.m. with no load connected. Calculate the frictional torque exerted by its bearings and air resistance.

18.60 An electric motor is run from a 24 V supply. When it is producing 120 W of mechanical power the armature current is 5.50 A. Calculate

(a) the e.m.f. induced in the armature

(b) the resistance of the armature.

18.61 The figure shows a 12 V power supply connected to a machine being used as a motor. The resistance of the armature is 1.0 Ω. When the switch is closed the current settles to 0.50 A and the speed of the motor is 1150 r.p.m. with no load connected.

(a) Explain why the current is not 12 A.

(b) What is the back e.m.f. in this situation?

(c) What is the power (i) drawn from the supply,

(ii) wasted in heating the armature, (iii) used in overcoming frictional forces in the motor?

(d) What would the back e.m.f. become if the motor was loaded (e.g. required to lift a sack) and its speed fell to 1000 r.p.m.?

(e) What would then be the current?

(f) What is then the power (i) drawn from the supply, (ii) wasted in heating the armature, (iii) used in overcoming frictional forces in the motor and doing useful work?

(g) A friend says 'It's a pity the back e.m.f. is always so large – it must make the motor very inefficient.' What would you say?

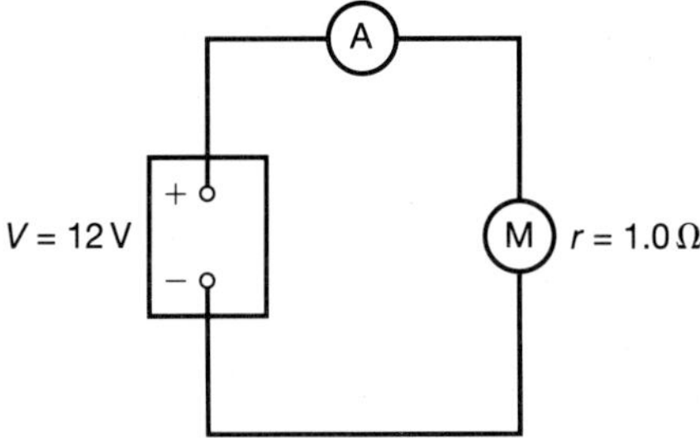

18.62 One of the coils in the armature of a motor has 25 turns each of area 50 cm^2; the coil's resistance is 0.50 Ω and it carries a current of 2.0 A.

(a) Draw a diagram showing the position of the coil in relation to the magnetic field when the torque acting on it is a maximum.

(b) If this maximum torque is 0.20 Nm, what is the flux density of the magnetic field in which the coil rotates?

(c) What is the e.m.f. induced in the coil in this position if its speed of rotation is 3000 r.p.m. (remember to convert the unit from r.p.m. to rad s^{-1})?

(d) What potential difference must be applied across the coil in this position to keep it turning at a steady speed?

18.63 The figure shows a circuit diagram for a machine being used as a motor. It is designed to be connected to a 12.0 V supply, and its armature resistance is 0.200 Ω.

(a) What is the initial current in the armature?

(b) Why does the current rapidly fall as the motor begins to rotate?

(c) The motor turns a pulley around which a rope is passed to act as a brake. The frictional force is 2.00 N and the distance from the force to the axle is 45.0 mm. The motor rotates this pulley at a steady rate of 1200 r.p.m. What is the rate at which the motor does mechanical work against the frictional force? (Remember to convert the unit of rate of rotation from r.p.m. to rad s^{-1}.)

(d) The current in the motor is then 0.980 A. What is the power drawn from the supply?

(e) What is the efficiency of the motor?

(f) What is the rate of production of internal energy in the resistance of the armature?

(g) Use your answers to *(c)*, *(d)* and *(f)* to calculate the rate of working of the motor against other resisting forces; e.g. frictional forces in the bearings.

(h) Find the total rate of mechanical working of the motor, and *hence* the back e.m.f. in the motor.

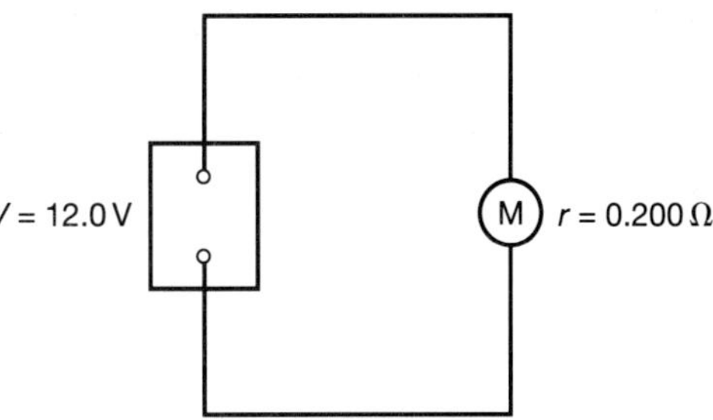

18.64 Refer to question *18.63*. The frictional force is now increased and the motor speed is found to fall.

(a) What effect does this have on (i) the back e.m.f., (ii) the current drawn from the supply?

(b) If the new motor speed is 1150 r.p.m. what is the new back e.m.f.?

18.65 The figure shows two ways in which the field coils for a motor's electromagnet may be connected to the supply: (i) shunt-wound and (ii) series-wound.

(a) Assuming that the p.d. provided by the supply

remains constant, describe how the current in the field coils varies as each motor is started from rest.

(b) Describe the effect on each motor when an additional load is applied.

(c) What are the relative advantages or disadvantages of these two methods of connecting the field coils?

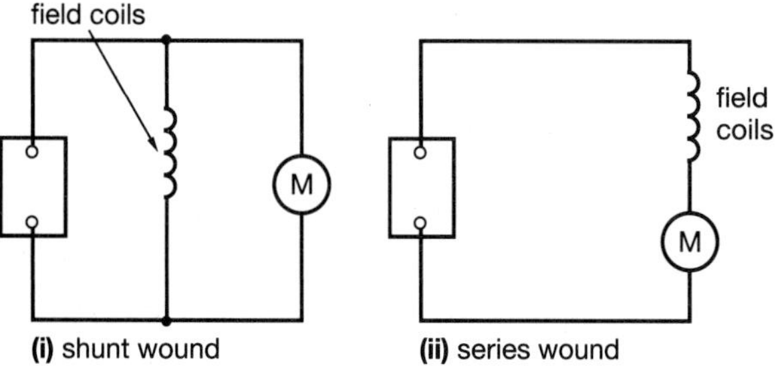

18.66 A small d.c. dynamo is connected to a light bulb. A thread is wrapped round the shaft of the dynamo and a weight is hung on this so that the dynamo is rotated by the weight falling to the floor. Describe the energy transformations which take place, and explain the physical process by which each transformation is brought about. What exactly is the *electrical energy* that appears in this circuit?

18.67 The figure shows a circuit diagram for a machine being used as a dynamo. The wires of the armature have resistance r; the load has resistance R.

(a) If the e.m.f. generated is $\mathcal{E}$ and the current delivered is I, write down an equation connecting $\mathcal{E}$, I, r and R.

(b) Multiply both sides of this equation by I. What does each term of this equation represent?

(c) A girl pedals a bicycle whose rear wheel is connected to this machine. Her feet each push on the pedals with a force of 450 N for half of each revolution, and these forces are each 0.25 m from the axle of the wheel. What is the torque of *one* of these forces?

(d) She pedals at a rate of 0.75 revolutions per second. What is her rate of working, in watts? (Remember to convert the unit of rate of rotation from rev s^{-1} to rad s^{-1}.)

(e) Assuming that the mechanical linkage in the bicycle is 90% efficient, what is the rate of working of the e.m.f. which she generates?

(f) If the armature resistance is 1.5 Ω, and the load is a bulb whose resistance under these conditions is 10 Ω, what is the current delivered, and the e.m.f. generated?

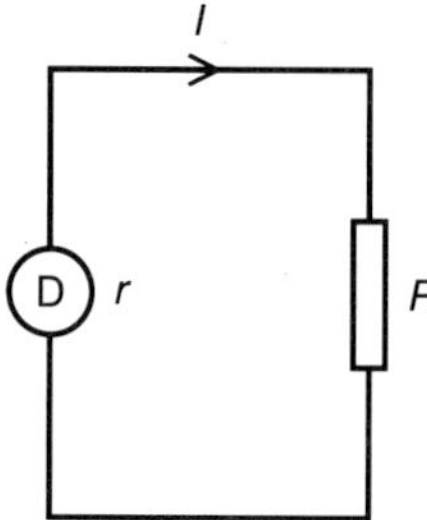

19 Alternating currents

19.1 Measurements

19.1 The figure shows graphs of how four different potential differences vary with time. Explain which of them are alternating p.d.s.

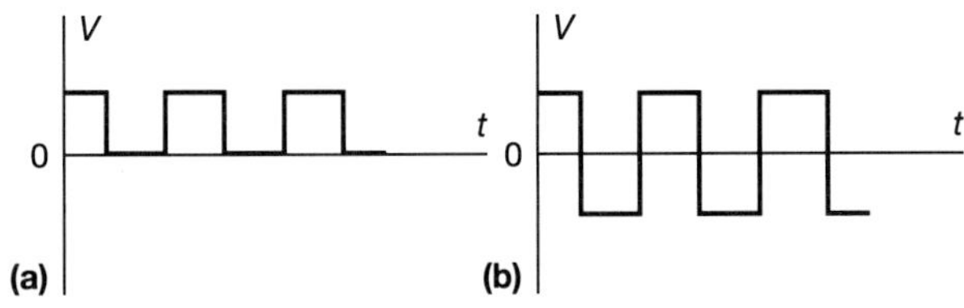

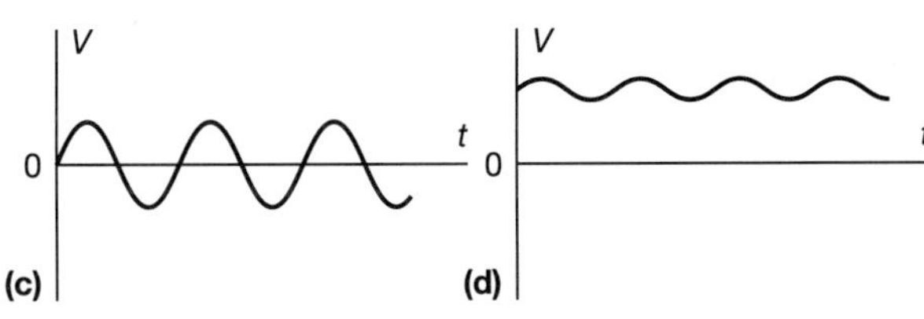

19.2 The r.m.s. value of a sinusoidal alternating current in a circuit is 2.0 A.

(a) What is its peak value?

(b) What is the peak value of the p.d. across a resistor of resistance 15 Ω which carries this current?

19.3 A 12 V car battery and a low voltage mains supply are joined alternately to a car headlamp bulb and both are found to keep it at the same brightness.

(a) What can you deduce about the mains supply?

(b) An oscilloscope is connected across the bulb while these tests are being conducted and the time-base is adjusted to give stationary traces. The a.c./d.c. switch is set to 'direct' and the sensitivity control is set at 5 V div^{-1}. Sketch what you would expect to see on the screen in each case.

19.4 An oscilloscope is connected across a sinusoidally alternating potential difference and the resulting trace is found to be 4.0 divisions in height from trough to crest. The sensitivity control is set at 5 V div^{-1}. Calculate

(a) the peak value of the alternating p.d.

(b) the r.m.s. value of the p.d.

(c) the r.m.s. value of the current in a resistance of 100 Ω to which this p.d. is applied.

19.5 A power supply which provides a sinusoidally varying p.d. of peak value 10 V is connected to a resistor of resistance 3.3 Ω. Sketch graphs with labelled axes to show, for two complete cycles, the variation with time of

(a) the p.d.

(b) the current in the resistor

(c) the power of the resistor.

(d) What is the mean power in the resistor?

19.6 A square-wave alternating p.d. generated by an oscillator may be described as follows. For a time interval of 1.0 ms the p.d. is constant at its peak value $+V_0$; the p.d. then changes very rapidly to a value of $-V_0$ at which it remains for a further 1.0 ms; it then reverts equally rapidly to its initial value $+V_0$, and so the cycle repeats continually.

(a) Sketch a graph of this waveform.

(b) What is the r.m.s. value of this alternating p.d.?

(c) What is the frequency of this p.d.?

19.7 An alternating current I is given by the equation
$I = (5.0\,\text{A})\sin 2\pi(50\,\text{Hz})t$

(a) What is the peak current?

(b) What is the r.m.s. current?

(c) What is the current when t is (i) 5.0 ms, (ii) 4.0 ms?

(d) At what time is the current 3.0 A?

19.8 A television set is labelled '240 V 150 W a.c. 50 Hz' at its main input.

(a) Write down an expression that shows how the current I taken by the set varies with time, and

state the value of any constants that appear in your expression.

(b) What is the maximum power taken by the set at any instant?

19.9 A current whose r.m.s. value is 13 A is being taken from the 50 Hz mains supply.

(a) What is the peak value of the current?

(b) What is the current 300 μs after it changes direction?

19.10 A student connected a diode in series with a resistor to a power supply which provided an alternating p.d. whose peak value was 2.0 V. With an oscilloscope connected across the resistor he expected to see the trace shown in (a) in the figure; instead he saw what is shown in (b). His teacher told him 'that is because the silicon diode has a turn-on p.d. of about 0.5 V'. How does that explain what he saw?

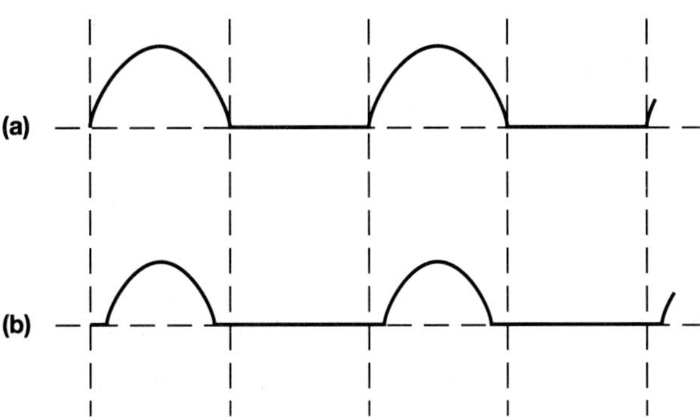

19.11 *(a)* Draw a circuit diagram to show how four diodes may be connected to a sinusoidally alternating supply to produce full-wave rectified current in a resistor.

(b) Sketch a graph to show two cycles of the alternating p.d., and beneath this graph another which shows the current in the resistor. Assume that the diodes have negligible resistance in the forward direction.

(c) Explain what effect there would be if a capacitor were connected across the resistor, and beneath your graph for *(b)* draw another graph to show the sort of current there would then be in the resistor.

19.12 The figure shows a form of rectifier circuit using a pair of diodes. It is supplied from a centre-tapped transformer, across the whole of which the r.m.s. potential difference is 12 V (at a frequency of 50 Hz). Describe how the circuit works, explaining what happens on successive half-cycles of the alternating supply.

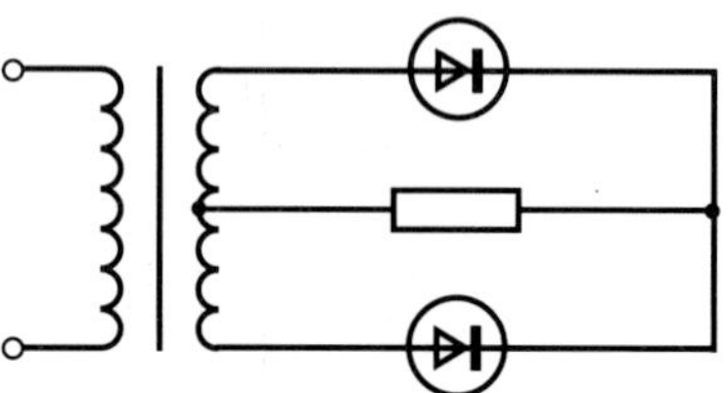

19.13 What trace would you expect to see on the oscilloscope in the circuit shown in the figure? The supply provides a p.d. of peak value 10 V. Label your graph with values of p.d. on the *y*-axis. Assume that the diodes have negligible resistance in the forward direction.

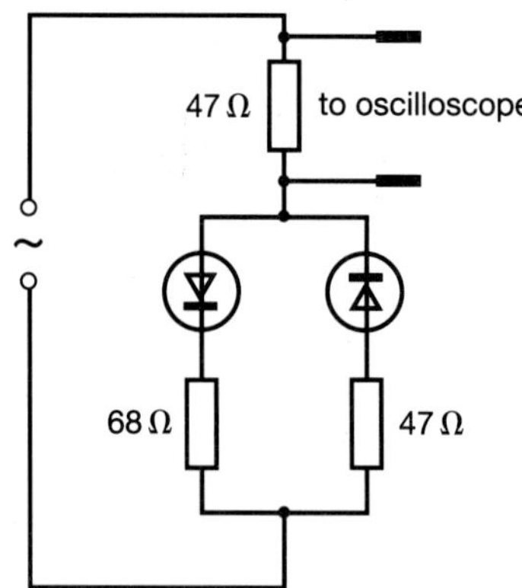

19.14 The figure below shows a circuit which is connected to the output of a full-wave rectified supply which has a peak value of 9.6 V.

(a) If the frequency of the original alternating supply is 50 Hz, what is the frequency of the full-wave supply?

(b) What is the maximum charge on the capacitor?

(c) What is the maximum current in the resistor?

(d) Approximately how much charge leaves the capacitor in the time between it having maximum values of charge?

(e) What, approximately, is the smallest value of the p.d. between A and B?

(f) Sketch a graph to show how the p.d. between A and B varies with time.

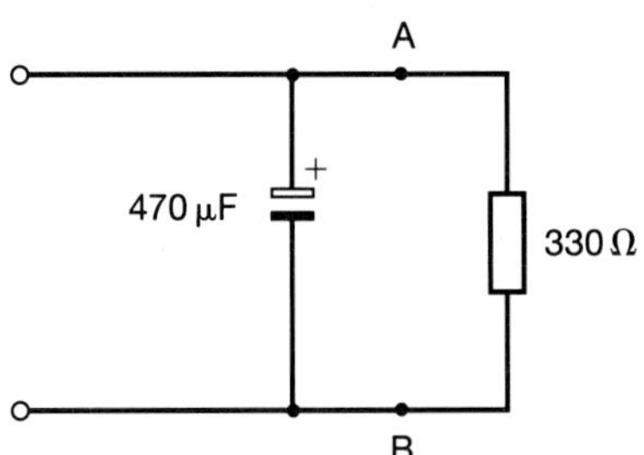

19.15 What would be seen on an oscilloscope screen if, connected to the X– and Y–inputs (which were set to the same sensitivity), there were

(a) two alternating in-phase p.d.s. of frequency 50 Hz, if the p.d. connected to the X–input had a peak value of 2.0 V and the p.d. connected to the Y–input had a peak value of 1.0 V?

(b) the same, except that one of the p.d.s. had a frequency very slightly less than 50 Hz?

(c) two alternating p.d.s. of peak value 2.0 V, if the p.d. connected to the X–input had a frequency of 50 Hz and the p.d. connected to the Y–input had a frequency of 100 Hz (if from time to time both p.d.s. are zero simultaneously)?

19.2 Circuits containing capacitors

19.16 An alternating p.d. which has a fixed peak value is connected to a purely capacitative circuit. Sketch graphs to show how the current varies with

(a) frequency

(b) capacitance.

19.17 In the circuit of the figure for question *19.16* what would be the effect on the current of, separately

(a) doubling the capacitance

(b) doubling the peak p.d.

(c) halving the frequency?

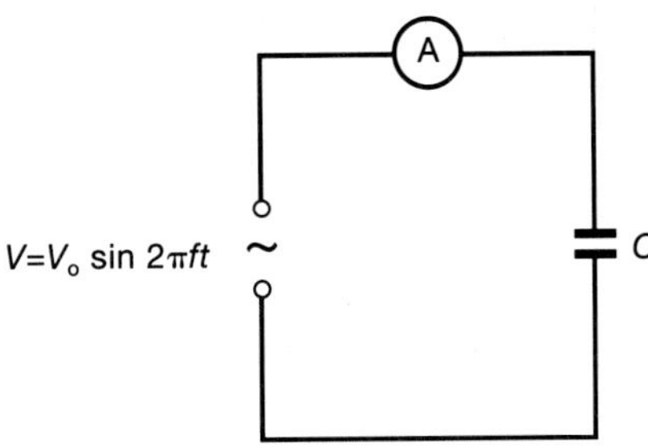

19.18 An alternating supply is connected to a capacitor through two ammeters as shown in the figure. The circuit has negligible resistance. The ammeters show that there is a current.

(a) How can there be a current in the circuit when there is a gap in it?

(b) Sketch a graph to show how the supply p.d. varies with time.

(c) Beneath this graph, with times coinciding, draw graphs to show the variation with time of (i) the charge on the capacitor, (ii) the current in the circuit, (iii) the power drawn from the supply.

(d) What is the average power drawn from the supply?

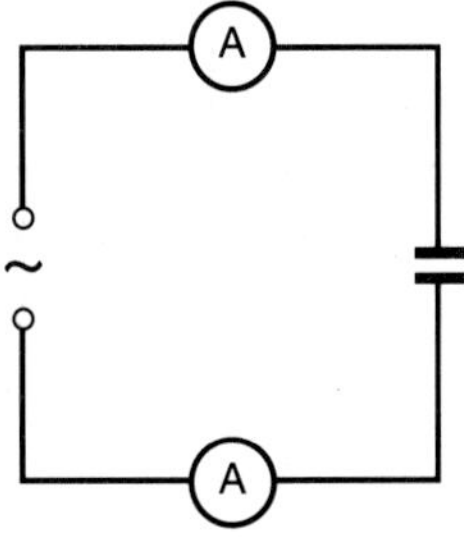

19.19 What is the reactance of a capacitor of capacitance 47 μF if it is connected to a supply of frequency *(a)* 50 Hz *(b)* 100 Hz *(c)* zero?

19.20 What is the r.m.s. current in a 4.7 μF capacitor connected to a 12 V r.m.s. 50 Hz supply?

19.21 The figure shows a varying p.d. whose maximum and minimum values are 7.0 V and 5.0 V: it can be thought of as a direct p.d. of 6.0 V on which is superimposed an alternating p.d. of peak value 1.0 V. In this case the alternating p.d. has a frequency of 100 Hz. What current flows through a capacitor of 2.2 μF?

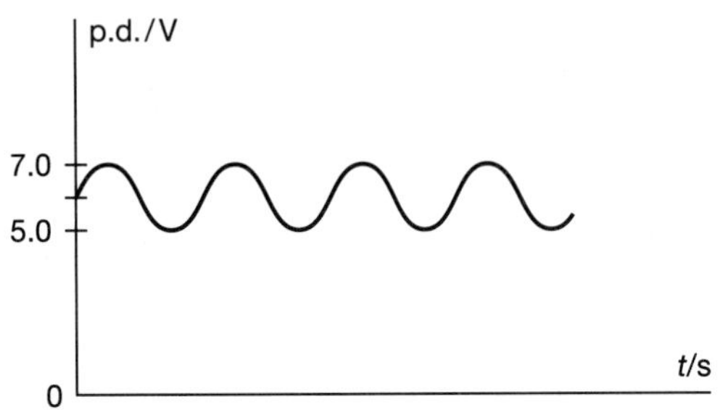

19.3 Circuits containing inductors

19.22 An alternating p.d. which has a fixed peak value is connected to a purely inductive circuit. Sketch graphs to show how the current varies with

(a) frequency
(b) inductance.

19.23 An alternating supply is connected to an inductor. The circuit has negligible resistance.

(a) Sketch a graph to show how the supply p.d. varies with time.
(b) Beneath this graph, with times coinciding, draw graphs to show the variation with time of the current in the circuit.

19.24 A 12 V 36 W lamp is connected in series with a coil to an alternating supply of r.m.s. p.d. 12 V. The lamp lights almost normally. Explain why the lamp dims when an iron bar is inserted into the coil.

19.25 An air-cored inductor has an inductance of 10 mH. What is its reactance when it is connected to a supply of frequency (a) 50 Hz, (b) 100 Hz, (c) zero?

19.26 An iron-cored inductor has an inductance of 6.0 H and negligible resistance.

(a) What is the r.m.s. current in it when it is connected to an alternating supply of r.m.s. value 12 V and frequency 50 Hz?
(b) If in fact the resistance of the inductor is 2.0 Ω, what current would flow if, instead, a direct p.d. of 12 V were connected to the inductor?

19.4 Mixed circuits

19.27 A resistor is connected in series with a capacitor to an alternating supply. An oscilloscope measures the peak p.d. across each in turn and it is found that the two peak p.d.s. are 4.7 V and 3.1 V respectively.

(a) Sketch graphs to show the variation of these p.d.s. with time, using the same axes for both graphs.
(b) Hence show that the supply must have a peak p.d. of less than 7.8 V.

19.28 What is the impedance of a series combination of a 470 Ω resistor and a 0.68 μF capacitor at frequencies of

(a) 50 Hz
(b) 500 Hz
(c) 5000 Hz?

19.29 What is the impedence of a series combination of a 470 Ω resistor and a 150 mH inductor at frequencies of

(a) 50 Hz
(b) 500 Hz
(c) 5000 Hz?

19.30 *(a)* What resistance must be connected in series with a lamp labelled '110 V 60 W' if the lamp is to light normally when connected to a 240 V, 50 Hz mains supply?
(b) We wish to achieve the same effect by replacing the resistor with a capacitor. What must be the total impedance of the capacitor and the lamp?
(c) Hence find the reactance of the capacitor, and its capacitance.
(d) What p.d. must the capacitor be designed to withstand?
(e) What is the advantage of the second method?

19.31 A power supply which provides an alternating p.d. is connected in series with an inductor which has negligible resistance. The inductor is then replaced by another, of the same inductance, but which does have appreciable resistance. Which of these quantities is now greater:

(a) the current in the circuit
(b) the rate of conversion of internal energy
(c) the impedance of the circuit
(d) the phase difference between the p.d. and the current?

19.32 The figure shows a circuit in which a 6.8 μF capacitor and a 6.8 mH inductor are connected in series with different types of loudspeaker. Calculate the reactances of

(a) the capacitor at frequencies of (i) 50 Hz, (ii) 5000 Hz. and
(b) the inductor at frequencies of (i) 50 Hz, (ii) 5000 Hz.

The output from an audio amplifier will consist of p.d.s. of frequencies in the range 30 Hz to 18 kHz. Explain the purpose of this circuit, indicating which of the two loudspeakers would be designed to reproduce low frequencies well.

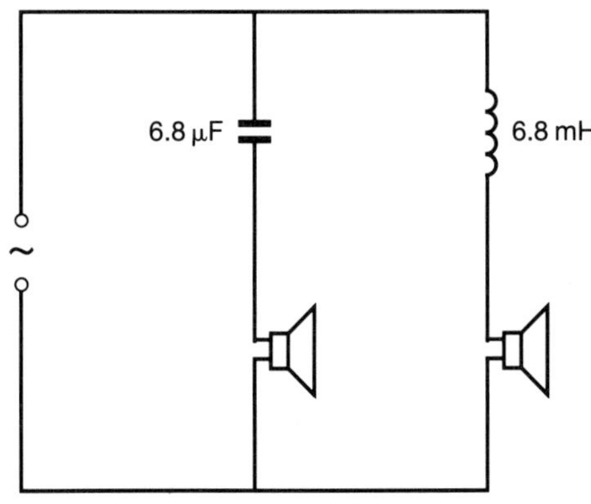

19.33 The following figure shows a bulb, a capacitor and an inductor connected in various ways to a signal generator. Sketch rough graphs to show how the current in the bulb in each circuit varies with the frequency of the supply. [Hint: it will help you to start by considering what happens when the frequency is zero, and when the frequency is very high.]

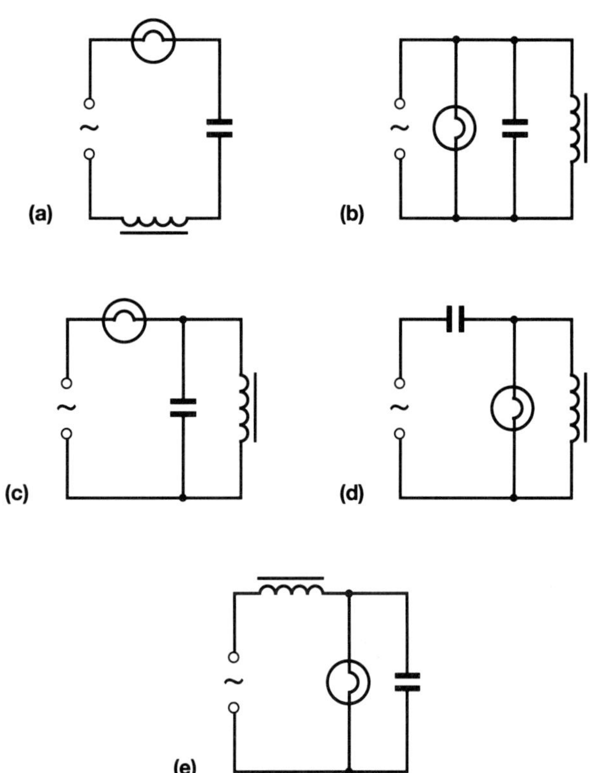

19.34 The figure below shows a resistor, a capacitor and an inductor connected in series. Explain

(a) why this is said to be a *series resonant circuit*
(b) why the resonant frequency f is given by $4\pi^2f^2LC = 1$
(c) which of the following quantities have their maximum values at the resonant frequency: (i) the

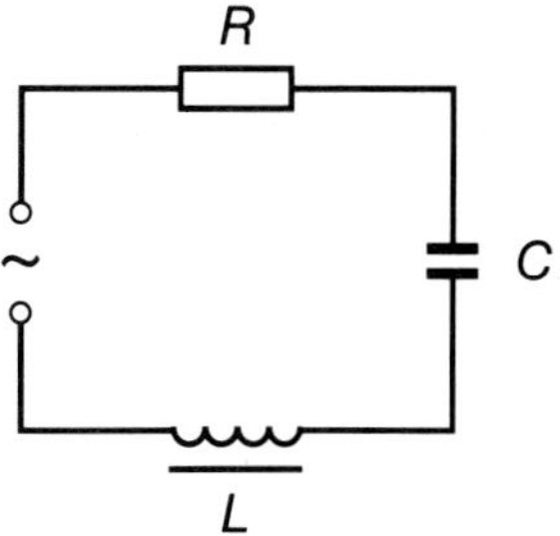

current (ii) the rate of conversion of internal energy (iii) the phase difference between the p.d. and the current.

19.35 The figure shows three identical bulbs connected in a circuit with a capacitor and an inductor to a signal generator. It is found that at a certain frequency f bulbs B and C are lit, but bulb A is not. When the frequency is raised bulb B brightens, and A is dimly lit; when the frequency is less than f bulb B goes out and bulb C lights instead, with bulb A again dimly lit.

(a) Explain these observations

(b) What traces would you expect to see on a double-beam oscilloscope connected across bulbs B and C when the frequency is f and both are lit?

(c) If the capacitor has a capacitance of 3.0 μF and f is 2.4 kHz, what is the inductance of the inductor?

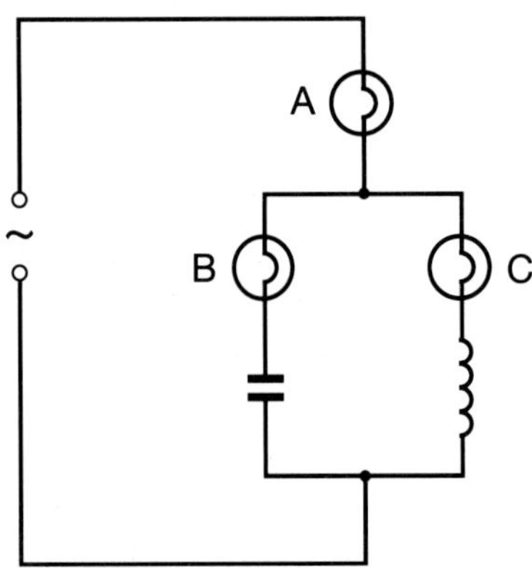

19.5 Electrical oscillations

19.36 A battery provides a p.d. of 6.0 V and is connected to a 470 μF capacitor. The capacitor is then disconnected from the battery and connected to a 10 mH inductor.

(a) What is the frequency of the oscillations?

(b) Explain why oscillations occur, referring to the different forms of energy in the circuit?

(c) Why does the amplitude of the oscillations decrease?

(d) Sketch a graph to show how the p.d. across the capacitor varies with time.

19.37 The inductor in a radio tuning circuit has an inductance of 470 μH.

(a) What is the frequency of the circuit when the variable capacitor has its maximum capacitance of 350 pF?

(b) Is this the lowest or highest frequency obtainable with this capacitor?

(c) To what value would the capacitance need to be changed if the radio is to receive the frequency at the other end of this waveband, if that is 1500 kHz?

19.38 It is possible to draw an analogy between the oscillation of a radio tuning circuit, and the oscillation of a mass oscillating between two springs on a horizontal surface. What features of the electrical oscillations correspond to the following features in the mechanical system:

(a) the mass

(b) the spring

(c) the kinetic energy of the mass

(d) the elastic potential energy of the spring?

19.6 Transformers

19.39 An 'ideal' transformer (i.e., one in which there are no power losses, and in which all the primary flux links the secondary coil) has 2400 primary turns and 120 secondary turns. It is used to light a 12 V 36 W bulb. What are

(a) the primary p.d.

(b) the primary current

(c) the primary power?

19.40 A 12 V alternating supply is connected to the primary terminal of a transformer which steps down the p.d. to 6.0 V. The secondary terminals are connected to a rheostat which is set to a resistance of 10 Ω.

(a) What is the power in the rheostat?

(b) If the resistance is reduced to 5.0 Ω, what does the power in the rheostat become?

(c) Where has the additional power come from?

19.41 An overhead projector lamp is labelled '24 V 250 W'.

(a) If the overhead projector is connected to the 240 V mains supply, and a transformer is used to step down the p.d. what must be the ratio of primary turns to secondary turns?

(b) What is the current in the projector lamp?

(c) Explain which of the following fuses you would use in the primary circuit: 13 A, 10 A, 2 A, 1 A.

19.42 A student places a 120-turn coil on an iron C core and connects it to a 12 V supply. She winds 24 turns of wire round a second C core and clamps the two C cores together so that there is a complete iron 'circuit'.

(a) Explain why a bulb, rated at 2.5 V, lights almost normally when connected to the second coil.

(b) If the current in the bulb is 0.20 A, what is the current in the primary coil?

(c) If she slides the 24-turn coil round the C cores until it is closer to the 120-turn coil she finds that the bulb is very slightly brighter. Why is this?

The student now winds a second 24-turn coil round one of the C cores, and connects an identical bulb to this coil. She is surprised to find that the brightness of the first bulb is the same as before, and that the second bulb is as bright as the first one.

(d) Explain why this outcome is to be expected, and where the additional energy has come from.

19.43 A student constructs a transformer which has a primary coil with 300 turns, and a secondary coil of 600 turns. He measures the resistance of the primary coil, and finds that it is 0.60 Ω. His teacher tells him that he can safely connect this coil to an alternating 6 V supply, provided the coil is placed on a complete iron core.

(a) What would be the current in the coil if it were connected to a 6 V d.c. supply?

(b) Why is it safe to connect the coil to a 6 V supply, *if* it is alternating, and *if* the coil is on an iron core?

The student finds that, with nothing connected to the secondary coil, an ammeter placed between the supply and the coil reads 0.10 A. He connects a 12 V, 24 W bulb to the secondary coil, and finds that the current in the primary coil rises to 4.1 A.

(c) What is the current in the secondary coil?

(d) Explain why the current in the primary coil is 4.1 A.

19.44 A building site has a transformer which steps down the p.d. from 11 kV to 415 V. In this question assume that the transformers have an efficiency of 100%.

(a) If the number of turns on the primary is 3000, what is the approximate number of turns on the secondary?

(b) The p.d. of 415 V is used to supply a crane which has a maximum power of 60 kW. What is the current drawn from the 11 kV supply when this crane is working at maximum power?

The site has a second transformer which, for safety reasons, steps down the p.d. of 415 V to 25 V for some hand lamps which are to have a power of 100 W. When five of these are in use, what is the current drawn from the 11 kV supply?

19.45 A laboratory power supply contains a transformer so that the mains p.d. of 240 V may be stepped down to low p.d.s. increasing in steps of 2 V from zero to 12 V. If the primary coil in the transformer has 1200 turns, explain how the secondary p.d.s. might be obtained.

19.46 A catalogue lists a transformer which is provided with two independent primary windings. It says that they can be connected in series for connection to a 240 V supply, or in parallel for connection to a 120 V supply. There are also two secondary coils, each described as '12 V 0.25 A'.

(a) With the manufacturer's suggested connections to the primary side of the transformer, what step-down ratios are possible with this transformer?

(b) What advantage would there be in connecting the two primary windings in parallel, rather than just using one of them?

(c) How would you expect the thickness of the wires in the primary and secondary windings to compare?

(d) If the primary of the transformer were connected to a 240 V supply, what current would be drawn from

it if a '12 V 100 mA' bulb were connected to one of the secondary coils?

19.47 In practice not all the magnetic flux produced by the primary coil links or threads the secondary coil. What effect does this have on

(a) the expected ratio (secondary p.d.)/(primary p.d.)

(b) the expected ratio (output power)/(input power)?

19.48 Transformers used for demonstrations in school and college laboratories often have the two coils on separate arms of an iron core, as shown in the figure (a), so that the coils can be removed and exchanged for others. Commercial transformers always have the two coils wound on the central part of a core which has the shape shown in (b). Why is (b) the preferred method of construction?

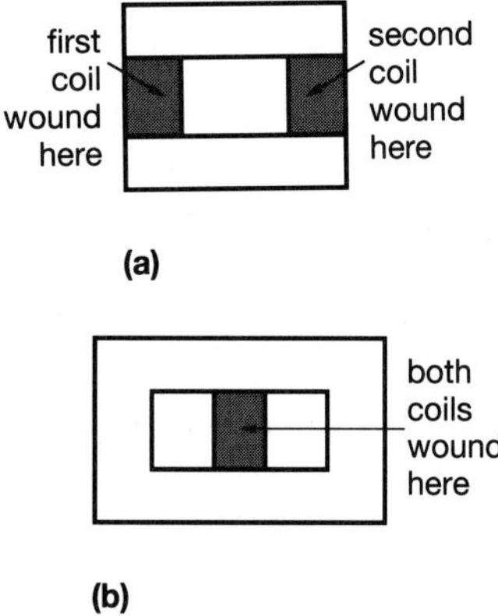

19.49 Transformers are not 100% efficient because of (a) resistance losses (b) eddy current losses (c) hysteresis losses. Explain each of these ways in which electrical energy is wastefully converted into internal energy.

19.50 A 12 V alternating supply is to be used to provide a current for an immersion heater which is to work at its normal power of 48 W.

(a) What is the resistance of the heater?

In one laboratory the heater may be connected to the power supply only through long leads, each of which has a resistance of 1.0 Ω.

(b) What is then the p.d. across the heater?

(c) What is the power of the heater in these circumstances?

(d) What supply p.d. would be needed if the heater was to have a power of 48 W?

(e) What would be the power wasted in the wires?

A transformer with a step-up ratio of 20 is now connected to the power supply, and the same long wires are used to connect the secondary of this transformer to the primary of a second transformer which is used to step down the p.d. in a 20:1 ratio. This output is used to supply the heater. The transformers may be assumed to be 100% efficient. The supply p.d. is adjusted so that in this new situation the heater does have a power of 48 W.

(f) What is the current in the long wires?

(g) What is the total p.d. across the two long wires?

(h) What was the supply p.d.?

(i) What was the power wasted in the wires?

(j) Comment on this method of reducing energy losses when energy has to be transmitted over long distances, explaining whether it would be possible if the supply had not been alternating.

19.51 Power stations generate alternating p.d.s. of 25 kV and a typical power output to the grid system is 1 GW.

(a) What current is being supplied to the grid system?

(b) If this current were sent along cables which have a resistance per unit length of $6.0 \times 10^{-5}\,\Omega\,m^{-1}$, calculate the p.d. across a 100 m length of this cable, and comment on your answer.

Your answer to *(b)* should show that the p.d. across even a short length of cable is much too high to be acceptable. Suppose that a transformer is used to step up the output p.d. from the power station to 400 kV.

(c) What current would now be supplied to the grid, if the power delivered were still 1 GW?

(d) What would be the p.d. across cable of length (i) 100 m, (ii) 20 km?

19.52 A student says 'It seems to me that what is important in the transformer is the turns-ratio, so why waste wire having, say, 1000 turns on the primary and 2000 turns on the secondary, when you could get the same turns-ratio using just one turn on the primary and two turns on the secondary?'. How would you reply?

20 Oscillatory motion

Data $g = 9.81\,\text{m}\,\text{s}^{-2}$

20.1 Describing oscillations

20.1 Estimate the time periods of each of the following motions and calculate (to 1 sig. fig.) their frequencies:

(a) a child on a playground swing
(b) a baby rocked in its mother's arms
(c) the free swing of your leg from the hip.

20.2 Sketch a large displacement-time graph for two periods of a simple harmonic motion.

(a) Mark with a P any instant where the speed is a maximum.
(b) Mark with a Q any instant when the speed is zero.
(c) Mark places where the acceleration is high and places where the acceleration is low.

20.3 Use your calculator to plot on graph paper a graph of $\sin\theta$ (up) against θ (along) from 0° to 360°. Add values of θ in radians. [It is useful to know the precise shape of sinusoidal graphs.]

20.4 The photograph shows a multiflash photograph of half an oscillation of a pendulum bob moving from left to right. The stroboscope was set to produce 30 flashes per second and the photograph is quarter full-size. Plot a graph to show how the horizontal displacements of the bob from the central position vary with time.

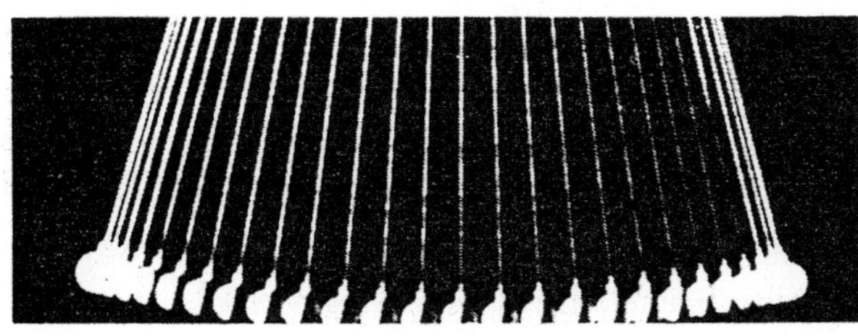

20.5 Draw a velocity-time graph for two bounces of a bouncing rubber ball. Is this an example of s.h.m? (Remember that the ball has a constant downward acceleration when in flight.)

20.6 What is (i) the period, and (ii) the frequency of

(a) the rise and fall of the sea
(b) the beat of a normal heart
(c) the oscillation of a ticker-timer arm
(d) piano strings which oscillate when middle C is played?

Express your answers in seconds (period) and hertz (frequency) respectively.

20.7 A piece of cork in a ripple tank oscillates up and down as ripples pass it. If the ripples travel at $0.20\,\text{m}\,\text{s}^{-1}$, have a wavelength of 15 mm and an amplitude of 5.0 mm, what is the maximum speed of the cork?

20.8 A potential difference which alternates sinusoidally is applied to the Y–plates of an oscilloscope which has a calibrated time base. A stationary trace, with an amplitude of 4.0 div and a wavelength of 1.5 div, is obtained with the time base set at $1.0\,\text{ms div}^{-1}$. When the time base is switched off the trace becomes a vertical line.
Calculate the maximum speed of the spot of light on the screen when producing the vertical line if 1 div is equal to a length of 10 mm.

20.9 The needle of a sewing machine moves up and down with simple harmonic motion. If the total vertical motion of the tip of the needle is 12 mm and it makes 30 stitches in 7.0 s what is the maximum speed of the tip of the needle?

20.10 The equation defining linear s.h.m. is

$$a = -(\text{constant})s$$

What units must the constant have?
Two s.h.m.s, A and B, are similar except that the constant in A is nine times the constant in B. Describe how these s.h.m.s differ.

20.11 A body oscillates with s.h.m. described by the equation

$$y = (1.6\,\text{m})\sin(3\pi\,\text{s}^{-1})t$$

What are

(a) the amplitude

(b) the period of the motion?

Calculate for $t = 1.5$ s

(c) the displacement

(d) the velocity

(e) the acceleration of the body.

20.12 In order to test how well pilots can recognise objects when seated in a juddering helicopter they are subjected to vibrations of frequency from 0.1 Hz to 50 Hz in a special rig. What is

(a) the maximum velocity

(b) the maximum acceleration

of a pilot who is being tested with vibrations of frequency 35 Hz and amplitude 0.60 mm?

20.13 A dock has a tidal entrance at which the water is 10 m deep at 12 noon, when the tide is at its lowest. The water is 30 m deep when the tide is at its highest, which follows next at 6.15 pm. A tanker, needing a depth of 15 m, needs to enter the dock as soon as possible that afternoon. Calculate the earliest time it could just clear the dock entrance. (Assume that the water rises and falls with s.h.m.)

20.2 Simple harmonic oscillators

20.14 The period t of vertical oscillations of a mass m supported by a light, helical spring of stiffness k (force per unit extension) is given by $T = 2\pi\sqrt{(m/k)}$.

(a) Two identical springs of force constant k are connected (i) in series (ii) in parallel, and support a mass m. What is the ratio of their periods of vertical oscillation?

(b) What mass would be required in case (ii) to make their periods of oscillation equal?

20.15 A man of mass 80 kg 'bounces' on the seat of a motorcycle. He finds that he passes through the centre of the oscillation 5 times in 3 seconds.
Calculate the spring constant of the suspension. State any assumptions you make.

20.16 A fisherman's scale stretches 2.6 m when a 1.9 kg fish is hung from it. What is the spring constant and what will be the frequency of vibration if the fish is pulled down and released?

20.17 A 'baby bouncer' is a device for amusing babies before they can walk. It consists of a harness suspended by elastic ropes from the lintel of a doorway. Such a device had ropes 1.20 m long which stretched to 1.42 m when a baby of mass 8.5 kg was placed in the harness. The baby was then pulled down 8.0 cm and released. Calculate

(a) the spring constant of the baby bouncer

(b) the period of the baby's motion

(c) the baby's maximum speed.

20.18 A body of mass 200 g is executing simple harmonic motion with an amplitude of 20 mm. The maximum force which acts upon it is 0.064 N. Calculate

(a) its maximum acceleration

(b) its period of oscillation

(c) its maximum speed.

20.19 What is the period of a pendulum on Mars, where the free-fall acceleration is about 0.37 times that on Earth, if the pendulum has a period of 0.48 s on Earth?

20.20 A pendulum 650 mm long is hung from the ceiling of a hotel lift. When the lift is in operation it is found to have a time period of 1.55 s. Describe the motion of the lift when the time period was measured. Be as quantitative as possible.

20.21 Two simple pendulums are suspended side by side from two fixed supports in the same horizontal plane. They are displaced by equal amounts and released simultaneously so that they oscillate, initially in phase with one another, in two parallel vertical planes. If the two pendulums differ in length by a small amount, describe their relative motions when viewed in a direction perpendicular to the vertical planes in which they oscillate.

20.22 Someone suggests that you could 'draw' a displacement–time graph for a body moving with s.h.m. as follows. (1) Hang a bucket of fine dry sand on a rope slung in a doorway. (2) Punch a small hole in the bottom of the bucket. (3) Move a long strip of carpet or paper at a steady speed beneath the bucket as it swings to-and-fro.

Draw a sketch of the suggested arrangement and discuss whether the experiment would succeed in its objective.

20.3 Oscillators and energy

20.23 The figure shows a 'time-trace' made by a fine brush attached to the end of a vibrating arm while moving a piece of paper steadily past it. Draw sketch graphs to show

(a) how the period T of the arm varies with the amplitude y_0 of its vibration

(b) how the amplitude y_0 varies with time t. (Measure the ratio of successive maximum displacements.)

(c) How does the total energy E of the vibrating arm vary with time t?

Sketch an experimental arrangement which could be used to produce the time-trace and describe how you would demonstrate the effect of increased damping on the system.

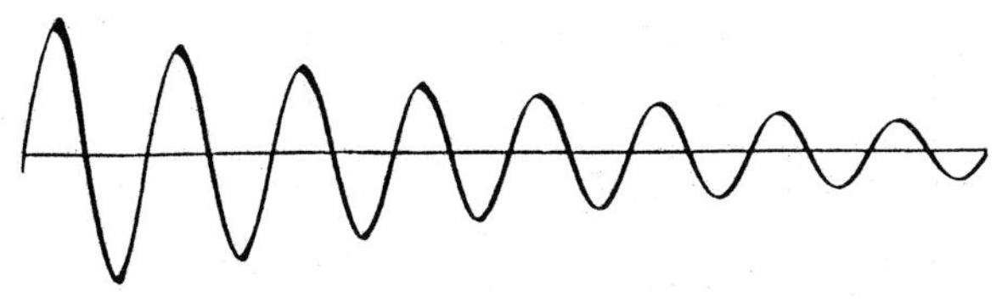

20.24 A block of wood of mass 0.25 kg is attached to one end of a spring of constant stiffness 100 N m^{-1}. The block can oscillate horizontally on a frictionless surface, the other end of the spring being fixed. The graph shows how the elastic potential energy E_p of the system varies with displacement s for a horizontal oscillation of amplitude 0.20 m.

(a) Show that the graph is correctly drawn.

(b) Copy the graph and sketch a second curve to show how the kinetic energy of the mass varies with the displacement s.

(c) Calculate the maximum speed of the block and its speed when the displacement is 0.10 m.

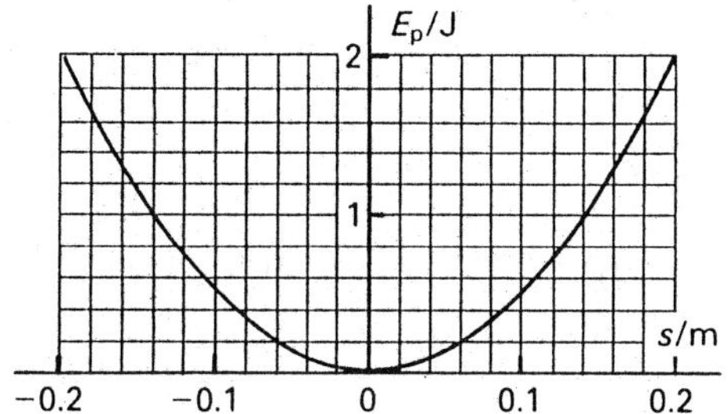

20.25 Provide, with as much detail as possible, a diagrammatic description of the energy changes which occur in an oscillating system which consists of a metal sphere on one end of a long spring attached to a firm support, after the sphere is pulled down and released so that it moves in a vertical line with s.h.m. Assume that a negligible amount of energy is converted to internal energy.

20.26 A bungee jumper demonstrated his skill, with police in attendance, and was timed to oscillate vertically with a period of 3.8 s.

(a) His mass was 85 kg. What was the spring constant of the elastic rope he used?

(b) The unstretched length of the elastic rope was 12 m. Show that the maximum safe height above the ground from which he could jump is just under 18 m. [Hint: consider the energy changes in a jump from 18 m.]

20.27 The relationship between the displacement s of a simple harmonic oscillator and the time t is

$$s = (1.2\,\text{m})\sin(4.0\,\text{s}^{-1})\,t$$

The variation of its elastic potential energy E_p with time is given by $E = \frac{1}{2}ks^2$, so that

$$E_p = (58\,J)\,[\sin(4.0\,s^{-1})t]^2$$

when k, the restoring force per unit displacement of the oscillator, is $80\,N\,m^{-1}$.

Plot a graph of s against t and below it, using the same scale on the time axis, a graph of E_p against t. [Be careful about the shape of the $E_p - t$ graph near points where $y = 0$.]

20.28 A punchbag of mass 0.65 kg is struck and oscillates with s.h.m. If the total mechanical energy of the oscillations is initially 55 J, what is the maximum speed of the punchbag? Describe how the energy of the punchbag changes as its oscillations die away.

20.29 If, in the previous question, the frequency of oscillation of the punchbag is 2.8 Hz, calculate

(a) the amplitude of its oscillation

(b) the stiffness, i.e. the force per unit extension, of the supporting spring system.

20.4 Resonance

20.30 Describe how you would demonstrate that the sharpness of resonance in an oscillating system depends on the amount of damping which it experiences.

20.31 The figure shows a thin strip of steel, like a hacksaw blade, clamped horizontally at one end. The natural frequency of the steel strip is 20 Hz.

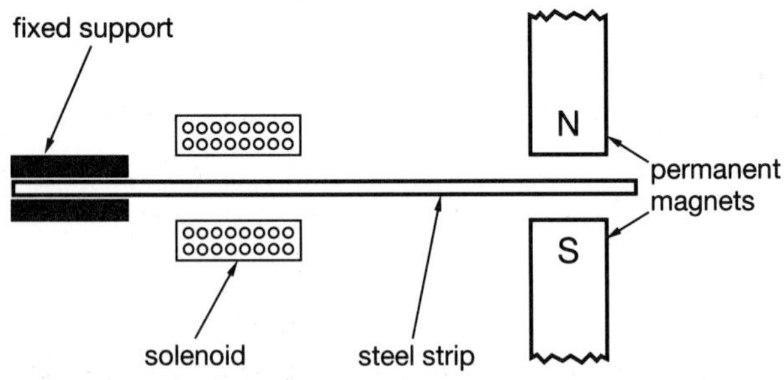

An alternating current of frequency f is passed in the solenoid, making the steel strip into a magnet. Describe the motion of the free end of the steel strip as f is gradually raised from 0 to 60 Hz.

20.32 Explain the meaning of the terms

(a) damped oscillation

(b) forced oscillation

(c) resonance.

Describe carefully one example in each of (i) mechanics, (ii) sound, and (iii) electricity.

20.33 A drilling machine was found to vibrate in such a way as to make accurate work impossible at certain frequencies. An investigation of its behaviour showed that the amplitude of the vibration of the drill bit s_0 was related to its frequency of rotation f as follows:

$s_0/10^{-2}$ mm	8	14	30	44	80	96
f/Hz	0	5	8	9	10	11

$s_0/10^{-2}$ mm	24	8	2	3	9	7	4
f/Hz	12	13	15	20	25	30	35

(a) Draw a graph of s_0 (up) against f (along) and explain its shape.

(b) Why is it advisable to start to drill a hole with the drill rotating at a frequency of between 15 Hz and 20 Hz?

20.34 At certain definite engine speeds, parts of a car, such as a door panel, may vibrate strongly. Explain the physical reason for this strong vibration and suggest how it might be reduced by alterations to

(a) the engine assembly and

(b) the door.

21 Mechanical waves

Data $g = 9.81\,\mathrm{m\,s^{-2}} = 9.81\,\mathrm{N\,kg^{-1}}$

21.1 Describing waves

21.1 The figure shows an idealised wave pulse travelling to the right along a heavy rope at $5.0\,\mathrm{m\,s^{-1}}$.

(a) Sketch a graph to show how the displacement y_P at P varies with time t during the next 0.50 s.

(b) Add a second graph using the same time axis to show how the displacement y_Q of Q varies with time t.

(c) How would your graphs differ if the wave pulse was travelling at $1.0\,\mathrm{m\,s^{-1}}$?

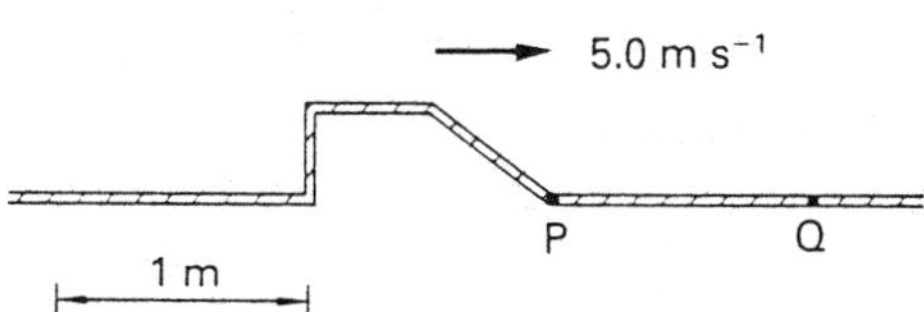

21.2 At large sports meetings the crowd sometimes produce what is called a 'Mexican wave'.
What would be a better name for this manoeuvre?
Describe what the crowd would need to do to produce a wave and suggest values for its frequency and amplitude.

21.3 The figure shows an idealised wave pulse, a 'step' travelling to the right along a long rope.

(a) Draw a graph to show how the *velocity* of the point P varies with time t. Mark scales on your graph axes.

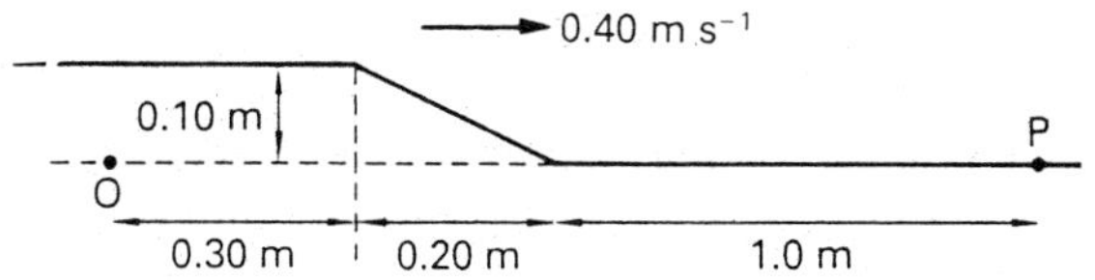

(b) Draw a second graph to show the transverve velocity of the rope against distance x from O at the instant shown in the diagram. Mark scales on your graph axes.

(c) How would your graph in *(b)* differ if the wave pulse was travelling at $2.0\,\mathrm{m\,s^{-1}}$?

21.4 The diagram shows an undisturbed slinky and the same slinky carrying a longitudinal wave pulse. The displacements of two points, A to A' and B to B', are shown.
Measure these and other displacements, y, and draw a graph of y against undisturbed position, x, along the slinky.

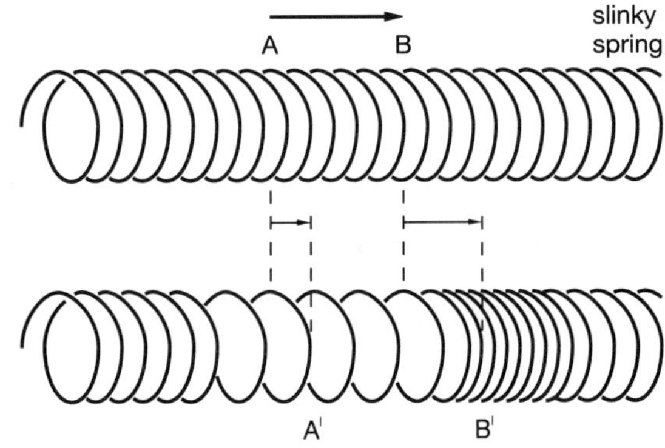

21.5 The photograph shows a wave pulse on a rope moving to the left. During the exposure the transverse movement of the rope has produced a blurring at some points.

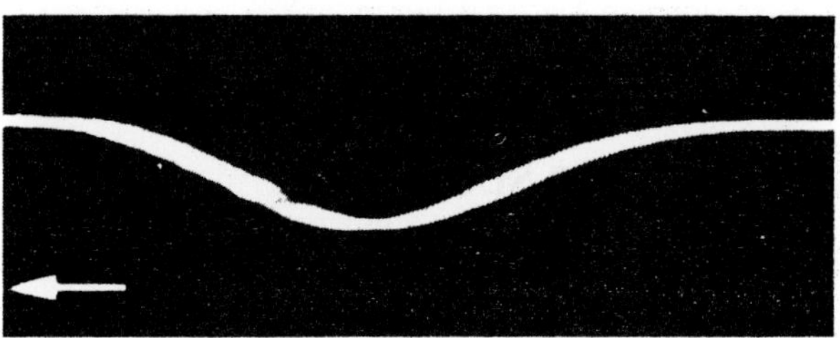

(*a*) Draw a sketch of the pulse and indicate on it which parts of the rope are moving and in what direction.
(*b*) Explain how the energy of the wave pulse is stored at different places.

21.6 A small loudspeaker emits sound energy uniformly in all directions in front of it with a total power of 5.0×10^{-5} W.
(*a*) What is the sound intensity (the rate of flow of sound energy per unit area) at a distance of (i) 2.0 m (ii) 12 m from the speaker?
(*b*) How does the amplitude of molecular vibration in the air around the speaker depend upon distance r from the speaker?

21.7 It is found that the intensity of a sound wave is $2.4\ \mu W\ m^{-2}$ at a distance of 1.3 km from a warning siren. Calculate the power of the siren. What assumptions, if any, do you need to make?

21.8 (*a*) Compare (i) the intensities and (ii) the amplitudes of an earthquake wave as it passes two points 200 km and 400 km from the source.
The intensity of an earthquake wave was $2.0 \times 10^{6}\ W\ m^{-2}$ at a distance of 200 km from the source.
(*b*) Calculate (i) the intensity at 10 km from the source and (ii) the total energy passing through an area of $10\ m^2$ perpendicular to the direction of wave propagation in 1.0 s at 10 km.

21.9 The maximum legal loudness for a car in Great Britain (measured under specified conditions) is 80 dB(A). It is found that a certain car exceeds this limit by 3 dB(A). The owner claims that the excess is negligible – 'less than 1 part in 25', while the local police official claims that an increase in loudness from 80 dB(A) to 83 dB(A) represents a doubling of sound intensity. Discuss who is right in this case.

21.1 Wave speeds

21.10 A transverse wave is seen to travel along a length of cotton thread stretched to a tension of 1.5 N at a speed of $60\ m\ s^{-1}$. Calculate the mass of 100 m of the cotton thread.

21.11 The speed of longitudinal waves in steel is $5100\ m\ s^{-1}$. If 20 m of steel wire of diameter 0.42 mm has a mass of 22 g, calculate the Young modulus of steel.

21.12 A heavy chain is hanging vertically with its lower end free.
(*a*) Describe the motion of a wave pulse which travels down the chain.
(*b*) If the chain is 8.0 m long and has a mass of 24 kg calculate the speed c of the pulse at distances d from the top given by d/m = 0, 2, 4, 6, 7, 7.5.
(*c*) Hence sketch a graph of c against d.

21.13 The speed c of longitudinal waves on a stretched spring of large diameter (e.g. a slinky) is given by $c = \sqrt{(kl/\mu)}$, where k is the spring constant, l the stretched length and μ the stretched mass per unit length of the slinky.
(*a*) Show that this expression for c has correct units.
(*b*) Calculate c for a slinky of mass 0.45 kg which stretches to a length of 3.0 m long when the tension in it is 6.0 N. (Assume the unstretched slinky has a negligible length.)
(*c*) Show that the time for a longitudinal wave pulse to travel from one end of the slinky to the other is independent of its stretched length.

21.14 A steel ball of diameter 62 mm is bounced on a massive steel place. The time of contact is found electrically to be equivalent to a trace of length 2.4 div on an oscilloscope screen with a time base set at $10\ \mu s\ div^{-1}$. Assuming that the time of contact is equal to the time taken for the longitudunal wave pulse to travel from the bottom of the steel ball to the top and back again, calculate the speed of the wave pulse in steel.

21.15 On an open field an experimenter A bangs two pieces of wood together producing a regular series of sharp claps. A second experimenter B walks way from A and notices that when he has moved 120 m he hears the claps half way in time between seeing them. Calculate the time interval between the claps. Take the speed of sound in air to be 340 m s^{-1}.

21.16 The speed of longitudinal waves in sea water is 1500 m s^{-1}. A fishing vessel uses pulses of these waves to search for shoals of fish.
Draw a diagram to illustrate the principle involved and calculate the times for a pulse to return from 35 m and from 40 m below the vessel.

21.17 It is suggested that the speed of sound c in free air depends upon the air pressure p, the density ρ of the air and the wavelength λ of the sound.
Use units or dimensions to predict the form of a possible relation between c, p, ρ and λ.
What important property of sound does your answer imply?

21.18 Suppose that the speed of propagation c of longitudinal waves in a metal rod depends only on E the Young modulus of the material, the density ρ of the material and d the diameter of the rod.

(a) Work out a possible expression relating c to E, ρ and d.

(b) Find a value for the constant given that for copper $E = 1.3 \times 10^{11}$ Pa, $\rho = 8.9 \times 10^3$ kg m^{-3}, and $c = 3.8 \times 10^3$ m s^{-1}.

21.19 A recording station observed that there was an interval of 68 s between the reception of *P* (push or primary) and *S* (shake or secondary) waves from an underground nuclear test explosion.
If the speed of the *P* and *S* waves in the Earth's crust are 7800 m s^{-1} and 4200 m s^{-1} respectively, find the distance of the test site from the recording station.

21.20 The graphs in the figure show the variation of the speed c of water ripples (such as you might see in a laboratory ripple tank) with their frequency f for a range of values of the depth of water h.

(a) Calculate the times taken for ripples of frequency (i) 5.0 Hz and (ii) 15 Hz to traverse a tank 0.80 m long when the water is firstly 20 mm deep and secondly 2.0 mm deep.

(b) Sketch a graph of wave speed c against depth of water h for ripples of frequency (i) 5.0 hz and (ii) 15 Hz.

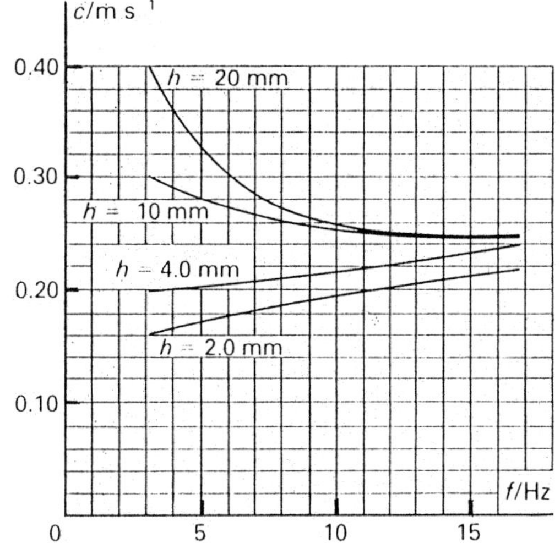

21.3 The principle of superposition

21.21 What is meant by the principle of superposition of waves? Are there any types of wave which do not obey the principle or any circumstances in which it does not apply?

21.22 Draw graphs to show the result of superposition when two waves of the same amplitude and frequency arrive at a point

(a) in phase

(b) in antiphase.

21.23 The figure overleaf shows two wave pulses at time $t = 0$. The markings on the x–axis are 1.0 m apart.

(a) Draw a series of y–x graphs at times t given by t/s = 1, 2, 3, 4, 5 to illustrate their superposition as they cross. [Hint: sketch the two pulses in lightly and then add the displacements to find the resultant pulse.]

(b) Draw two y–t graphs, one for the point P and one for Q, during the time $t = 0$ to $t = 8$ s.

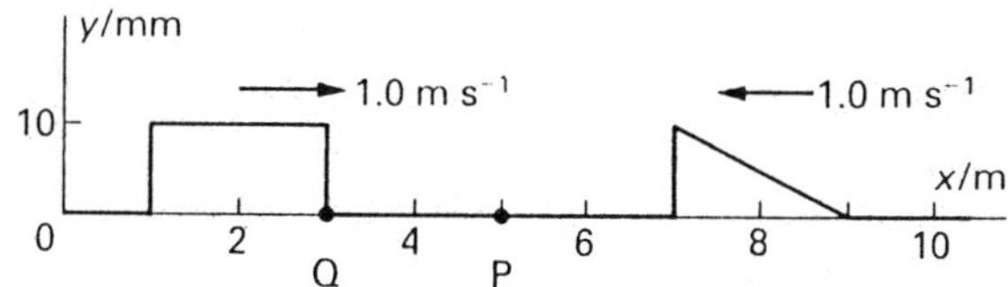

21.24 Dolphins communicate by emitting ultrasonic waves of frequencies in the range 100 kHz to 250 kHz. What wavelength range in water does this represent? The speed of the waves in sea water $1500 \mathrm{m\,s^{-1}}$.

21.25 Two seagulls are observed to be bobbing up and down in antiphase as water waves pass them. The wave crests are perpendicular to the line joining the seagulls. The frequency of the seagulls' oscillation is 0.40 Hz, they are 15 m apart and the wave speed is $4.0 \mathrm{m\,s^{-1}}$. Are these values compatible with the observation?

21.26 The figure shows a sinusoidal wave travelling to the right along a rope. The dark line represents the wave at $t = 0$ and the dashed line the wave at $t = 0.25$ s.

(a) What is (i) the amplitude y_0 and (ii) the wavelength λ of this wave?

(b) Calculate (i) the speed c (ii) the frequency f and (iii) the period T of the wave.

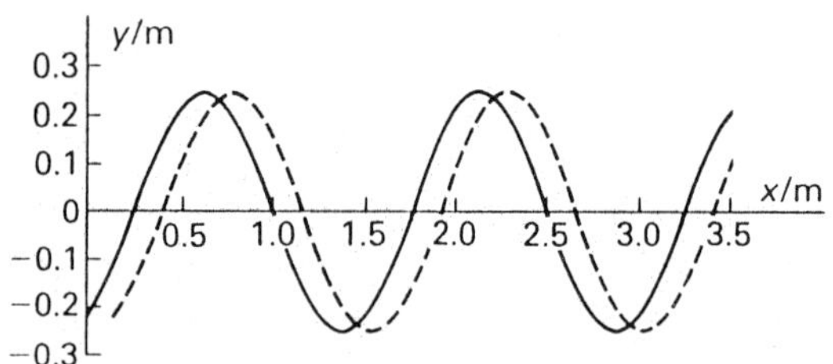

21.27 A photograph of a sinusoidal transverse wave on a string can be described by the equation

$$y = (0.020 \mathrm{m})\sin(10 \mathrm{m^{-1}})x$$

What is

(a) the wavelength and, if the speed of the wave was $25 \mathrm{m\,s^{-1}}$

(b) the frequency of the wave?

(c) What is the maximum transverse speed of a point on the string as the wave passes?

21.28 Explain the general conditions for locating maxima and minima in an interference pattern produced by two in-phase ripple tank dippers. What will happen to the pattern if the dippers suddenly start to move in antiphase?

21.29 What is the result of superposing two sinusoidal waves of the same frequency, one of which has twice the amplitude of the other, at a place where they arrive with a phase difference of 90° ($\pi/2$ rad)? [Draw two y–t graphs on the same axis for the waves to be added and find the resulting y–t graph using the principle of superposition.]

21.30 The photograph shows a typical ripple tank two-source superposition pattern.

(a) If the scale is such that 10 mm on the photograph is equivalent to 120 mm on the water surface, calculate the wavelength of the water ripples.

(b) By measuring distances such as S_1P and S_2P, verify that the bright patches on the photograph represent places where the two wavefronts from S_1 and S_2 arrive in phase.

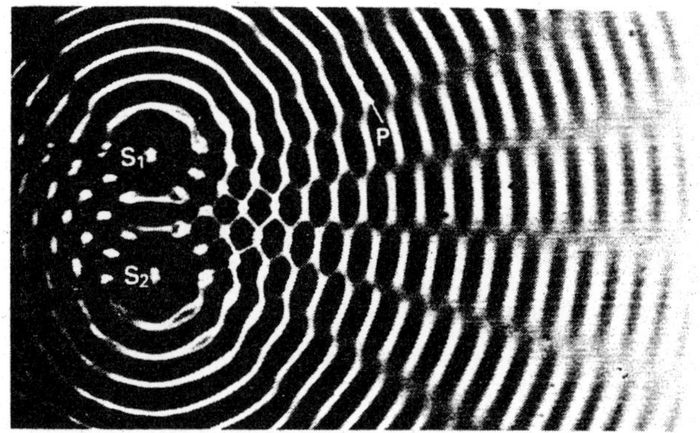

21.31 Two ripple tank dippers S_1 and S_2 are vibrating *in antiphase*.

(a) Draw (you will need a compass) a series of arcs to represent the wavefronts from S_1 and S_2, using a wavelength such that $S_1S_2 = 3.5\lambda$.

(b) Mark on your diagram the nodal and antinodal lines and state how this pattern of superposition differs from that where $S_1S_2 = 3.5\lambda$, but S_1 and S_2 are in phase.

21.32 Two in-phase coherent sources of sinusoidal waves are placed at the points S_1 and S_2 in the figure. A detector registers a maximum at both P and Q, and when moved from P to Q detects a single minimum between them.

(a) Deduce the wavelength of the waves emitted by S_1 and S_2. [You will need a ruler. Assume the figure is reduced by a factor of ten from the real situation.]

(b) Describe and explain what the detector will register when placed at (i) N and (ii) M.

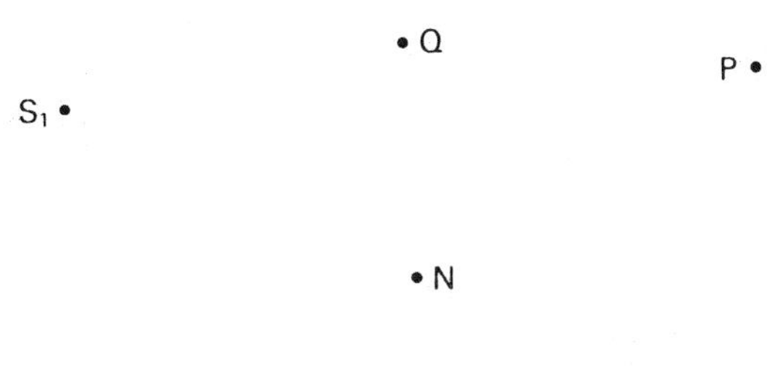

21.33 The diagram shows an experimental arrangement for investigating the superposition of sound from two sources S_1 and S_2.

If the wavelength of the waves from S_1 and S_2 is 80 mm in air and the distance $S_1M = 0.80$ m, suggest three possible values for S_2M

(a) when the height of the trace on the oscilloscope is a maximum

(b) when the height of the trace on the oscilloscope is a minimum.

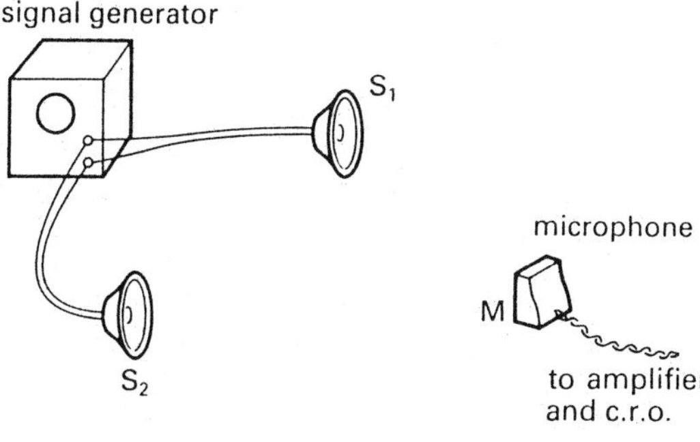

21.34 In another experiment with the apparatus described in the previous question the height of the trace on the oscilloscope is found to be a minimum when $S_1M = 0.80$ m and $S_2M = 1.00$ m.

Why can the wavelength λ of the sound waves in air not be found from these measurements alone? What further observations are needed before λ can be found?

21.35 Two loudspeakers L_1 and L_2 driven from a common oscillator are set up as shown in the figure. A detector is placed at D.

It is found that, as the *frequency* of the oscillator is gradually changed from 200 Hz to 1000 Hz the detected signal passes through a series of maxima and minima.

(a) Explain why this is so.

(b) Calculate the frequency at which the first minimum above 200 Hz is observed.
(Take the speed of sound in air to be 340 m s^{-1}.)

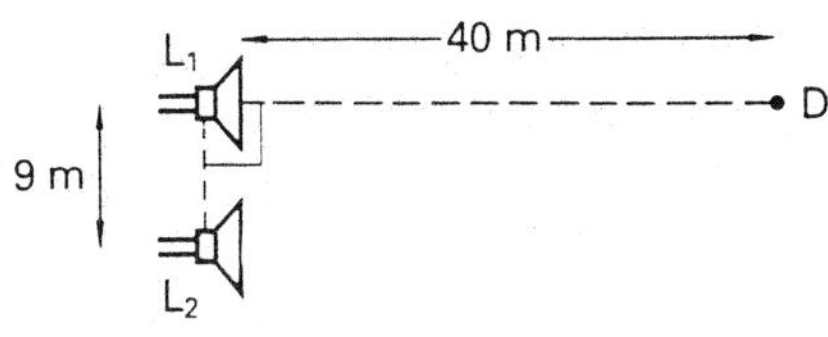

21.4 Hearing

21.36 A car travels with uniform speed along a long straight road (represented by the horizontal axis in the figure) sounding its horn continuously. A microphone connected to a frequency meter is placed close to the side of the road. It is found that the frequency f recorded by the meter varies with the position x of the car as shown. Explain the graph.

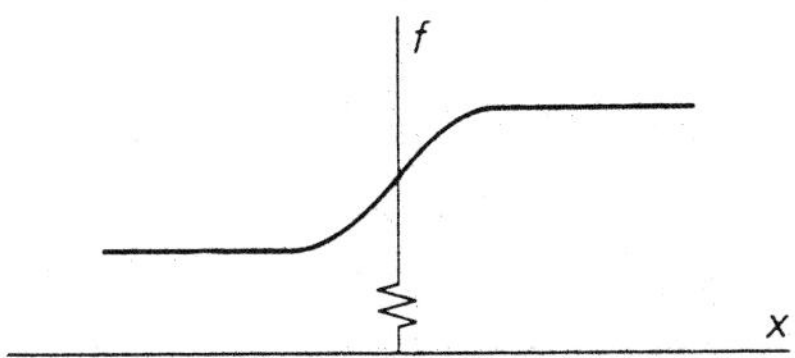

21.37 An object is vibrating vertically in a water surface with a frequency of 10 Hz. At the same time it is moving in a horizontal straight line with a speed of $20\,\text{mm}\,\text{s}^{-1}$. The waves it produces travel with a speed of $120\,\text{mm}\,\text{s}^{-1}$.

(a) Draw a diagram showing the positions of the waves emitted during the previous half second.

(b) Calculate the wavelength of the waves (i) ahead of (ii) behind the moving objects.

21.38 An observer accelerates from a speed of $170\,\text{m}\,\text{s}^{-1}$ to a speed of $400\,\text{m}\,\text{s}^{-1}$ while moving away from a source of sound of frequency 500 Hz. Describe what she would hear.

22 Electromagnetic waves

Data $c = 3.00 \times 10^{8}\,\text{m}\,\text{s}^{-1}$
$e = 1.60 \times 10^{-19}\,\text{C}$

22.1 The electromagnetic spectrum

22.1 Light and X–rays are both said to be electromagnetic waves. What kind of experimental observations suggest that both are wave motions?

22.2 Estimate the time for light to travel

(a) the width of an atom

(b) across a room

(c) from the Earth to the Moon.

22.3 Who will hear an opera singer first – a person in the theatre belcony 45 m from the stage, or a person 2400 km away at home? Assume the microphone is very close to the singer and that the radio listener is sitting close to the radio. Take the speed of sound to be $340\,\text{m}\,\text{s}^{-1}$.

22.4 The following data represents some frequencies and wavelengths used in radio and television broadcasting:

200 kHz/1500 m (AM radio),
92.6 MHz/3.24 m (FM radio),
0.516 GHz/0.581 m (UHF TV).

Show that the waves associated with these broadcasts all travel with the same speed.

22.5 Mark a logarithmic scale of wavelengths down the left side of a piece of paper where $\lambda/\text{m} = 10^{4}, 10^{3} \ldots, 10^{-19}, 10^{-20}$.

(a) Mark a parallel scale for the frequencies of electromagnetic waves.

(b) Indicate the main regions of the electromagnetic spectrum to the right of your scale showing the range of wavelengths, etc. for each region.

(c) [If you have studied section 26.1] Add a parallel scale for photon energies.

22.6 Outline the methods by which electromagnetic waves of wavelength of the order of *(a)* $10^{-10}\,\text{m}$ *(b)* $5 \times 10^{-7}\,\text{m}$ *(c)* $10^{-1}\,\text{m}$ are detected.

22.7 In early measurements of the surface-to-surface Earth–Moon distance d using the reflection of radar waves, there was an uncertainty of about $\pm$ 75 m in d.

Assuming that this uncertainty was wholly the result of the measurement of the time taken for the round trip, what was the uncertainty in the measured time?

22.8 The spectrum of atomic hydrogen contains a bright line at a wavelength of 486 nm. When the spectrum of light from a distant galaxy was analysed this same hydrogen line was measured to have a wavelength of 497 nm.
Calculate the speed of recession of the galaxy from the Earth.

22.9 A police speed-trap uses radar waves of wavelengths 100 mm. A car moving at $13.4\,\mathrm{m\,s^{-1}}$ (30 m.p.h.) reflects these waves and a change in frequency of Δf is observed. Calculate Δf. Did you need to know the speed of the radar waves in your calculation?

22.10 Lines in the spectrum of light from one edge of our sun are found to have a slightly lower wavelength than the same lines from the opposite edge. Explain why this is the case.

22.2 The nature of e-m waves

22.11 The figure represents a plane electromagnetic wave moving to the right.

(a) Describe the figure in detail and thus explain in what way it represents such a wave.

(b) If the maximum value of E is $1.0 \times 10^{-7}\,\mathrm{V\,m^{-1}}$, calculate the maximum electric force experienced by an electron in the path of the wave. (See the data above.)

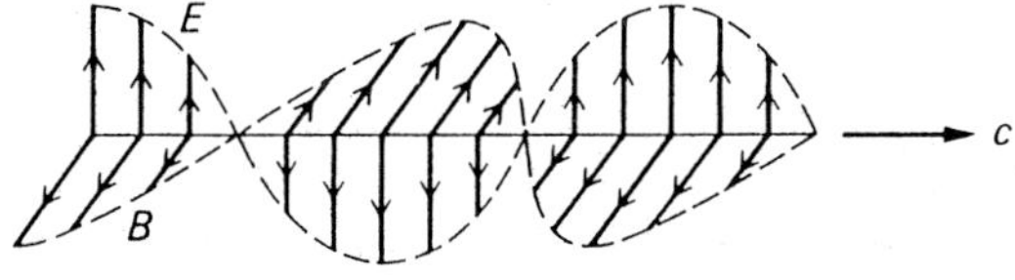

22.12 Draw a diagram to show the varying E– and B–fields in an electromagnetic wave a long way from their source.

(a) Show the positions in which (i) a straight metal wire would need to be placed to receive energy from variations in the E-field and (ii) a coil of wire would need to be placed to receive energy from the B–field.

(b) Explain the mechanism by which the electrons in the wire and the coil absorb the energy from the wave.

22.13 Draw a graph to show the variation of the E–field with distance along a plane polarised sinusoidal electromagnetic wave of wavelength 1.2 m and amplitude $4.0\,\mu\mathrm{V\,m^{-1}}$.

(a) Calculate (i) the frequency of the wave and (ii) the r.m.s. value of its E–field.

(b) What is the r.m.s. potential difference produced by this wave across an aerial 0.60 m long?

22.14 A sodium atom emits a wavetrain of light of wavelength 590 nm. If the time taken by the atom to undergo the energy transition which produced the wavetrain was $3.0 \times 10^{-9}\,\mathrm{s}$, how many oscillations of the E–field are there in this wavetrain?

22.15 *(a)* A transmitter T of e–m waves of wavelength 30 cm is placed 4.0 m from a receiver R. When a reflecting sheet AB is moved slowly up to R as shown in the diagram, a series of maximum and minimum received signals is detected. Explain this observation.

(b) Justify the predictions that (i) AB will need to be moved through 15 cm in order for the received signal to go from one maximum to the next maximum and (ii) that when AB is moved to be up against R the received signal will be zero.

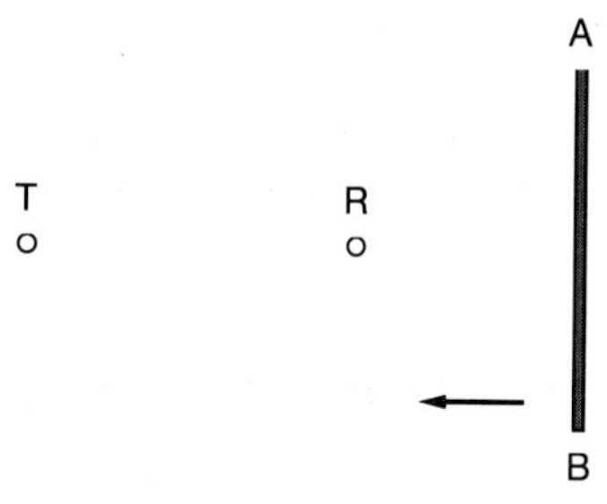

22.16 How could you tell whether or not a pair of sunglasses contains polarising lenses?

22.17 The figure below shows a transmitter of electromagnetic waves of wavelength $\lambda = 0.30\,m$ placed at T which is a distance of 6.0 m from a receiver at R. A plane reflecting surface M is held as shown in such a way that the perpendicular distance from M to the direct line TR is 2.0 m.

(a) Express the path lengths of the two wavetrains from T to R in terms of λ.

(b) If the wave which reflects from M undergoes a phase change of π rad, are the two waves arriving at R in phase or in antiphase?

(c) Describe as fully as possible how the signal received at R varies as M is slowly moved towards the line TR until it almost lies on it.

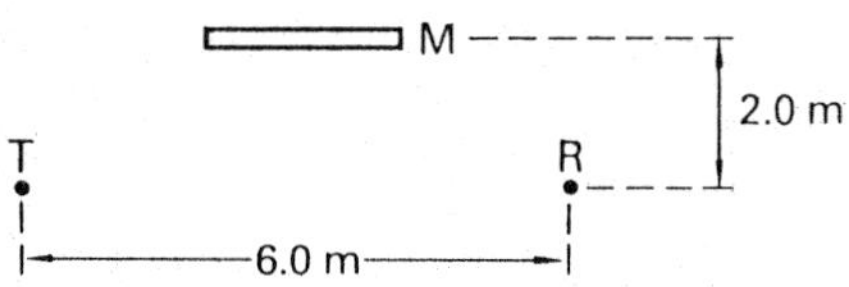

22.18 A 'ghost' image is seen on a television screen 40 mm to the right of the proper picture. What does this tell you about the received signal if the electron beam covers the entire screen of 625 lines twenty-five times per second and the screen is 0.50 m wide?

22.19 Given that $\epsilon_0 = 8.85 \times 10^{-12}\,F\,m^{-1}$ and $\mu_0 = 4\pi \times 10^{-7}\,N\,A^{-2}$ show that the units of $(\epsilon_0\mu_0)^{-1/2}$ are $m\,s^{-1}$.

22.20 Mica crystals are said to be doubly refracting, i.e., the speeds of e–m waves in mica depend on their plane of polarisation. For light of wavelength 589.0 nm in air the refractive indices of mica, $n = c\,(\text{vacuum})/c(\text{mica})$, for two mutually plane polarised waves are 1.605 and 1.612.

(a) Calculate the speeds of the two plane polarised waves in mica.

(b) For a sheet of mica 40.0 μm thick, calculate the number of oscillations undergone by each wave as it passes through the mica.

(c) Hence establish the phase differences between the emerging waves.

22.21 A human face emits infra-red radiation with a peak wavelength of about 10 mm. If the total power radiated is 12 W calculate the intensity at a distance of *(a)* 15 cm and *(b)* 3.0 m from the centre of the head.

What assumptions have you made in your calculations?

22.22 Solar radiation arrives at the Earth's orbit at the rate of $1.4\,kW\,m^{-2}$. The average radius of this orbit is $1.49 \times 10^{11}\,m$.

(a) Calculate the power output of the Sun.

(b) What rate of mass loss does this represent?

22.3 Radio communication

22.23 Draw a block diagram to show the essential components of a simple radio receiver. Add an energy flow diagram to describe the energy changes which occur, starting with an incoming radio wave and finishing with outgoing sound. Indicate any sources of energy and any places at which energy is 'wasted'.

22.24 Explain what is meant by the statement: 'The amplitude of the 30 mm microwaves is modulated sinusoidally at 1000 Hz'.

22.25 A portable radio has an extensible metal aerial of maximum length 0.80 m. What is the optimum length of the aerial for broadcast signals of frequency

(a) 92 MHz

(b) 102 MHz?

22.26 The average rate per unit area at which a plane electromagnetic wave transmits energy can be expressed as $E_0B_0/2\mu_0$ where E_0 and B_0 are the amplitudes of the electric and magnetic field variations in the wave. ($\mu_0 = 4\pi \times 10^{-7}\,NA^{-2}$.) If the values of E_0 and B_0 at a distance of 10 m from a point source of light are $6\,V\,m^{-1}$ and $2 \times 10^{-8}\,T$ respectively, calculate the power output of the light.

22.27 Information is now increasingly being carried at frequencies in the infra-red or optical parts of the electromagnetic spectrum. Explain the advantage(s) of this development.

22.28 You are given a box T which you are told is a source of plane polarised electromagnetic waves of about 80 mm wavelength and a second box R which can detect such waves.
Describe what simple experiments you would perform with the resources of a school laboratory to test that T is what it is said to be.

22.4 Electromagnetic wave spectra

22.29 'γ–ray spectra give us evidence about the atomic nucleus, ultra-violet and optical spectra evidence about the outer atom and infra-red spectra evidence about the nature of interatomic bonding.'

Write brief notes on this statement, including such things as reference to the scale of the energy changes which take place in each region.

22.30 A steerable dish 77 km in diameter is used as a radio-telescope to study electromagnetic waves reaching the Earth's surface from space.

(a) If the amplifying equipment needs an input power of at least 10^{-9} W, estimate the intensity of the weakest incoming wave which the telescope can detect.

(b) When the telescope is being used to investigate the distribution of atomic hydrogen in our galaxy (the Milky Way), estimate the smallest angle between two areas of hydrogen which it could resolve. (Atomic hydrogen radiates strongly at a wavelength of 0.21 m.)

23 Interference patterns

Data speed of e-m radiation $c = 3.00 \times 10^8\,\mathrm{m\,s^{-1}}$
speed of sound in air $= 340\,\mathrm{m\,s^{-1}}$

23.1 Stationary waves

23.1 A demonstrator wishes to use a vibrator and a stretched rubber cord to show the production of stationary waves. If the cord has a mass of 0.12 kg and when stretched to a length of 2.4 m has a tension of 6.0 N in it, at what frequencies of vibration will the cord settle into stationary wave patterns?

23.2 A violin string of mass per unit length equal to $3.75 \times 10^{-4}\,\mathrm{kg\,m^{-1}}$ is stretched to a tension of 15.0 N.

(a) What is the fundamental frequency of a note played on this string when its length is restricted to (i) 0.300 m (ii) 0.200 m (iii) 0.150 m?

(b) What harmonics (overtones) may be present when the fundamental note is played on the 0.300 m length of string?

23.3 Draw successive positions in the vibration of a stretched string oscillating in its third harmonic. Hence explain why adjacdent nodes in the stationary (standing) wave pattern are $\lambda/2$ apart, where λ is the wavelength of the superposing waves which are producing the stationary wave.

23.4 An aluminium rod 1.20 m long is suspended horizontally from two threads. When one end of the rod is tapped by a hammer the rod 'rings', emitting a note of frequency 2130 Hz.
Explain how the note is produced and calculate a value for the speed of longitudinal mechanical waves in the aluminium rod.

23.5 A wire stretched above a sounding box has a fixed mass per unit length μ. The tension T in the wire and the length l of the wire can be independently varied. An experimenter measures the frequency f of the fundamental vibration of the wire under various conditions of T and l.

(a) Draw sketches to show the form of graph he gets when he plots
 (i) f against T, keeping l constant
 (ii) f^2 against T, keeping l constant
 (iii) f against l, keeping T constant
 (iv) f^{-1} against l, keeping T constant.

(b) Explain the theory behind your sketches and state, for any of the graphs which is linear, what is represented by its gradient.

23.6 The lowest note on a piano has a frequency of 27.5 Hz. The wire which produces this note when struck is 2.00 m long and has a tension of 320 N. What is the total mass of the wire?

23.7 A wire of mass per unit length $1.6\,\text{g}\,\text{m}^{-1}$ is attached to a fixed block A and pulled by a spring balance B as shown in the diagram. The stretched piece of wire is 1.8 m long and its centre is placed between the poles of a large magnet. An alternating p.d. of frequency 50 Hz is connected across the wire.

(a) Describe qualitatively what happens as the tension in the wire is slowly increased. [Hint: consider the possible motion of the centre of the wire.]

(b) Calculate the tension in the wire when it oscillates in its fundamental mode.

(c) Write down one other tension at which the wire vibrates resonantly.

(d) If the amplitude of oscillation of the centre of the wire in its fundamental mode is 12 mm, calculate the maximum speed of this part of the wire.

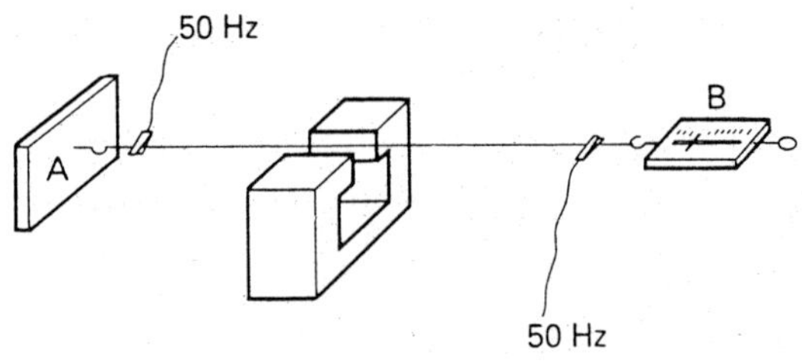

23.8 When the table on which a cup of tea or coffee is standing is knocked, a stationary wave pattern often appears on the liquid surface for a short time. Sketch the form of the pattern and explain how it is produced.

23.9 A tuning fork of frequency 440 Hz is sounded together with a stretched metal wire. When the tension in the wire is 100 N, the experimenter hears exactly 2 beats per second.
When she gradually reduces the tension in the wire without altering its length the beat frequency decreases to zero and then increases again to exactly 2 beats per second. Calculate the value of the new tension in the wire.

23.10 A small loudspeaker emitting a note at 600 Hz is held above a tall glass measuring cylinder which is 0.50 m tall.
Sketch a graph of the sound intensity I heard by a nearby observer against the depth of the water d as water is poured down the side of the measuring cylinder until it is full. Mark a scale on the d axis.

23.11 Two loudspeakers face each other at a separation of about 30 m. They are connected to the same sinusoidal oscillator which is set at 170 Hz.
Describe and explain the variation of sound intensity heard by a man who walks at a slow steady speed of $0.50\,\text{m}\,\text{s}^{-1}$ along the line joining the two speakers.

23.12 The air in a resonance tube closed at one end is made to vibrate by a small loudspeaker placed over the other end. The length l of the tube can be varied. The lowest frequency f which produces resonance for various values of l is found to be as follows:

l/mm	100	200	300	400	500
f/Hz	720	385	270	205	165

(a) Plot a graph of l against $1/f$.

(b) Deduce a value for the speed of sound in the tube.

(c) Is the end correction negligible?

23.13 In the diagram T is a microwave transmitter and P a detecting probe. As P is moved towards the metal sheet maxima are found separated by 16 mm.

(a) Deduce, with a full explanation, the wavelength of the microwaves.

(b) As P approaches the metal sheet the intensity of the minima is found to become closer and closer to zero. Explain why this is so.

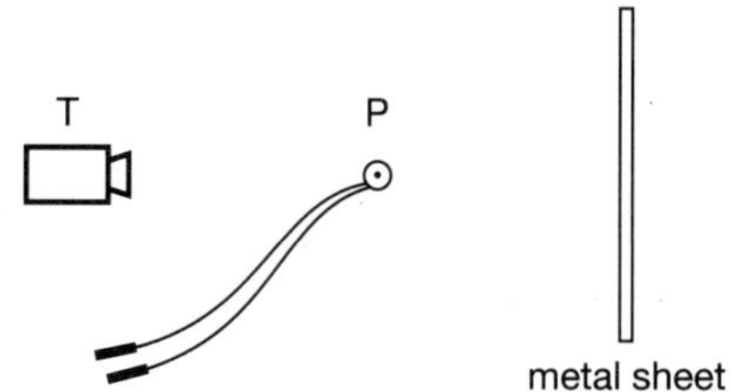

23.14 (a) A microwave transmitter T and receiver R are placed side by side as shown in the figure facing two sheets of material N and M. It is found that a very small signal is registered by R; what can you deduce about the experimental set-up?

(b) When M is moved towards N a series of maxima and minima is registered by R. Explain this and deduce the wavelength of the electromagnetic waves transmitted by T if the distance from the 2nd to the 7th minimum is 70 mm.

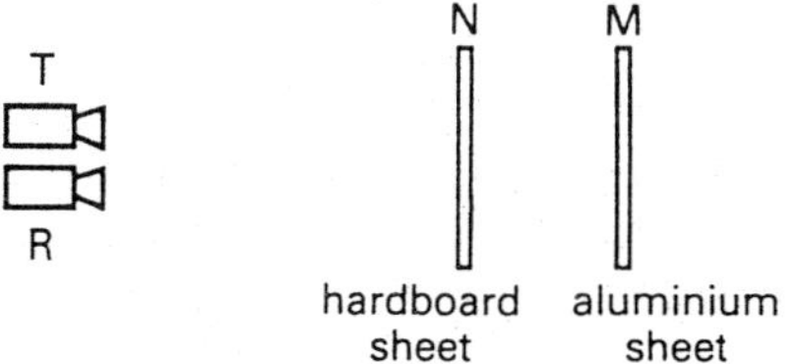

23.15 (a) Two radio transmitters T_1 and T_2 emit vertically polarised electromagnetic waves at a frequency of 1.44 MHz. A stationary wave pattern is set up along the line T_1T_2; what is the distance between adjacent nodes in this pattern?

(b) A car is driving alng the line between the transmitters (e.g. along the M4) and its radio is receiving the programme carried by the 1.44 MHz waves. Describe what the driver hears if the car is travelling at just over $30\,\mathrm{m\,s^{-1}}$.

23.16 In order to cut out unwanted reflections from a glass surface, e.g. a camera lens or a safety cover over a painting, a process called blooming is used. This involves coating the surface of the glass with a very thin film of calcium fluoride in which light travels at a speed v, less than c.

(a) The figure shows two reflected rays, R_1 and R_2, which will superpose to the left of the film. For light of wavelength λ in air, what thickness of film, t, will give rise to R_1 and R_2 being in antiphase?

(b) Calculate t for $\lambda = 580\,\mathrm{mm}$, given that $v = 0.69c$.

(c) Explain why, for this thickness of film, other wavelengths will not be fully cut out.

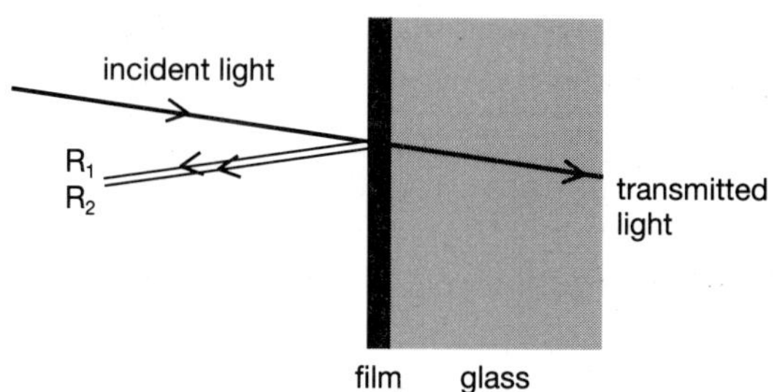

23.17 The figure shows two microscope slides M_1 and M_2 arranged so as to enclose a wedge-shaped air film. The slides are illuminated with monochromatic light. An interference pattern consisting of a series of equally spaced fringes parallel to the line where the slides meet is observed as a result of light waves reflected from the lower surface of M_1 and the upper surface of M_2. Explain what would be seen if, separately, the following changes were made:

(a) the metalfoil was moved very slowly to the right

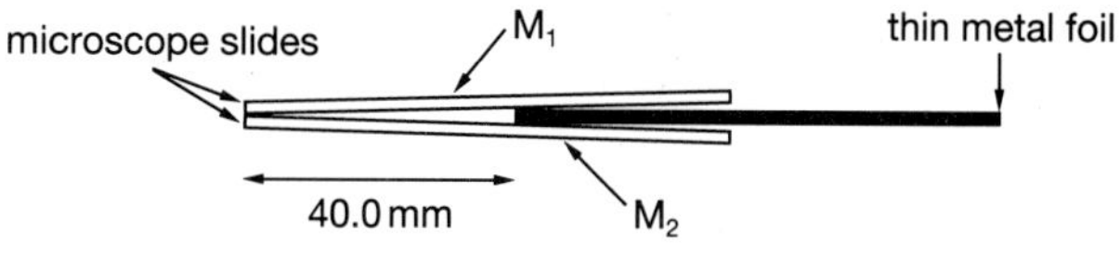

(b) the top microscope slide was exchanged for one which was not quite flat

(c) the space between the microscope slides was filled with water

(d) the wavelength of the light used to illuminate the microscope slides was increased by about 10%

(e) the temperature of the metal foil was raised.

23.18 If in the previous question the distance occupied by 20 fringe-spacings was measured and found to be 4.9 mm, and the wavelength of the light used was 590 nm, calculate the thickness of the metal foil. (Assume that the illumination and the viewing are from directly above the slides.)

23.2 Diffraction

23.19 Sketch a series of diagrams to illustrate the behaviour of plane water waves for values of the wavelength λ given by $\lambda/\mathrm{m} = 0.1, 0.5, 1.0$ as they arrive at a barrier in a children's paddling pool in which there is a gap of width 1.0 m.

Describe what is happening to the wave energy passing through the gap when $\lambda = 1.0\,\mathrm{m}$.

23.20 Take two pencils and hold them vertically and *very close* together (but not touching). Look through the narrow gap between them at a vertical edge or bar in a nearby window. Describe what you see.

What do you see, again with the gap held vertically, if you look at a horizontal edge or bar in the window? Explain your observations.

23.21 A plane sound wave of frequency 8.5 kHz is incident on a large heavy board in which there is a slit of width 0.10 m. Sound is diffracted through the slit and a small omni-directional microphone is moved about in the region beyond the slit.

Draw a sketch to show the direction(s) in which the microphone detected a minimum of sound.

23.22 The graph shows the diffraction pattern produced by a single slit illuminated by a parallel beam of light of wavelength λ. If the width of the diffracting slit is 0.20 mm, calculate λ.

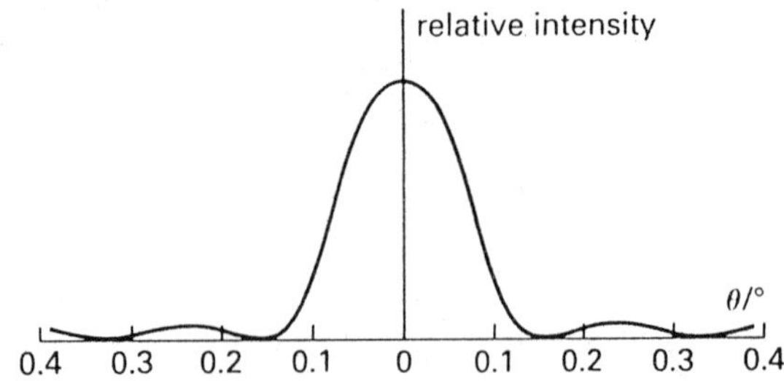

23.23 A laser beam is used to illuminate a flag at night. The flag is 400 m from the laser and is approximately 2 m square. The laser produces light of wavelength 6.6×10^{-7} m and the initial beam width is 2.0 mm. Will the laser light adequately illuminate the flag? (Assume that the light spreads out by diffraction through the circular end of the laser.)

23.24 An optical telescope with an aperture of 250 mm is used to observe two stars which are known to have an angular separation of 3 μrad. Can they be resolved? Take an 'average' value of 600 nm for the wavelength of the light from the stars.

23.25 A parabolic reflecting dish is used to reflect a radar beam emitted from a source placed at its focus. The figure shows how the intensity in the reflected beam varies with direction.

(a) Explain how this figure relates to the graph which accompanies question *23.22*.

(b) If the dish has a width of 1.05 m and the radar system operates at 10 GHz calculate the angular diameter 2θ of the main beam.

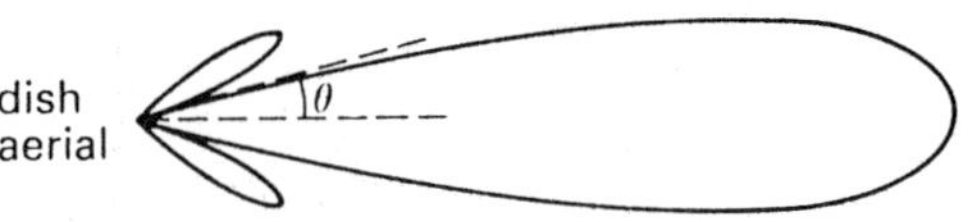

(c) Copy the figure and draw two lines from the dish aerial to points where the intensity is $1/\sqrt{2}$ times the maximum intensity. (The angle between these lines is called the beam width.)

23.3 Young's slits

23.26 the only practical way to produce visible patterns of superposition (interference patterns) with light is, in effect, to derive two sources from a single source. Explain why this is so and describe how diffraction may be used to produce such a double source.

23.27 This is a question about the geometry of the two-source Young's fringes experiment. (You will need a calculator with an 8-digit display.)

(a) In the figure which is *not* to scale sources at S_1 and S_2 send light to a point P. If $a = 0.400$ mm, $D = 0.800$ m and $x = 3.00$ mm, calculate the lengths
S_2P and S_1P (using Pythagoras's theorem) and the path difference $(S_2P - S_2P)$ between light arriving at P from S_1 and S_2.

(b) Explain whether for light of wavelength 600 nm from coherent sources at S_1 and S_2 there will be a maximum or a minimum intensity at P.

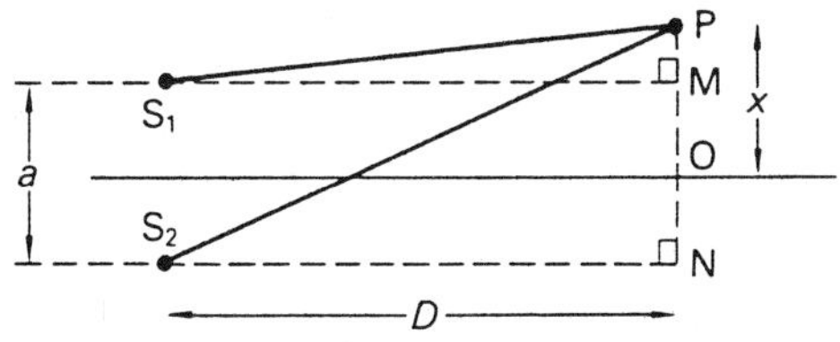

23.28 Using the photograph which accompanies question 21.30 calculate the wavelength λ of the ripples by measuring the distance between the sources a, and the ratio $\Delta x/D$ where Δx is the separation of the maxima at a distance D from the sources. Take the scale of the photograph to be 1/12 real size and use the relationship $\lambda \approx a\Delta x/D$.
In the ripple tank experiment λ was 40 mm. Does your calculation of λ support the use of the (approximate) formula in this case?

23.29 An experimenter wishes to demonstrate the wave nature of the output from a small ultrasonic generator consisting of a quartz crystal oscillating at 50 kHz. Explain how he could arrange the apparatus to get a two-source interference pattern. Give approximate dimensions of the arrangement which would produce intensity minima separated by 200 mm at his detector.

23.30 Microwaves, when they are reflected from a metal sheet, and light, when it is reflected at the front surface of a piece of glass, both undergo a phase reversal, i.e. a phase change of π rad. Outline one experiment for each of these types of electromagnetic radiation which would provide support for this statement.

23.31 In a Young's slit type of experiment with microwaves of wavelength 30 mm the distance between maxima detected at a distance of 42 m from the sources while moving across the line of symmetry was found to be 2.5 m. What was the separation of the two microwave sources?

23.32 In the figure P and Q are two radio navigation stations transmitting continuous sinusoidal radio waves at a wavelength of 3500 m. The stations are 70 km apart and transmit signals which are in phase and of equal amplitude. A ship moves from Y, equidistant from P and Q, towards P.

(a) Describe how the received radio signal varies during the first 3 km of its journey.

(b) Another ship is at X where it receives a maximum signal. It moves on line XZ which is parallel to YQ. By considering the kind of interference fringe pattern produced by two sources, how would you expect the signal received by this second ship to compare to that received by the first?

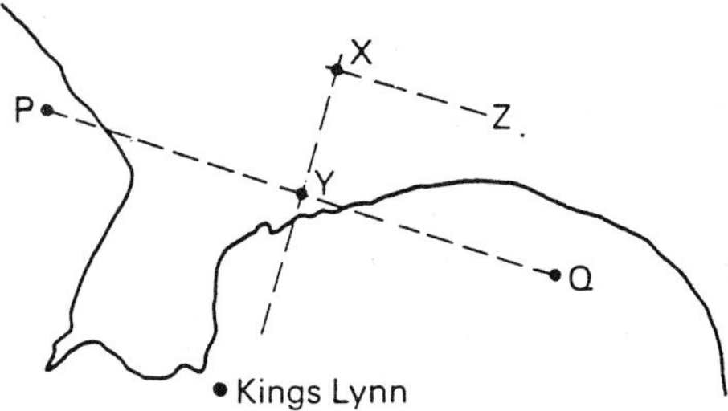

23.33 The figure overleaf shows a graph of intensity against distance on a screen placed 2.0 m away from an illuminated double slit in a typical 'Young's slits'

experiment. Explain the general shape of the curve (the full line).

(a) If the light was of wavelength 590 mm and the minima on the full curve occur every 4.2 mm, what was the slit separation?

(b) Calculate also the *width* of each slit. Explain any approximations in your calculation.

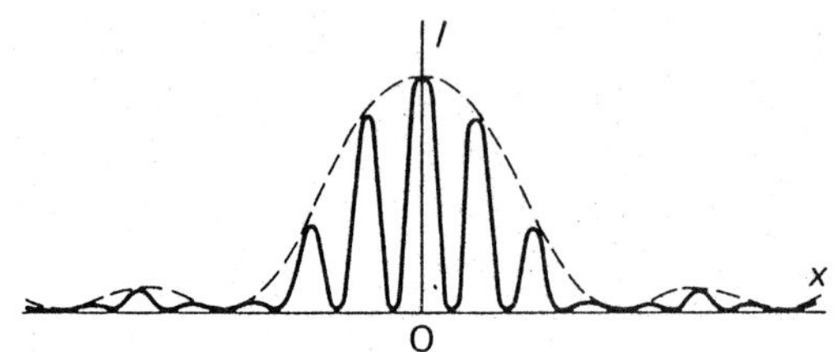

23.4 The diffraction grating

23.34 A diffraction grating is set up so that parallel light is perpendicularly incident on it. For light of wavelength 589 nm the first order spectral lines are observed in directions making an angle $\theta = 22.0°$ with the straight through position.

(a) Calculate the value of the slit separations s in the grating and the number of slits per millimetre.

(b) Calculate the wavelength of light which would give a first order spectral line at $\theta = 24.3°$.

23.35 How many spectral orders are produced within 15° of the incident direction when a parallel beam of yellow light of wavelength of 590 nm falls on a coarse diffraction grating the lines of which are 18 μm apart.

23.36 Plane water ripples of wavelength 5 mm arrive at a barrier which lies parallel to the waves and has small gaps in it at intervals of 12 mm. Show, by drawing a *scale diagram*, that there will be first and second order diffracted waves but no third order.

23.37 'When white light passes through a diffraction grating the grating *disperses* the light. Each slit in the grating *diffracts* the light and the resulting superposition of light from different slits leads to a pattern of peaks or maxima of light intensity at angles of *deviation* which vary from colour to colour.'
Write brief notes, including diagrams where appropriate, to explain in your own words each of the italicised words.

23.38 A diffraction grating having 5.00×10^5 lines m^{-1} is illuminated with a parallel beam of white light of extreme wavelengths $\lambda_r = 750$ nm and $\lambda_b = 400$ nm.

(a) Calculate the angular dispersion between the red and violet in the first order spectrum.

(b) A lens of focal length 200 mm is used to form an image of this first order spectrum in order to record it photographically. What will be the distance between the red and the violet ends of the spectrum on the film? Support your calculation with a diagram.

23.39 Show that the second and third order spectra of visible light produced by a diffraction grating will *always* overlap regardless of the number of lines per millimetre in the particular grating used. (Take values of λ_r and λ_b from the previous question.)

23.40 A sodium lamp is viewed through a diffraction grating held close to the eye. The lamp is 2.5 m from the grating. Three images of the lamp are seen, a central image and one on either side of the position of the lamp, each apparently about 0.6 m from it, as read from a tape measure laid on the bench directly beneath the lamp.
If the grating has 400 lines per millimetre, calculate an approximate value for the wavelength of sodium light.

23.41 A small detector of infra-red radiation which does not respond noticeably to visible light is moved across a line spectrum produced by a diffraction grating. It detects only one strong signal at a place occupied by a green line of wavelength 520 nm in the second order visible spectrum. What is the wavelength of this infra-red radiation?

23.42 Suggest how you might construct a diffraction grating for use with

(a) microwaves of frequency about 10^{10} Hz

(b) sound waves of frequency about 10^4 Hz.

24 Optics

24.1 Reflection

24.1 A plane wave moving at 0.40 m s^{-1} approaches a flat reflecting barrier at an angle of incidence of 30°. Draw a series of diagrams at intervals of 0.25 s to show the progress of a piece of wavefront AB, 0.50 m long, from the moment A reaches the barrier to the moment B reaches it.

24.2 Draw, using a compass, a circular wavefront, part of which has reflected from a straight barrier. Add to your diagram several rays, with arrows, showing the direction of energy propagation. Mark the position of the image of the source.

24.3 Draw a diagram showing a ray of light being reflected by a plane mirror, the angle of incidence being 20°.

(a) Through what angle is the reflected ray deviated? If the mirror is rotated until the angle of incidence is 25°, through what angle is the reflected ray rotated?

(b) If the mirror is now rotated through an angle x (i) what is the new angle of incidence, (ii) what is the new angle of reflection, (iii) through what angle has the reflected ray been rotated?

24.2 Refraction

24.4 Plot a graph of the angle of refraction θ_g against the angle of incidence θ_a for values of θ_a = 0°, 10°, 20°, 30°, 45°, 60°, 75° and 90° for a ray of light refracted from air into glass of refractive index 1.50. For what part of your graph is $\theta_g \propto \theta_a$ to within 2°?

24.5 *(a)* A ray of light travelling in water of refractive index 1.33 strikes its horizontal surface at an angle of incidence of 40°. Find the angle θ_a at which it emerges into the air.

(b) If a layer of oil of refractive index 1.44 is poured onto the water surface the ray emerges into the air at an angle θ. Calculate the path of the ray in the oil and show that $\theta = \theta_a$.

24.6 A narrow beam of light enters one long side of a rectangular block of glass at an angle of incidence of 45°.

(a) Calculate the angle of refraction in the block if the refractive index of the glass if 1.54.

(b) If the block is 80 mm wide find by drawing or by calculation the *sideways* displacement of the beam when it emerges into the air.

24.7 The refractive index of air varies with temperature. Describe two different everyday observations which support this statement.

24.8 The graph shows how the deviation D varies with the angle of incidence θ of a ray of light entering a triangular (60°–60°–60°) glass prism.

(a) What is the minimum deviation D_m? [Hard: Use the graph to explain why the minimum deviation must occur when the light passes symmetrically through the prism.]

(b) What are the two angles of incidence for which the deviation is 45°? Draw careful diagrams to show the paths of rays incident at these two angles through the prism. What do you notice about your diagram?

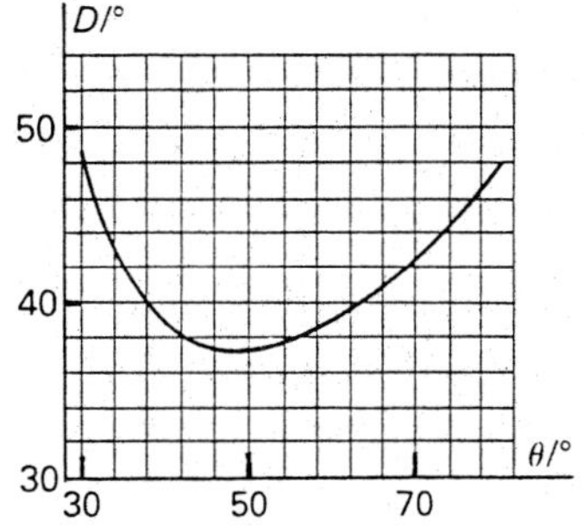

24.9 Explain what is meant by the dispersion of white light. Describe an experiment to compare qualitatively the dispersion produced by two prisms of identical shape made of different types of glass.

24.10 The diagram shows a plane wavefront of width b at almost normal incidence on a thin prism of refracting angle A made of glass of refractive index n. By considering the distance nl travelled in air by the part of the wave incident at the apex of the prism compared to the distance l travelled in the prism in the same time by the wave incident a distance b below the apex, write down

(a) an expression for the angle A

(b) an expression for the angle (D–A).

(c) Hence show that, for small angles, the deviation of the wavefront is given by
$D = (n - 1)A$.
(Remember that an angle, in radians, is expressed as arc/radius.)

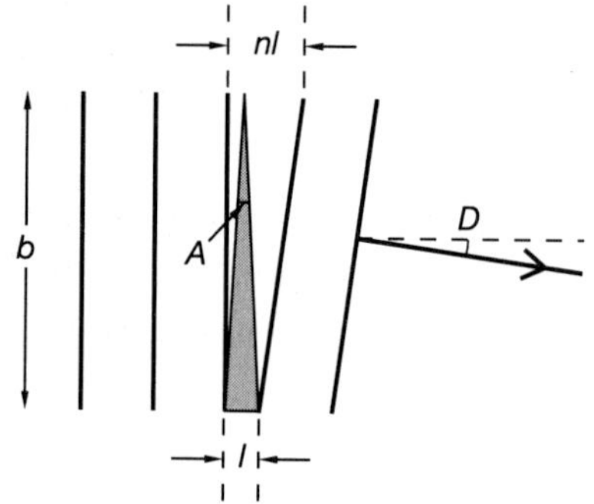

24.11 The table gives the refractive indices of two glasses for various wavelengths of light in the optical part of the spectrum.

λ/nm	405	486	546	589	656
n_{crown}	1.532	1.523	1.519	1.517	1.515
n_{flint}	1.685	1.664	1.655	1.650	1.644

Plot two graphs with λ along the x–axis to show the variation of n with λ for crown and flint glass.

(a) For a thin prism of flint glass with a refracting angle of 6.00° calculate the deviation of (i) red light: $\lambda = 650$ nm (ii) blue light: $\lambda = 450$ nm, using the formula in the previous question.

(b) What is the difference of the deviations, i.e, the angle of dispersion produced by the prism?

(c) Repeat *(a)* and *(b)* for a crown glass prism with a refracting angle of 13.0° and comment on the results.

24.12 Sound, of frequency 500 Hz, travels at 340 m s^{-1} in air and at 1510 m s^{-1} in sea water. Draw a scale diagram showing wavefronts in air and in sea water to illustrate the refraction of sound. Take the angle of incidence of the sound energy in air to be 65°.

24.13 The speed c of water waves in a ripple tank of depth h can be written (approximately) as $c = k\sqrt{h}$ where k is a constant. Plane waves, moving at 0.25 m s^{-1} in a region where $h = 25$ mm, are refracted at a straight boundary at which the depth h changes to 4.0 mm.

(a) Calculate the speed of the refracted waves.

(b) What is the angle of deviation of the waves (the angle between the incident and the refracted wavefronts) if the incident waves meet the boundary between deep and shallow water at an angle of 45°?

24.14 In an experiment to measure the speed of light a light pulse is reflected up and down a straight tube which is 1200 m long.

How much longer will the light take to make 20 journeys there and back if the tube is full of air rather than if it is evacuated? Take the refractive index of air to be 1.00029.

24.15 Describe how you would measure the refractive index of tap water in the laboratory. Estimate the uncertainties in the measurements you take and hence suggest an overall maximum uncertainty in your result.

24.3 Total internal reflection

24.16 What is the difference between the critical angles of red light and blue light for a glass for which $n_{blue} = 1.639$ and $n_{red} = 1.621$? How could you demonstrate that the critical angles were different?

24.17 A step-index optical fibre has a core of refractive index 1.48 and cladding of refractive index 1.46. A narrow beam of light in air enters the (flat) end of the core at an angle of 12° to the axis of the fibre.

(a) Will the beam be propagated along the fibre or not? Support your calculations with an appropriate diagram.

(b) What is the maximum angle to the axis for propagation to occur?

24.18 (a) Draw a diagram to illustrate the paths taken by rays travelling along a straight step-index optical fibre if (i) the ray is axial (ii) the ray meets the core-cladding boundary at an angle greater than the critical angle.

(b) A square pulse of monochromatic light is fed into such an optical fibre. Explain how the pulse shape will have changed after it has propagated along several kilometres of fibre.

24.19 An optical fibre of length l has a core and cladding of refractive indeces n_1 and n_2 respectively. The speed of light in air is c.

(a) Calculate the time taken for a ray of light propagating parallel to the axis of the fibre to travel along it.

(b) By what factor is this time increased for a ray which crosses the axis and reflects from the core-cladding boundary at an angle of incidence θ? Explain your answer.

(c) Hence show that the longest time for a ray to travel along this fibre is given by $l(n_1)^2/cn_2$.

24.20 Water waves of frequency 8.0 Hz, travelling in a region where the wave speed is $0.32\,\mathrm{m\,s^{-1}}$, are obliquely incident on the boundary of a region of deeper water where the wave speed is $0.40\,\mathrm{m\,s^{-1}}$.

(a) Sketch a wavefront diagram of the situation if the angle of incidence is equal to the critical angle θ_c.

(b) Calculate the value of θ_c in this case.

24.21 The figure shows an optical dipstick, a device for checking the level of petrol in a tank. Whether or not the laser beam emerges at the photodiode detector depends on the tightness of the curve at the bottom of the optical fibre.

(a) Explain the way in which the dipstick works for a fibre made of glass of refractive index 1.48, if the refractive index of petrol is 1.38.

(b) If the fibre is of diameter 50 μm, calculate the minimum radius into which the fibre can be bent in order for the dipstick to work. (The beam escapes into the petrol when $\theta <$ the critical angle.)

(c) Is there a maximum radius above which the dipstick won't work? Explain your reasoning.

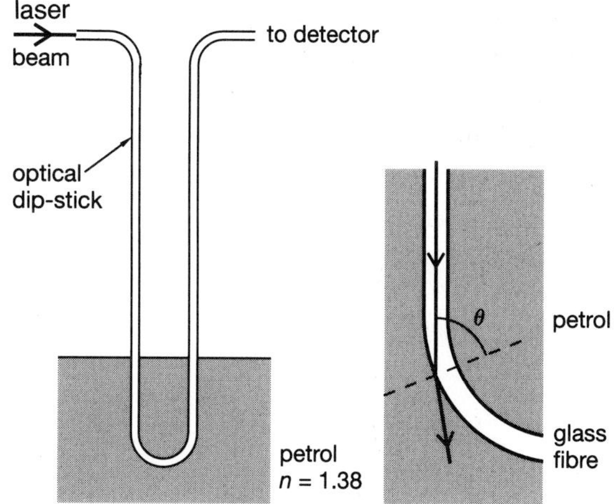

24.4 Images

24.22 Copy the figure drawing a semicircle of radius 100 mm. Taking each of your 16 evenly spaced lines to

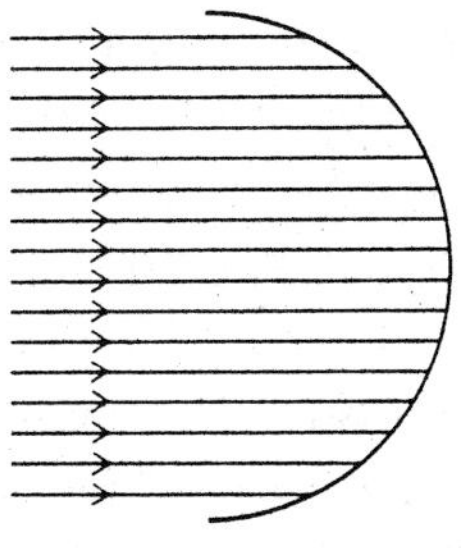

be a ray incident on a concave mirror (the semicircle) draw the normals at the points of incidence and construct a series of reflected rays. They will not form a perfect image of the distant object but will form a cusp-shaped figure very much like the bright patch on the surface of a cup of tea cast by sunlight or by the light from a single bulb.

By considering only the central (i) 12 rays (ii) 8 rays and (iii) 4 rays, explain how reducing the aperture of the mirror sharpens the image.

24.23 The figure shows circular wavefronts which are being refracted at a plane boundary between shallow water and deep water.

(a) Which part of the diagram represents deep water?

(b) Find the ratio of the wave speeds in deep and shallow water. Explain your calculation.

(c) Locate as precisely as possible the centres of the circles of which the two sets of wavefronts form parts and calculate the ratio of the radii of the two parts of a wavefront, e.g. PS and QR.

(d) Comment on your answers to *(b)* and *(c)*.

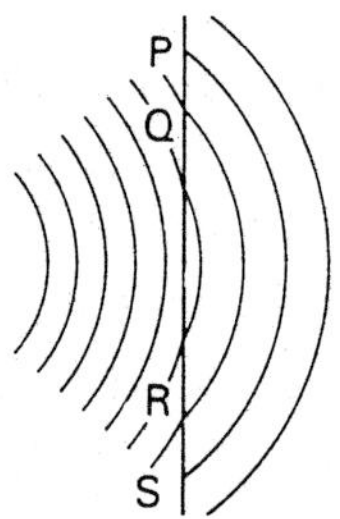

24.24 ***(a)*** What is the apparent depth *d* of water (of refractive index 1.33) in a swimming pool known to be 3.00 m deep, i.e. which is of real depth 3.00 m? Assume that the observer is looking straight down into the water.

It is not easy to measure *d* experimentally. One method is to place a plane mirror on the surface of the water and to look at the image of an object held a distance *h* above the mirror. When this image exhibits no parallax with the apparent position of a mark on the bottom of the pool, $h = d$.

(b) Explain what is meant by *no parallax* and draw a diagram to describe this experiment.

24.5 Lenses

24.25 ***(a)*** The lenses of a long-sighted person's spectacles are known to be +2.5 D (left) and +2.0 D (right). Explain what this means and calculate the focal lengths of the two lenses.

(b) While using these spectacles the person adds a pair of clip-on sunglasses. These are −1.0 D in both lenses. What are now the effective focal lengths of the two pairs of combined lenses?

24.26 When showing holiday slides a man wants to provide as large an image as possible. He achieves a magnification of 33 times across a room which is 4.6 m long. If the slide measures 40 mm by 25 mm what is

(a) the size of the image on the screen

(b) the effective focal length of the lens in the projector?

24.27 The diagram shows how a converging lens acts as a magnifying glass to produce an upright virtual image of a caterpillar.

(a) If the image is 300 mm from the lens and the caterpillar is 150 mm from the lens calculate the focal length of the lens.

(b) Where would the image of the caterpillar be if it was placed 300 mm from the lens?

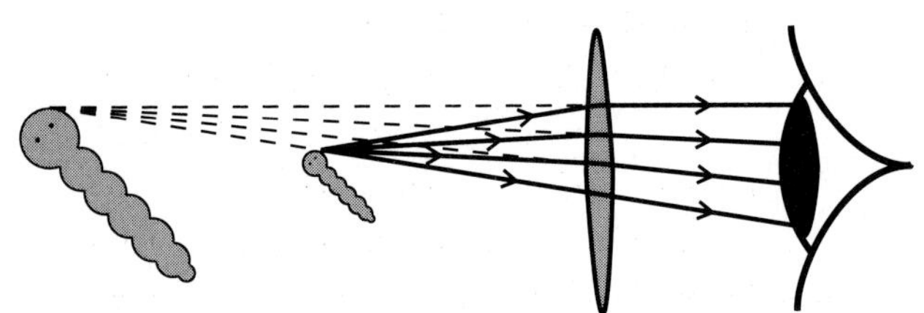

24.28 A converging lens has a focal length of 0.20 m. Find the position and size of the image of an object

5.0 mm high which is placed the following distances from the lens:

(a) 1.00 m
(b) 0.40 m
(c) 0.22 m
(d) 0.15 m.

State whether the image is upright (U) or inverted (I) in each case and whether it is real (R) or virtual (V).

24.29 *(a)* Draw a graph of u against v relating the positions of an object and its real image for a lens of focal length 150 mm. Show values of u up to 5.0 m and down to 0.16 m.

(b) Describe the shape of the graph for values of u from 5 m to 1 m. What does it tell you about using such a lens in a camera to take photographs?

24.30 Tabulate a series of values of u and v for a converging lens of focal length 0.20 m for real objects and images.

Sketch graphs of

(a) v/u against v
(b) $1/v$ against $1/u$
(c) $c + v$ against u.

(Plot the first mentioned quality on the y–axis in each case.)

24.31 A naturalist wants to photograph a rhinocerous which is 75 m away. The beast is 3.8 m long, and its image is to be 12 mm long on the film.

(a) What focal length lens should be use?
(b) What would the image size have been if he had used a normal 50 mm focal length lens?

24.32 For an equiconvex thin lens, of which the radii of curvature r of the faces are each 462 mm, the refractive indices for red light and for blue light are: $n_{red} = 1.64$ and $n_{blue} = 1.68$. A small white light source is placed on the axis of the lens and 500 mm from it.

Calculate the positions of the images formed by *(a)* the red light *(b)* the blue light from the source, given that the focal length f can be calculated from the formula.

$$\frac{1}{f} = \frac{2}{r}(n - 1)$$

24.33 The figure shows the image formation described in the previous question. The dashed lines represent the rays of red light and the full rays the blue light. Describe as fully as possible what is seen on a screen placed *(a)* at S_b and *(b)* at S_r if the lens has an aperture of 60 mm. (You will need to use the answers to the previous question.)

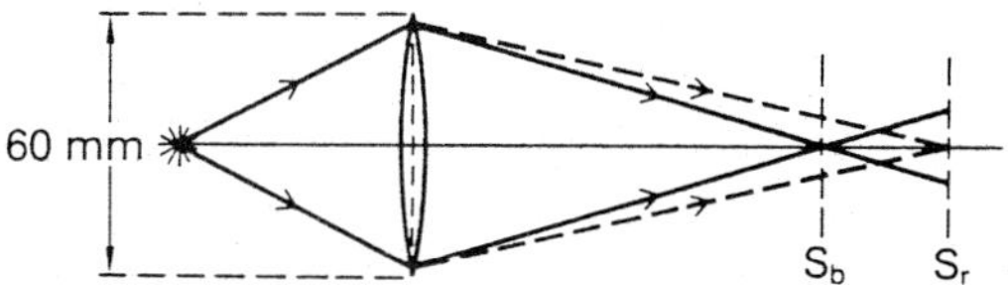

24.6 The eye

24.34 A man with eyeballs of effective length 25 mm (i.e. with this distance from refracting region to retina) walks towards a white post which is 4.0 m high. Calculate the size of the image of the post on his retina when he is a distance d from the post given by d/m = 400, 100, 20, 5.

24.35 The Moon subtends an angle of 0.52° at the Earth's surface.

(a) What is the size of the image of the Moon on the retina of an eye of length 21 mm from refracting system (the cornea plus lens) to retina?

(b) Describe how (i) the size, and (ii) the intensity of the image varies when the pupil of the eye changes from 2.0 mm to 6.0 mm in diameter.

24.36 The power of a normal eye is ≈ +40 D when it is relaxed and it can accommodate by about +4 D. Amplify and explain this statement as fully as possible.

24.37 *(a)* What is the visual angle subtended by the sides of this letter

H

when the page is 0.75 m from your eye?

(b) How much bigger would the visual angle be if the page was held at the least distance of distinct

vision, 25 cm, for a normal eye?

(c) Estimate the greatest distance at which you can 'read' the letter and hence the visual angle at which your eyes can just resolve the sides of the H.

24.38 In the figure an object O of height 40 mm has an image I at the near point (i.e. 0.25 m) from a normal eye E.

(a) If the lens is of focal length 0.20 m and is 0.55 m from the eye find the linear magnification m of the image.

(b) Also calculate (i) the visual angle α_i of the image, and (ii) the visual angle α_o of the object as seen by the eye with the lens removed. (iii) Hence find the angular magnification M of the system.

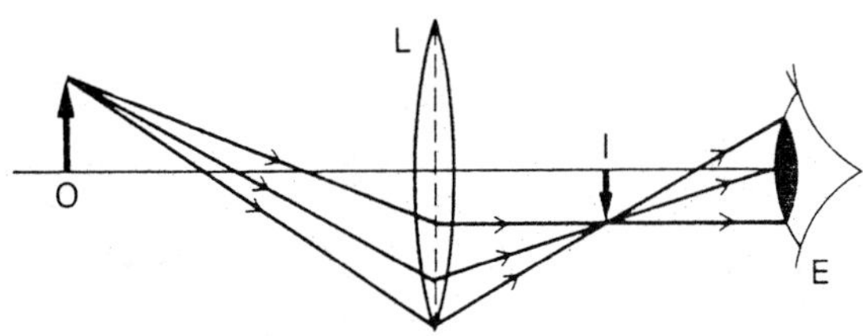

24.39 The eye can just resolve two objects which are separated by an angle of about 3×10^{-4} rad. A magnifying glass has a maximum useful magnifying power of about 10. Can a single lens be used to count the scratches on a diffraction grating with 100 lines per millimetre? [Hint: calculate the visual angle subtended at an unaided eye by two adjacent scratches on the grating with the grating at the near point, 250 mm from the eye.]

24.7 Optical instruments

24.40 The lens of a relaxed eye has an effective focal length of 21 mm. The diameter of the eye pupil varies from 1.5 mm to 6.5 mm.

(a) What are the corresponding f–numbers of the eye?

(b) How many times greater is the intensity of light incident on the eye when the pupil contracts to 1.5 mm than when it dilates to 6.5 mm? (Assume the pupil adjusts to give an image on the retina of constant brightness.)

24.41 *(a)* Show that f–numbers 2.8, 4, 5.6 and 8 represent apertures whose areas double as one moves from one f–number to the next.

(b) On a day when opening the camera shutter for 5.0 ms correctly exposes the film using an aperture of $f/2.8$, what will be the best shutter speeds for the other three f–numbers quoted above?

(c) Under what circumstances might one wish to use (i) a high f–number (ii) a very low f–number?

24.42 The converging lens in a typical miniature camera has a focal length of 50 mm. The lens can be moved relative to the film in order to focus objects from infinity down to about 0.50 m.
What is the range of movement of the lens?

24.43 A camera with a lens of focal length 60 mm is used to take a colour slide of a tree which subtends an angle of 0.13 rad at the photographer. Later the slide is held up to the light and viewed with the unaided eye from a distance of 200 mm. Calculate

(a) the size of the tree's image on the slide

(b) the angle subtended by this image at the eye of the person who views the slide

(c) the overall magnifying power obtained.

Draw diagrams to explain your calculations.

24.44 An astronomical telescope has an objective lens with a focal length of 1.45 m and an aperture of diameter 80 mm. Its eyepiece lens has a focal length of 0.12 m. With the incident light parallel to the axis and the final image at infinity, calculate the minimum diameter of the aperture of the eyepiece lens if all of the light from the objective lens is to pass through the eyepiece lens and reach the observer.

24.45 *(a)* When using the telescope described in the previous question what will be the angular magnification?

(b) Explain why it is not possible to give the (linear) magnification when using telescopes in this way.

24.46 The focal length of the objective lens of the Yerkes Observatory's largest refracting telescope (the biggest of its kind in the world) is 20 m. A photograph of the Moon is made using this telescope.

How should the photographic plate be mounted and how large must the plate be in order to record the whole of the Moon's image? The moon is 3.5×10^3 km in diameter and is 3.8×10^5 km from the Earth.

24.47 If the Yerkes Observatory telescope described in the previous question uses an eyepiece lens system of effective focal length 36 mm what is the angular magnification of the telescope with the final image at infinity?

25 Probing the nucleus

Data $e = 1.60 \times 10^{-19}$ C
$c = 3.00 \times 10^8$ m s^{-1}
$h = 6.63 \times 10^{-34}$ J s
mass of electron $= 9.11 \times 10^{-31}$ kg
u $= 1.66 \times 10^{-27}$ kg
mass of α–particle = 4.0015 u
mass of neutron = 1.0087 u
mass of proton = 1.0073 u
Avogadro constant $= 6.02 \times 10^{23}$ mol^{-1}

25.1 Radioactivity

25.1 Make a table to display the main properties and characteristics of the radiations from natural sources. (Your table might, for example, give relative masses and relative ionising abilities as well as typical energies.)

25.2 A radium source is mounted in total darkness above a rectangular photographic plate as shown in the figure; this is seen from the side in (i). After some time the plate is removed and developed, and is found to be fogged as shown in (ii).

(a) Explain what kinds of radiation are responsible for the different areas of fogging, and how their properties give rise to the pattern shown.

To investigate these properties further an experimenter repeats this test with a photographic plate covered partly with a strip of thin card and partly with a strip of aluminium about 2.5 mm thick, as shown in (iii).

(b) Explain what you would expect to find when this plate is developed. Would you expect to find any parts of it totally free from fogging?

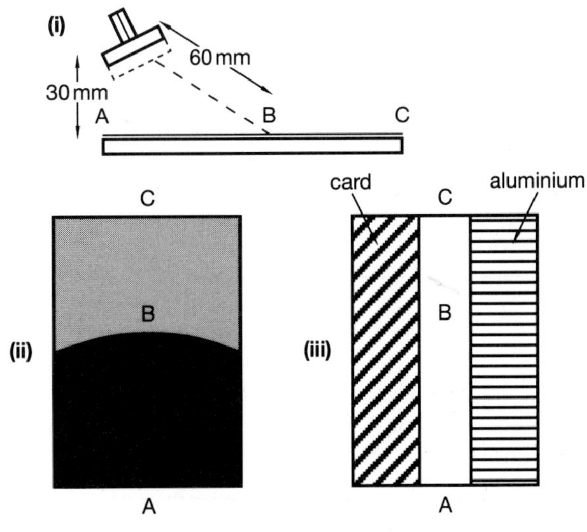

25.3 Describe how you would positively identify which types of nuclear radiation are emitted by an unknown radioactive source.

25.4 A source containing radium–226 is found to emit γ–radiation of wavelength 6.5×10^{-12} m (as well as the usual α–radiation). What quantity of energy (in MeV) is carried away from the nucleus by each γ–ray photon?

25.5 The α–particles from an americium–241 source have energies of either 2.44 MeV or 2.49 MeV.

(a) What are these energies in joules?

(b) What is the ratio of the initial speeds of these two α–particles?

(c) Calculate the wavelength of a photon which has an energy, $E = hf$, equal to the difference of energy of these two α–particles.
(See the data on page 149.)

25.6 'Strontium–90 emits particles which are identical to the electrons in the beam of a TV tube.'

(a) What is the experimental evidence for this statement?

(b) How would you convince a student that β–particles and electrons are *identical*?

25.7 The graphs show the percentage of (i) α–particles from one source which penetrate a given distance *t* in air (upper scale on *x*–axis) (ii) β–particles from one source which penetrate a given thickness *t* of aluminium (lower scale on *x*–axis).

(a) Describe the graphs in words.

(b) Make any possible deductions about the α–particles and the β–particles from the graphs.

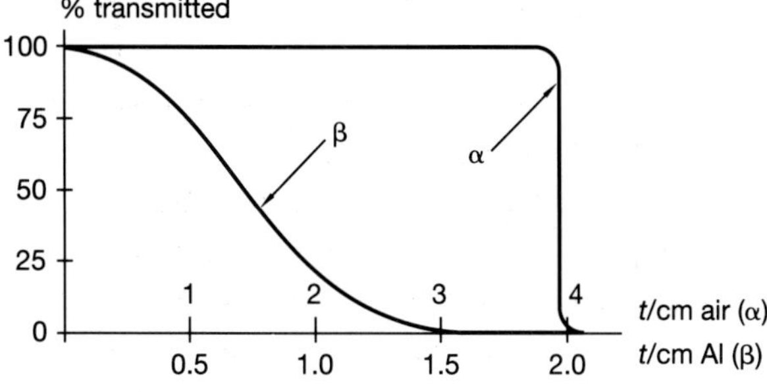

25.8 Sheets of lead are placed between a γ–source and a γ–detector, the output of which is a current in pA (10^{-12} A). The results are as follows:

thickness of sheet added/mm	0	2.0	2.0	2.0	2.0	4.0	4.0	8.0
detector current/pA	31	27	24	21	18	14	11	7

Plot a suitable graph and deduce the half-thickness of lead for these γ–rays. State any assumptions which you make.

25.9 A student tries to demonstrate the magnetic deflection of α–particles in a school laboratory. He has an evacuated tube and a strong permanent magnet which produces a uniform *B*–field of 220 mT over a distance of nearly 10 cm.

If the α–particles he is using each have an energy of 4.8 MeV, use the equation $F = BQv$ to calculate the radius of the circle which they follow in the field and discuss whether or not the demonstration will be effective. (See the data on page 149.)

25.10 In an experiment to measure the speed v and specific charge e/m of β–particles in a vacuum the following measurements are obtained:

$v/10^8\,\mathrm{m\,s^{-1}}$	1.5	2.0	2.5	2.7	2.9
$(e/m)/10^{11}\,\mathrm{C\,kg^{-1}}$	−1.54	−1.29	−0.96	−0.78	−0.45

According to the special theory of relativity e/m should decrease with speed v according to the relation

$$\frac{e}{m} = \frac{e}{m_o}\sqrt{(1 - v^2/c^2)}$$

where m_o is the rest mass of β–particles and *c* is the speed of light.

(a) Plot a graph of e/m against $\sqrt{(1 - v^2/c^2)}$.

(b) Use your graph (i) to decide whether the measurements confirm the special theory of relativity, (ii) to find the value of e/m at low speeds ($v \rightarrow 0$).

(c) Compare your value with the specific charge of electrons, and comment on the result.

25.11 Calculate the flux density of the magnetic field that will deflect into an arc of radius 0.10 m

(a) β–particles of speed $2.0 \times 10^7\,\mathrm{m\,s^{-1}}$

(b) α–particles of speed $2.0 \times 10^7\,\mathrm{m\,s^{-1}}$ (whose specific charge is $4.8 \times 10^7\,\mathrm{C\,kg^{-1}}$).

25.2 Background radiation

25.12 It is suggested that, in order to reduce exposure to background radiation, it is preferable to live in a house built of granite which is well sealed against draughts than in a large tent designed to allow cool breezes to flow through it. Explain what you think of this suggestion.

25.13 The diagram shows how the *average* annual radiation dose of 2 mSv (millisievert) is made up for people living in the United Kingdom.

(a) What percentage of the average dose comes from artificial sources?

(b) The dose received varies considerably over the British Isles. Suggest why some regions are regions of high dose.

(c) In the year following the Chernobyl accident the average dose over the whole of Britain increased by about 0.1 mSv. Express this as a percentage of the average dose (i) from natural and (ii) from artificial sources.

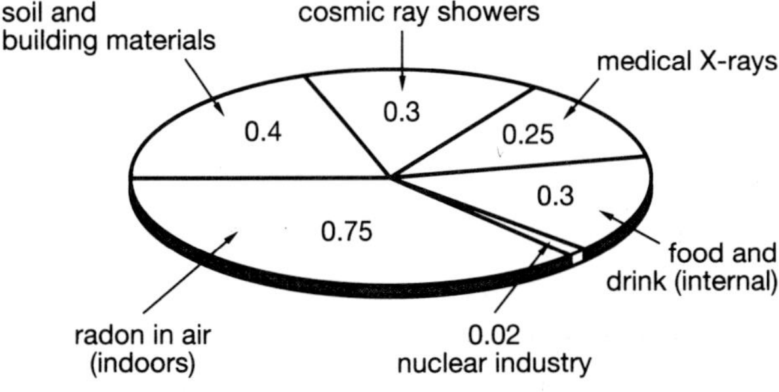

25.14 A radioactive source is to be mixed with some mud in preparation for a study of the movement of sediment in an estuary. The team involved handle the source with very long pincers and complete the task as quickly as possible after removing the γ–source from its lead-lined box.

Explain how they are reducing the dose they receive to as small a value as practicable.

25.15 Under what circumstances would you expect the intensity of radiation from a small source to vary inversely with the square of the distance from the source (i.e. so that doubling the distance reduces the intensity to a quarter as much)?

Discuss to what extent you would expect such a variation to apply in the following cases:

(a) a light source in clear air

(b) an α–particle source in air

(c) an β–particle source (i) in a vacuum (ii) in air

(d) a γ–ray source in air.

25.16 You are given a small metal disc, the size of a penny, which you are told is a source of γ–radiation with a long half-life.

Describe how you would show that the intensity of the radiation from the source was inversely proportional to the square of the distance from it. List any safety precautions you would take.

25.17 A school γ–source is often a tiny quantity of cobalt–60 with a 'strength' of 5 μCi (microcurie). If a one-curie source produces 3.7×10^{10} γ–photons per second, calculate how many γ–photons pass through each of your eyes, taken to be spheres of radius 2.0 cm, every second when you look at a school source from a distance of *(a)* 0.50 m *(b)* 2.50 m.

25.3 Ionising radiations

25.18 *(a)* If an α–particle loses on average 30 eV of energy for each ion pair that it creates in a collision, how many ion pairs would you expect a 6.5 MeV α–particle to create?

(b) An α–particle source that emits particles of this energy is placed inside an ionisation chamber in such a way that all the ions created are collected by the electrodes in the chamber. If the source emits 2.5×10^5 particles per second, estimate the current through the ionisation chamber. Explain what assumption about the ions you are making.

25.19 *(a)* Describe some form of particle detector that will respond only to α–particles.

(b) Explain how you would establish that it is only α–particles to which this detector responds.

(c) Explain how the behaviour of this detector leads you to believe that the radiation detected is in the form of *particles*.

25.20 Describe a form of GM tube that can be used to detect α, β and γ–radiation. Explain how you would use this detector to establish that all three kinds of radiation are present in the emissions from a 'radium' source.

25.21 *(a)* The path of a charged particle in a cloud chamber is seen as a bright white line. Explain precisely what makes up the line.

(b) The path of a β–particle is found to be like that shown in the diagram in which it is known that a magnetic field is directed out of the paper. Deduce (i) the direction of motion of the β–particle and (ii) the sign of its charge. Explain your reasoning.

A

B

aluminium sheet

25.22 Cloud chamber photographs of trails left by α–particles tell us that all the α–particles from a given source have *almost* the same energy. Explain how this deduction is made from the trails. (You will need to find some typical cloud chamber photographs in textbooks or other sources in order to answer this question.)

25.23 The density of ionisation produced by α–particles is shown in the graph as the number of ion pairs produced in air per millimetre of track plotted against the distance, x, from *the end of the track*.

(a) For an α–particle which leaves a track 36 mm long, estimate the total number of ion pairs it produces.

(b) If the creation of each ion pair requires 32 eV what was the initial energy of the α–particle?

(c) Estimate the length of the track which would be produced by an α–particle with an initial energy of 2.4 MeV.

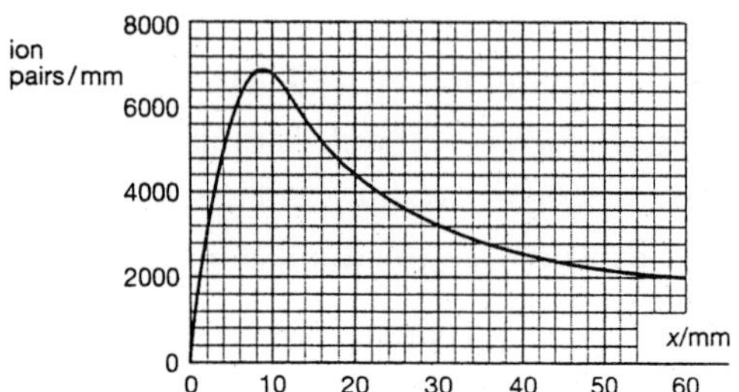

25.24 *(a)* Describe the differences that may be observed between the tracks of individual α–particles in cloud chambers filled with hydrogen, helium and air.

(b) Explain how information about the mass of an α–particle can be obtained from such data.

(c) Describe briefly an experiment with relatively large colliding bodies that supports your explanation.

25.4 The nucleus

25.25 Describe an experiment which suggests that most of the mass of an atom is concentrated in a small central region called a nucleus.

25.26 Two α–particles, each of energy 4.0 MeV, collide head on. Calculate the distance between their centres at the moment that they both come instantaneously to rest.

Take $1/4\pi\varepsilon_0 = 9.0 \times 10^9\,\mathrm{m\,F^{-1}}$.

25.27 The maximum kinetic energy which an α–particle can transmit to an electron occurs during a head–on elastic collision.

Calculate the kinetic energy lost by an α–particle of initial energy 6.2 MeV in such a collision. (See the data on page 149.) Are we justified in neglecting this energy loss in analysing the results of the Rutherford scattering experiment?

25.28 Tin, symbol Sn and atomic number 50, has more stable isotopes than any other element. The number of neutrons can be 64, 65, 66, 67, 68, 69, 70, 72 or 74. Give a list of the symbols for these nuclides.

25.29 Copper (atomic number 29), has two stable isotopes of mass number 63 (69.2%) and 65 (30.8%), where the numbers in brackets are the relative proportions of the isotopes. Calculate the relative atomic mass of copper.

25.30 The mass of an atom of sodium, ${}^{23}_{11}Na$, is 3.82×10^{-26} kg. What is the mass, in grams, of one mole of sodium atoms? Comment on your answer.

25.5 Nuclear reactions

25.31 What is the evidence that α–particles are identical to helium nuclei?

25.32 Samarium–147 (atomic number 62, symbol Sm) decays by α–emission. The following is a list of neighbouring elements with their atomic numbers (in brackets): cerium (58), praseodymium (59), neodymium (60), promethium (61), europium (63), gadolinium (64). Explain what isotope it must decay into.

25.33 Potassium–40 (symbol ${}^{40}_{19}K$) is an isotope that decays by β^+–emission.

(a) How many protons, neutrons and electrons are there in each neutral atom of this isotope?

(b) From the information in the following list (with the atomic number given in brackets) write down the symbol of the isotope into which potassium–40 decays: chlorine (17), symbol Cl; argon (18) symbol Ar; calcium (20), symbol Ca; scandium (21), symbol Sc.

25.34 Copy the grid which gives the number of neutrons, N, in a nucleus (up) against the number of protons, Z, (along), i.e. it is a grid of neutron number against atomic number in the region $N = 81$, $Z = 57$.

(a) Explain why the arrow shows an α–decay and write the nuclear equation for this decay.

(b) Add two labelled arrows to your grid to show (i) a possible β^-–decay and (ii) a possible β^+–decay. Give the appropriate nuclear equations.

(c) Discuss how the arrows you have drawn from β–decays support the fact that nuclides with an excess of neutrons tend to undergo β^-–decay whereas those with too few neutrons tend to undergo β^+–decay.

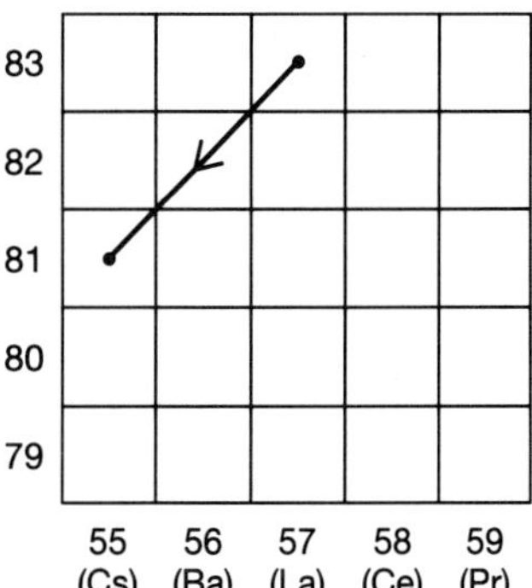

25.35 A nucleus of radon–220 (${}^{220}_{86}Rn$) decays by emission of an α–particle (a nucleus of ${}^{4}_{2}He$) of energy 6.3 MeV. Find, using also the data on page 149

(a) the mass of the radon–220 atom

(b) the mass of the α–particle

(c) the nucleon number, atomic number, and the mass of the resulting nucleus

(d) the speed and momentum of the α–particle

(e) the speed of recoil of the resulting nucleus

(f) the kinetic energy (in MeV) of the resulting nucleus.

25.36 *(a)* ${}^{87}_{37}Rb$ is a radioactive isotope of rubidium that decays by emission of a β^- –particle. Write down the atomic number and nucleon number of the isotope into which it decays.

(b) If the atomic masses of the two isotopes are 86.9092 u and 86.9089 u respectively, calculate the maximum possible energy of the emitted β^-–particle (i) in J (ii) in MeV. (See also the data on page 149.)

25.37 An atom of phosphorus–32 decays by β^-– emission into an atom of sulphur–32, and in the process 1.7 MeV of nuclear energy is transferred to the kinetic energy of the particles.

If the atomic mass of sulphur–32 is 31.9721 u, calculate the atomic mass of phosphorus–32. (See also the data on page 149.)

25.38 Under certain circumstances γ–radiation can cause the production of pairs of electrons and positrons, the energy of each γ–ray photon being converted into the mass of an electron–positron pair. Take the rest mass of an electron as equivalent to an energy of 0.512 MeV.

(a) What is the smallest energy (in eV) that a γ–ray photon must have in order to give rise to an electron–positron pair?

(b) What is the wavelength of such a γ–ray?

(c) If a γ–ray of half this wavelength produces an electron–positron pair and its energy is equally shared between the particles, what is the energy (in eV) of each of the particles produced?

25.39 Write full nuclear equations for the following reactions. (You may need to look up the atomic numbers of some of the elements involved.)

(a) $^{14}N\ (\alpha, p)^{17}O$

(b) $^{27}Al\ (\alpha, n)^{30}P$

(c) $^{27}Al\ (p, \alpha)^{24}Mg$

(d) $^{113}Cd\ (n, \gamma)^{114}Cd$

(e) $^{238}U\ (n, \beta^-)^{239}Np$

(f) $^{12}C\ (p, \beta^+)^{13}C$

(g) $^{56}Fe\ (p, n)^{56}\ Co$.

25.40 A proton can be taken as having a mass m and a charge $+e$, while an α–particle has a mass of $4m$ and a charge $+2e$. When these particles are accelerated from rest through the same potential difference, what is

(a) the ratio of the energies they gain from the electric field?

(b) the ratio of the speeds they attain?

25.41 A useful radioactive isotope of zinc, $^{63}_{30}Zn$, is produced by the bombardment of $^{60}_{28}Ni$ with α–particles. Use the following information to calculate the minimum energy which the α–particle must have to induce this reaction.

^{63}Zn has atomic mass 63.9332 u

^{60}Ni has atomic mass 59.9308 u.

(See also the data on page 149.)

25.42 Cobalt–60, a γ–emitter widely used in the treatment of cancers, is produced when cobalt–59 absorbs a neutron. Calculate the minimum energy of the γ–photon and its equivalent wavelength. Use the data below and those on page 149.

^{59}Co has atomic mass 58.9332 u

^{60}Co has atomic mass 59.9338 u.

25.6 Radioactive decay

25.43 Iodine–124 decays by β^+–emission and is used in medical diagnosis. In a sample of $^{124}_{53}I$ any individual atom has a 50% chance of decaying in 4.2 days.

Estimate the fraction of these atoms which, when introduced into the body, will remain undecayed after 10 days.

25.44 The half-lives of sodium–21 and sodium–26 are 24 s and 60 s respectively.

(a) If two samples are prepared, each containing the same number of sodium atoms, which one will have the greatest initial activity?

(b) Calculate the initial activity of the samples if each contain 1.0×10^6 atoms.

(c) Draw two graphs showing the subsequent decay of these samples and estimate the time when their *activities* will be the same.

25.45 A sample of a radioactive isotope with a half-life of 1.0 minute is obtained by chemical extraction from a nuclear reactor and deposited in a filter.

(a) If the sample contains initially 1000 atoms of the isotope, tabulate the number of atoms to be expected at subsequent intervals of 1 minute for the next 5 minutes, and represent your results graphically.

(b) Draw a tangent to the graph at the 2–minute mark and calculate the rate of decay at this moment.

(c) Calculate also the average decay rate between

1.5 minutes and 2.5 minutes from the start.

25.46 In an experiment to determine the half-life of the nuclide $^{63}_{30}Zn$, a sample containing some of the radioactive zinc was placed close to a GM tube and the following readings taken:

time/hours	0	0.5	1.0	1.5	2.0	2.5	3.0
counts in one minute	259	158	101	76	56	49	37

During the following morning the counter registered 29, 32, 33, 29, 28 and 30 counts over a one-minute period on the hour each hour.

(a) Make a table of the counts during the experiment taking note of the background count.

(b) Plot a graph of this count rate against time and use it to deduce *three different values* of the half-life of ^{63}Zn. Find the mean of your values.

(c) Plot a second graph of ln(count) against time and use it to deduce a value for the half-life of ^{63}Zn.

(d) Discuss which of *(b)* and *(c)* provides the more reliable value.

25.47 Technetium–99 (atomic number 43, chemical symbol Tc) decays by emission of a negative β–particle into ruthenium (chemical symbol Ru). Write down the full symbols with superscript and subscript for these two nuclei.

A sample containing 0.10 μg of technetium–99 is found to emit β^-–particles at a rate of $135\,s^{-1}$.

(a) How many atoms are there in 99 g of ^{99}Tc?

(b) Calculate the decay constant λ of ^{99}Tc.

(c) What is the half-life, in years, of ^{99}Tc?

25.48 A sample of iodine–131, of half-life 8.04 days, has an activity of 7.4×10^7 Bq. What will be the activity of the sample after four weeks?

25.49 Calculate the mass of caesium–137 that has an activity of 2.0×10^5 Bq, given that the half-life of this isotope is 30 years.

25.50 In an experiment to measure the half-life of radon–220, an α–emitter, a volume of air mixed with 80 000 atoms of this radon gas is pumped into an ionisation chamber.

(a) If the inital rate of production of α–particles is $1050\,s^{-1}$, what is (i) the decay constant and (ii) the half-life for radon–220?

(b) Suggest how the rate of production of α–particles might be measured.

(c) How is it possible to provide a sample of a radioactive material, such as this radon–220, which has such a small half-life?

25.51 Explain how you would attempt to measure the half-life, $t_{½}$, of an isotope when it is known that $t_{½}$ is more than 500 years. You may assume that small fractions of a gram of the isotope can be isolated.

25.52 Ordinary potassium contains 0.012% of a naturally occurring radioactive isotope ^{40}K which has a half-life of 1.3×10^9 years. What is

(a) the number of atoms of ^{40}K in 100 g of potassium

(b) the activity of 100 g of potassium?

25.53 The half-life of carbon–14 is 5730 years and decays by β^-–emission.

(a) Calculate the decay constant for carbon–14 and hence find the number of these carbon atoms required to produce 150 β^-–particles per second.

(b) If one atom in 8×10^{11} atoms of natural carbon is radioactive, what mass of carbon is required to produce this count rate?

25.54 In order to find the volume of water in a central heating system a small quantity of a solution containing the radioactive isotope sodium–24 (half-life 15 hours) is mixed with the water in the system. The solution has an activity of $1.6 \times 10^4\,s^{-1}$.

When 30 hours have elapsed, it is assumed that the sodium–24 has mixed thoroughly with the water throughout the system, and a 100 ml sample of the water is drawn off and tested for radioactivity. It is estimated that the activity of the sample is $2.0\,s^{-1}$.

What is the total volume of water in the central heating system?

25.55 In a piece of living timber the fraction

1.25×10^{-12} of the total carbon content is in the form of the radioactive isotope carbon–14 (half-life 5730 years). A sample of carbon dioxide containing 2.00 g of carbon from living timber is introduced into a GM tube. Calculate

(a) the number of atoms of carbon–14 in the sample

(b) the decay constant of carbon–14

(c) the average number of disintegrations to be expected in 10 minutes, if the background count obtained with a non-radioactive gas in the GM tube is 10 per minute.

(d) If the count rate obtained with an identical sample prepared from an ancient piece of timber is 307 in 10 minutes, calculate the age of the ancient piece of timber.

25.56 A sample of a gaseous compound of uranium–235 is injected into the space inside a GM tube, and a count rate of 2000 per minute is obtained. In the absence of the uranium compound the background count rate was 100 per minute. If the sample of the gaseous compound contained 0.40 mg of uranium–235, calculate

(a) the amount (in mol) of uranium–235 atoms in the sample

(b) the number of uranium–235 atoms in the sample

(c) the activity of the sample

(d) the decay constant of uranium–235

(e) the half-life (in years) of uranium–235.

After the above measurements have been made it is found that the count rate increases over a period of hours, and when the measurements are repeated several days later the additional count rate caused by the uranium–235 has almost doubled. How do you account for this?

25.7 Nuclear energy

25.57 In a beam of slow neutrons uranium–238 ($^{238}_{92}U$) tends to absorb one neutron per nucleus, thereby turning into another isotope. This isotope decays by β^-–emission into neptunium (Np). The neptunium also decays by β^-–emission into plutonium (Pu). The plutonium is an α–emitting isotope.

(a) Write down the symbols (complete with superscripts and subscripts) for each of the isotopes involved, including the isotope into which the plutonium decays.

(b) Calculate the relative atomic mass of this isotope if the total kinetic energy of the particles emitted in the above processes is 11.05 MeV.
The atomic mass of uranium–238 is 238.050 u.
(See also the data on page 149.)

25.58 $^{15}_{6}C$, $^{15}_{7}N$ and $^{15}_{8}O$ are three nuclides with the same mass number; they are called isobars. Their atomic masses are 15.0073 u, 14.9963 u and 14.9987 u respectively.

(a) Calculate the mass defect (in u) and the binding energy (in MeV) for each nuclide. Take $m_p =$ 1.0073 u and $m_n =$ 1.0087 u.

(b) Suggest which is the most stable nuclide. By what process might the other two nuclides decay?

25.59 Calculate the mass defect per nucleon of the nuclides ^{56}Fe and ^{238}U. Express your answers in MeV. The atomic masses of the two nuclides are 55.9349 u and 238.0508 u. Take other data from the previous question.

25.60 You will require the following data together with some of that on page 149 for this question.

^{235}U atomic mass = 235.0439 u
^{236}U atomic mass = 236.0456 u
^{238}U atomic mass = 238.0508 u
^{239}U atomic mass = 239.0543 u

(a) Find the energy difference (i) between ^{235}U + n and ^{236}U and (ii) between ^{238}U + n and ^{239}U.

(b) By comparing your results for (i) and (ii) above, explain why ^{235}U will undergo violent fission (create a bomb) more readily than ^{238}U.

(c) In the controlled fission of a reactor very slow neutrons are required. Explain how this is achieved.

25.61 The fission of one atom of uranium–235 releases 200 MeV of energy. A nuclear power station that uses uranium–235 has an output of 1.0 MW and is 40%

efficient. Calculate

(a) the number of atoms of uranium–235 that it uses per hour

(b) the quantity of uranium–235 atoms (in mol) that it uses per hour

(c) the mass of uranium–235 that it uses per hour.

25.62 One possible neutron-induced fission reaction for uranium–235 is

$$^{235}_{92}U + ^{1}_{0}n \; ^{134}_{52}Te + ^{97}_{40}Zr + 4^{1}_{0}n$$

The masses of the nuclides involved are

uranium–235: 235.0439 u

tellurium–134: 134.0913 u

zirconium–97: 97.0980 u

Use these data and those on page 149 to calculate

(a) the energy released in one such fission reaction

(b) the energy available from the complete fission by this process of 1.00 g of uranium–235.

25.63 Plutonium–238 decays by emitting α–particles of energy 5.5 MeV with a half-life of 88 years. It is to be used as a power source in a heart pacemaker.

(a) Discuss why plutonium–28 is a suitable isotope for this application.

(b) If the required power is 50 nW calculate (i) the minimum number of plutonium–238 atoms in the source (ii) the mass of this source.

25.64 The rest mass of an electron is 9.11×10^{-31} kg.

(a) Calculate the minimum energy of a γ–photon which could produce an electron–positron pair.

(b) What will be the speed of recoil of the particles if a γ–photon with 1% more than this minimum energy causes pair production? State any assumptions which you make.

25.65 The fusion of two dueterium nuclei produces a nuclide of helium plus a neutron and liberates 3.27 MeV of energy.

(a) Write a nuclear equation for this fusion process.

(b) Calculate the atomic mass of the helium nucleus given that a deuterium nucleus has a mass of 2.0136 u and $m_n = 1.0087$ u.

(c) How many such fusions per second would be needed to produce a power output of 200 MW? What mass of deuterium is being 'used up' in this case?

25.66 In the interior of the Sun, thermonuclear reactions take place whose net result is the conversion of hydrogen atoms into helium atoms with the release of energy.

(a) Calculate the energy released when four hydrogen atoms are converted into one helium atom, given that the atomic masses of hydrogen and helium are 1.0078 u and 4.0026 u respectively.

(b) If it was possible to harness this reaction to provide the energy for a power station on Earth at an overall efficiency of 10%, estimate (i) the number of hydrogen atoms (ii) the mass of hydrogen required per day to operate a 1000 MW power station.

26 Photons and electrons

Data speed of light $c = 3.00 \times 10^8 \, m\,s^{-1}$
Planck constant $h = 6.63 \times 10^{-34} \, J\,s$
electronic charge $e = 1.60 \times 10^{-19} \, C$
mass of electron $m_e = 9.11 \times 10^{-31} \, kg$

26.1 Photons

26.1 The solar constant (the mean intensity of solar radiation arriving at the Earth) is $1.4 \, kW\,m^{-2}$. If the mean distance of the Earth from the Sun is $1.5 \times 10^{11} \, m$ what is

(a) the power of the Sun
(b) the rate of loss of mass of the Sun?

26.2 Calculate the energies of

(a) a photon of infra-red radiation of wavelength 1500 nm
(b) a photon of green light of wavelength 546 nm
(c) a photon of ultraviolet radiation of wavelength 365 nm
(d) a photon of X–radiation of wavelength 154 pm.

26.3 A laboratory helium–neon laser emits light of wavelength 632.8 nm in a beam of diameter 2.0 mm.

(a) What is the energy of one photon of this light?
(b) If its power is 0.70 mW, how many photons are passing any point in the beam each second?

26.4 A 60 W filament lamp hangs from the ceiling in a room. Assume that 5% of the electrical energy is converted into visible radiation. Stating any further assumptions you make, calculate an approximate value for

(a) the intensity of the visible radiation on a table which is 1.5m below the lamp
(b) the number of photons striking an A4 sheet of paper which is placed on the table, if the average wavelength of the visible radiation is 550 nm.

26.5 The wavelengths of the two D lines in the spectrum of a sodium lamp are both close to 590 nm.

(a) What is the energy of one photon of sodium light?
(b) A 500 W sodium vapour lamp has an efficiency of 30% (i.e. 30% of the supplied energy is emitted as the D light). How many photons does it emit per second?
(c) Someone stands 50 m from the lamp. If his eye pupil in these conditions has a diameter of 3.5 mm, how many photons enter one eye each second?
(d) What is the average distance between photons along the line from the lamp to the eye?

26.6 A spacecraft in orbit round the Earth has solar panels to supply it with electrical energy. The solar constant is $1.4 \, kW\,m^{-2}$, and the mean wavelength of the radiation from the Sun is 550 nm.

(a) What is the momentum of a photon of wavelength 550 nm?
(b) How many photons arrive each second on each square metre of the solar panels, assuming that the radiation strikes them normally?
(c) Find the pressure exerted by the radiation on the solar panels, assuming that it is totally absorbed.

26.7 Orthochromatic photograph film was in use in the 1940s and 1950s. Its advantage was that it was not sensitive to red light, so could be developed in a darkroom fitted with a red safelight (and the processor could see what he was doing). Why would you have expected it to be less likely that there should be a type of film which was not sensitive to blue light?

26.8 A photon collides with an electron which is loosely bound to an atom and, as a result, changes direction. The collision is elastic because there are no other forms of energy into which the kinetic energy may be changed. Before the collision the electron may be considered to be stationary. Because the photon behaves like a particle we can say that momentum and kinetic energy are conserved.

(a) Why must the electron have some kinetic energy after the collision?

(b) What can you say about the energy of the scattered photon, compared with the energy of the incident photon?

(c) How does the wavelength of the scattered photon compare with the wavelength of the incident photon? (This change of wavelength is called the Compton effect and is striking evidence that photons may be treated as particles.)

26.2 The photoelectric effect

26.9 How do the following observations of the photoelectric effect support the idea that light is quantised?

(a) There is no noticeable delay between the arrival of photons and the emission of electrons.

(b) For a particular metal surface, only light of a certain minimum frequency will cause emission of electrons.

26.10 How does the quantum theory explain that

(a) electrons are emitted by a particular metal only when radiation of less than a certain wavelength falls on it

(b) the rate of emission of electrons is proportional to the intensity of the radiation

(c) the maximum speed of the emitted electrons is independent of the intensity of the radiation?

26.11 The minimum frequency of light which will cause photoelectric emission from a lithium surface is 5.5×10^{14} Hz.

(a) Calculate the work function of lithium.

If the surface is lit by light of frequency 6.5×10^{14} Hz. Calculate

(b) the maximum energy of the electrons emitted

(c) the maximum speed of these electrons.

26.12 The work function of a freshly cleaned copper surface is 4.16 eV. Calculate

(a) the minimum frequency of the radiation which will cause emission of electrons, and state whether this radiation is visible

(b) the maximum energy of the electrons emitted when the surface is lit by radiation of frequency 1.20×10^{15} Hz.

26.13 The equation $hf = \phi + eV_s$ relates the energy hf of a photon, the work function ϕ of the metal on which the photon is falling, and V_s the p.d. required to completely stop emission of photons. If corresponding values of f and V_s are measured

(a) what shape would be expected if these values are plotted on a graph, with V_s on the y–axis and f on the x–axis

(b) what would be the significance of the slope and intercepts?

26.14 An experiment was performed using a photoelectric cell which contained a potassium surface as the cathode. Light of some particular wavelengths was shone on the surface and it was found that for each wavelength a different potential difference was needed to reduce the current in the cell to zero:

wavelength λ/nm	579	546	436	405
stopping p.d./V	0.14	0.27	0.84	1.06

Plot a graph of stopping p.d. V_s (on the y–axis) against frequency f (on the x–axis) and use your graph (and the value of the electronic charge given in the data) to deduce the value of

(a) the Planck constant

(b) the work function of potassium

(c) the minimum frequency needed to liberate electrons from potassium.

26.15 Monochromatic radiation of wavelength 546 nm falls on a potassium surface of area 7.5 cm^2 in an evacuated enclosure. The intensity at the surface is 60 mW m^{-2}, and it may be assumed that 1% of the photons emit electrons from the surface. What is the photoelectric current?

26.16 The work function of a freshly cleaned zinc

surface is 3.6 eV. If it is illuminated with ultraviolet radiation of wavelength 253 nm

(a) what will be the maximum k.e. (in eV) of the emitted electrons?

(b) what p.d. would be needed to stop the electrons being emitted?

If the radiation is shone on the freshly cleaned zinc cap of an uncharged leaf electroscope, explain

(c) why the emission of electrons will soon stop

(d) whether you would expect there to be any deflection of the leaf.

26.17 The graph shows how the photoelectric current in a photocell varies with p.d. for monochromatic light of a particular intensity. Explain

(a) why the photoelectric current is constant for positive p.d.s. which are greater than a certain value.

(b) why there is no photoelectric current for negative p.d.s. below a certain value.

(c) why there is some photoelectric current even when the p.d. is zero.

Copy the graph and on the same axes sketch additional graphs which show the current which would be obtained if

(d) twice as many photons (of light of the same frequency) arrived each second

(e) the same number of photons, of light of a higher frequency, arrived per second.

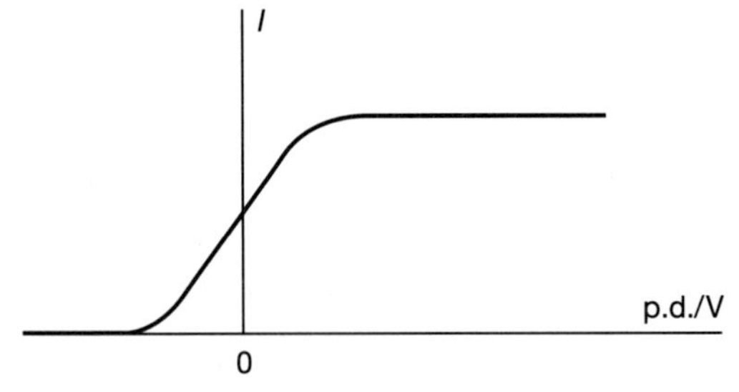

26.18 What kind of experiment could you do to convince someone that the charge carriers in the photoelectric effect were electrons?

26.3 Energy levels

26.19 ***(a)*** Explain what is meant by saying that a collision between an electron and a gas atom is elastic.

(b) In a succession of such collisions what effect is there on the energy and speed of the electron?

(c) What happens to the energy of the electron when the collision between it and a gas atom is not elastic?

26.20 The ionisation energy of hydrogen is 13.6 eV.

(a) What is the speed of the slowest electron that can ionise a hydrogen atom when it collides with it?

(b) What is the longest wavelength of electromagnetic radiation that could produce ionisation in hydrogen?

26.21 The two lowest excited states of a hydrogen atom are 10.2 eV and 12.1 eV above the ground state.

(a) Calculate three wavelengths of radiation that could be produced by transitions between these states and the ground state.

(b) In which parts of the spectrum would you expect to find these wavelengths?

26.22 The energy levels of hydrogen are given by $-13.6\,\text{eV}/n^2$, where n is 1, 2, 3 etc. Calculate the energy levels for values of n from n = 1 to n = 5, and draw an energy level diagram to illustrate these values.

26.23 ***(a)*** The first energy level for mercury is 4.9 eV above the ground state. When the atom returns from this level to the ground state, what is the wavelength of the radiation emitted, and in what part of the spectrum is this radiation?

(b) How do you account for the following?

(i) Cool mercury vapour strongly absorbs the ultraviolet from a mercury vapour lamp.

(ii) Cool mercury vapour is completely transparent (i.e. non-absorbing) to the visible light from a mercury vapour lamp, provided the ultraviolet light is excluded by a glass filter.

(iii) Cool mercury vapour partly absorbs the visible light from a mercury vapour lamp if the ultraviolet radiation from the lamp is also present.

26.24 In an experiment to investigate the energy levels in helium atoms electrons were accelerated through a p.d. of 50.0 V and then allowed to strike helium atoms. The energies of the electrons after the collisons were measured.

(a) What is one energy which you might expect some of the electrons to have after the collisions?

(b) Other energies which the electrons had after the collisions included 28.9 eV, 26.8 eV and 26.0 eV. What are the wavelengths of the radiation which might have been observed in this experiment?

26.25 The table gives the frequencies of some of the lines which occour in three groups in the hydrogen spectrum (traditionally the series have the names given at the top of each column):

Lyman $f/10^{14}$ Hz	Balmer $f/10^{14}$ Hz	Paschen $f/10^{14}$ Hz
24.659	4.5665	1.5983
29.226	6.1649	2.3380
30.824	6.9044	2.7399
31.564	7.3084	2.9822

(a) Which series is in the visible part of the spectrum?

(b) Which series is in the infra-red part of the spectrum?

(c) Can you see any numerical relationship between the frequencies in adjacent columns? If so, why is that relationship to be expected?

(d) Predict the next two highest frequencies in the Lyman series.

(e) How many different energy levels are responsible for the frequencies shown in the table?

(f) What is the longest wavelength in the Lyman series?

26.26 The figure shows an energy level diagram. Sketch a possible line spectrum for the light emitted when electrons make the transitions shown. Label the lines, using the letters shown in the diagram, and indicate on your spectrum diagram which end corresponds to the higher frequency.

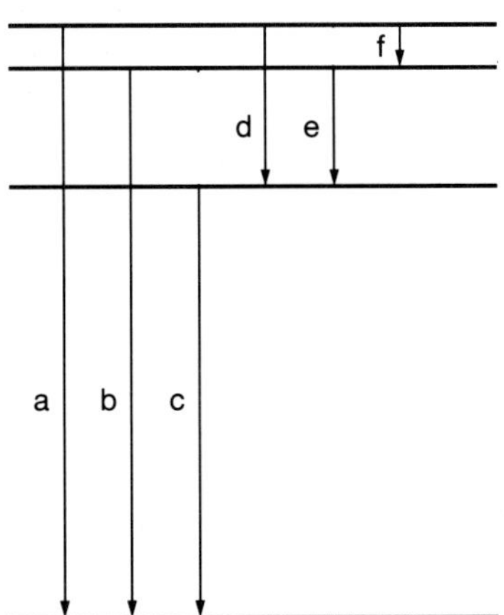

26.27 The four lowest energy levels for an atom consists of the ground state and three levels above that. How many transitions are possible between these four levels?

26.28 The figure shows three energy levels for a particular atom. When an electron moves from level 1 to the ground state the light emitted is blue. In what part of the spectrum would you expect to find the radiation emitted when an electron moves from level 2 to the ground state?

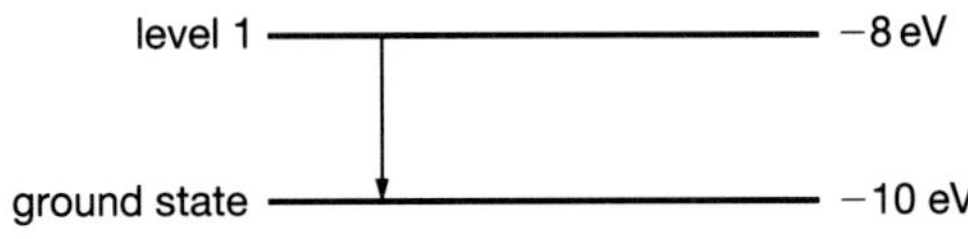

26.29 Suppose an atom has two energy levels E_1 and E_2 above the ground state. To these energies correspond radiation frequencies of f_1 and f_2 respectively.

(a) Sketch the energy level diagram of this atom.

(b) What other frequency will be emitted by this atom?

26.4 X–rays

26.30 *(a)* Describe, with the help of a diagram, an apparatus for producing X–rays.

(b) What is meant by (i) the penetrating power of X–rays (ii) their intensity?

(c) What effect would there be on the penetrating power and intensity of increasing (i) the p.d. across the X–ray tube (ii) the current used to heat the filament?

26.31 The variation with frequency of the intensity of X–rays produced by a typical X–ray tube is shown in the figure.

(a) With reference to the figure explain why the tube is sometimes said to have a *spectrum* which may be thought of as a *line spectrum* superimposed on a *continuous spectrum* .

(b) Which of these two parts depends only on the accelerating p.d. in the tube, and which depends only on the material of the anode?

(c) Copy the figure and add another graph to show the variation of intensity for the same tube when it is operated at twice the p.d.

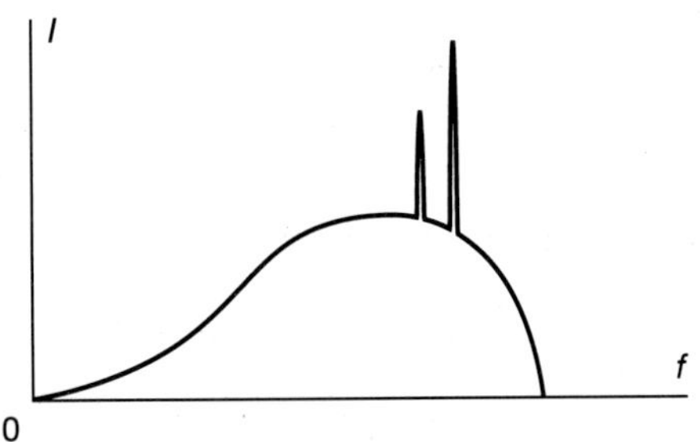

26.32 Explain what happens to the electrons when they strike the anode in an X–ray tube if they produce

(a) X–rays of a range of frequencies

(b) X–rays of just a few precise frequencies.

26.33 The anode in an X–ray tube often consists of a tungsten core surrounded by solid copper.

(a) Why are these two materials used?

In a certain X–ray tube the accelerating p.d. is 50 kV and the anode current is 3.0 mA.

(b) How many electrons strike the anode each second?

(c) What is the rate of delivery of kinetic energy to the anode?

26.34 *(a)* What is the kinetic energy (in J) of an electron accelerated through a p.d. of 100 kV?

(b) If a photon is emitted from the tube with the whole of this energy what is its frequency and wavelength?

26.35 *(a)* At what points in a typical house containing the usual electrical equipment would you expect to find electromagnetic radiation of the following wavelengths:
(i) 5×10^{-7} m, (ii) 3×10^{-10} m, (iii) 2×10^{-6} m, (iv) 0.12 m, (v) 1.5×10^{3} m?

(b) What are the energies of photons of these wavelengths?

26.36 If a TV tube has an accelerating p.d. of 20 kV, what is the

(a) maximum frequency of the X–rays produced

(b) range of wavelengths of the X–rays?

26.5 Waves and particles

26.37 *(a)* What are the energies (in eV) of the following types of photon: (i) a radio wave of wavelength 1500 m, (ii) infra-red radiation of wavelength 5.0×10^{-5} m, (iii) a gamma ray of wavelength 2.0×10^{-12} m

(b) Does any of this radiation behave *entirely* like a wave or *entirely* like a particle?

(c) Which type would you think of as being most like a wave, and which most like a particle?

26.38 *(a)* Show that for low speeds (compared with the speed of light) the kinetic energy E of an electron of mass m and its momentum p are related by the equation $E = p^2/2m$.

(b) What are the kinetic energy, momentum and wavelength of an electron accelerated through a p.d. of 10 V ?

(c) What are these quantities when it is accelerated through a p.d. of 100 V ?

26.39 Calculate the momentum and wavelength of the following particles, when each has an energy of 10 keV:

(a) an electron

(b) a proton (mass of proton = 1.7×10^{-27} kg)

(c) an alpha particle (mass of neutron = mass of proton).

26.40 An experimenter wishes to investigate the diffraction of electrons by thin foils. He wants to use wavelengths of 1.5×10^{-10} m.

(a) What momentum should the electrons have?

(b) What kinetic energy do these electrons have?

(c) What p.d. should be used to accelerate the electrons?

26.41 In an electron diffraction tube the electron beam passes through a very thin crystalline foil. The beams diffracted by the crystals form circles on the end face of the tube. The diameter *d* of one prominent particular circle is measured for a range of values of the accelerating p.d. *V*, and the following values are obtained:

V/kv	1.5	2.0	3.0	4.5	6.0
d/mm	68	58	48	40	35

The theory of this experiment leads us to expect that *d* should be proportional to $1/\sqrt{V}$.

(a) Plot a graph of *d* against $1/\sqrt{V}$, and comment on the result.

(b) What p.d. would be required to give a diffraction circle of diameter 25 mm?

26.42 When light srikes a circular target of radius *r* it is diffracted and there is a minimum intensity at an angle θ given by $\sin\theta = 0.61/r$.
Similarly electrons approaching a nucleus are found to be diffracted. In one experiment electrons with an energy of 420 MeV were used.

(a) Show that if you could use the equation $eV = \frac{1}{2}mv^2$ to calculate the speed of electrons with an energy of 420 MeV you would find that their speed was apparently $1.2 \times 10^{10}\,\mathrm{m\,s^{-1}}$. Why is this an impossibility?

(b) At speeds approaching the speed of light the Newtonian laws of mechanics cannot be used: at the speeds of these electrons the relationship between energy *E* and momentum *p* is (approximately) $E = pc$, where *c*, is the speed of light. Use this relationship to calculate the momentum of electrons which have an energy of 420 MeV.

(c) What is the wavelength of these electrons?

(d) It was found that the first minimum of intensity when the electrons were scattered from carbon nuclei occurred at an angle of 50°. What does this information tell us about the radius of the carbon nucleus?

(e) Electrons accelerated through 183 MV were used for larger nuclei. What was their wavelength, and what is a possible reason for using this different wavelength for larger nuclei?

26.43 How could you distinguish, experimentally, between a photon and an electron, if each has a momentum of 5×10^{-23} N s?

27 Electronics

27.1 Analogue and digital systems

27.1 Make a list of physical quantities which vary continuously. Add to the list the names of the transducers (if any) which convert the physical quantity into a voltage. Suggest, where possible, the order of magnitude of the voltage produced for a given change in the physical quantity. Your list might start with:

magnetic field, Hall probe, mV for 100 mT change

27.2 Draw block diagrams to represent

(a) a microphone – loudspeaker system such as might be in use at an athletics meeting

(b) a domestic refrigerator cooling system which pumps a liquid round a closed circuit to reduce the temperature inside the fridge.

27.3 A thermistor has a resistance R which, for a limited range of temperatures between 0°C and −10°C can be expressed as $R = R_0 (1 + a\theta)$
where R_0, its resistance at $\theta = 0°C$, is 15 kΩ and $a = -0.10 K^{-1}$.
It is connected in series with a fixed resistor of resistance 20 kΩ to form a potential divider between supply rails at 0 V and +5.0 V. One side of the thermistor is at 0 V.

(a) Calculate the voltage V_x at the point X, between the thermistor and the resistor, when
(i) $\theta = 0°C$
(ii) $\theta = -5°C$
(iii) $\theta = -10°C$.

(b) Estimate the rate of change of V_x with temperature at $\theta = -5°C$.

27.4 ***(a)*** What are the following binary numbers in decimal notation:
1001, 110111, 10110, 111, 100011?

(b) What are the following decimal numbers in binary notation:
12, 283, 74, 16, 164?

27.2 Inverting amplifiers

27.5 An op-amp has an open-loop gain of 200000. The voltage of its non-inverting input is held at 0 V and small voltages between +15 μV and −15 μV are fed to its inverting input V_-.
Draw a graph to show how the output voltage V_{out} varies with V_-. Why would it be difficult to study this experimentally?

27.6 Suppose in the figure the potentials at X, Y and Z are called V_x, V_y and V_z and that, under all circumstances $V_z = 0V$.
What is V_y when $V_x = +5.0V$ and the value of R is
(a) 22 kΩ ***(b)*** 220 kΩ ***(c)*** 10 kΩ?

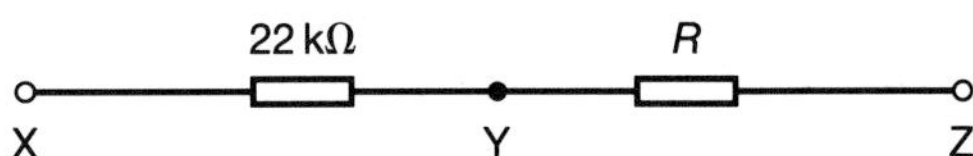

27.7 Suppose that in the previous question V_y is kept at 0 V under all circumstances but there is no current to or from earth at Y.
Calculate the size of V_z is −2.0 V and the value of R is
(a) 22 kΩ ***(b)*** 2.2 kΩ ***(c)*** 10 kΩ.

27.8 Suppose that in question 27.6, V_x is kept at 0 V.
What is V_x when $V_y = +1.0V$ and the value of R is
(a) 22 kΩ ***(b)*** 220 kΩ ***(c)*** 10 kΩ?

27.9 The diagram on the next page represents the traces on a double beam oscilloscope with Y_1 and Y_2 connected to the input and output, respectively, of an amplifier.
Y_1 is set to 30 mV div^{-1} and Y_2 to 1 mV div^{-1} and the time base is set to 50 μs div^{-1}.
Calculate

(a) the frequency of the signal

(b) the voltage gain of the amplifier

(c) the r.m.s. value of the output voltage.

What else can you deduce about the amplifier?

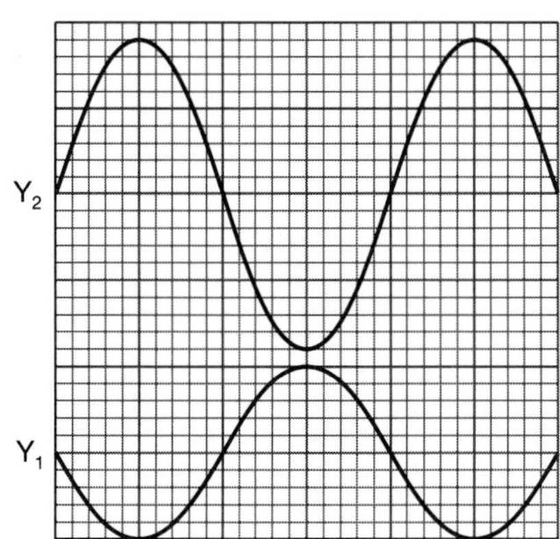

27.10 Explain why, for an inverting amplifier using an op-amp with V_+ connected to 0 V, the connection to the inverting input is called a virtual earth.

(a) Copy the circuit shown in the figure. Calculate, explaining any assumptions you make, the currents in each of the input resistors when $V_A = 0.30$ V and $V_B = 0.20$ V. Hence calculate V_{out}.

(b) This circuit performs the sum $V_A + 10V_B$. Draw two separate circuits, giving component values,
(i) which performs the sum $2V_A + 5V_B$, and
(ii) which performs the sum $V_A - 10V_B$.

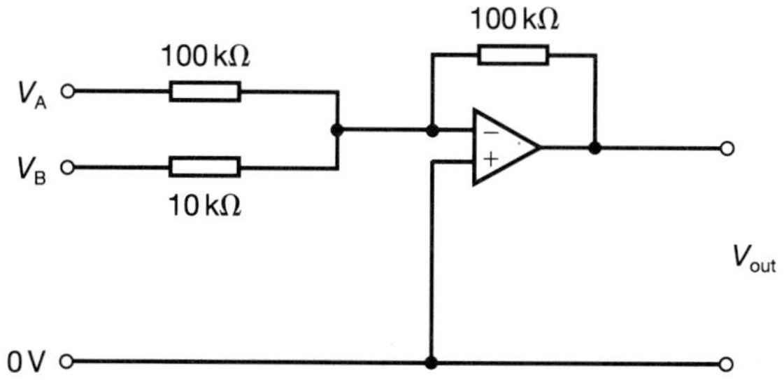

27.11 The following circuit shows an op-amp which can have one of three inputs via a switch S. They are:
$V_P = 1.2$ V d.c.
$V_Q = 0.5$ V r.m.s.
$V_R = 12.0$ V r.m.s.
If the supply voltage to the op-amp is ±5 V draw sketch graphs to show how the output voltage V_{out} varies with time *t* for each input.

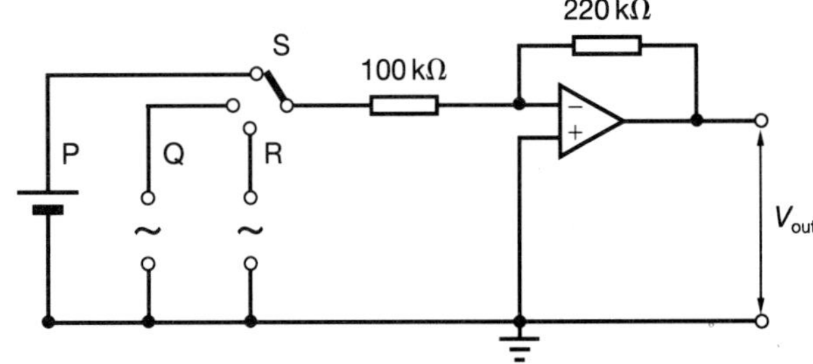

27.12 For the circuit shown below the input voltage is held at −0.20 V. What is

(a) the current in the 220 kΩ resistor

(b) the rate of flow of charge onto the capacitor

(c) the rate of rise of voltage across the capacitor?

What two assumptions did you need to make?

(d) Draw to scale a diagram showing the trace on the oscilloscope screen for the first 30 s after the switch S is closed if the time-base is set to 10 s div^{-1} and the Y–gain to 10 mV div^{-1}.

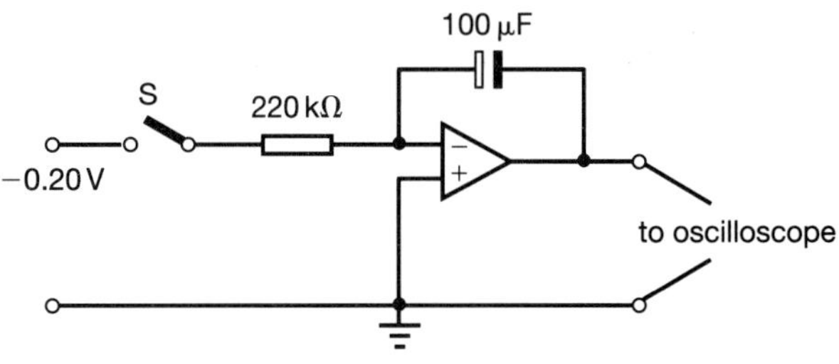

27.13 The LDR in the circuit shown overleaf has a resistance *R* which varies inversely with the intensity of illumination *I*, i.e. $R = k/I$. In bright sunlight $I = 600$ W m^{-2} and $R = 500\,\Omega$.

(a) What is the resistance when $I = 0.30$ W m^{-2}, i.e. in near darkness.

(b) Calculate V_{out} for these extremes of illumination and suggest an application for this circuit.

(c) Repeat *(b)* for a similar circuit but one in which the LDR is in parallel with a fixed resistor of resistance 1000 Ω.

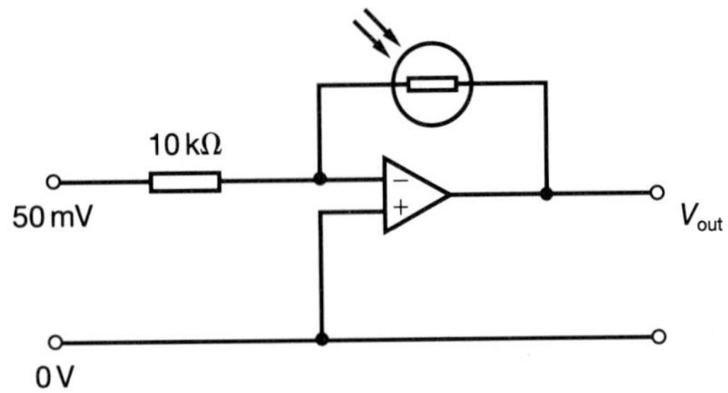

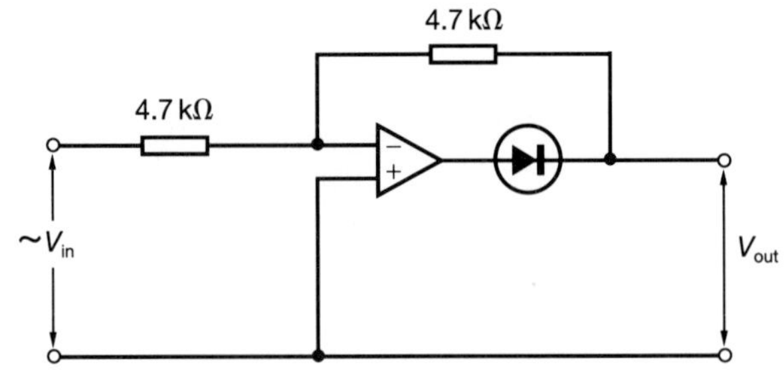

27.14 ***(a)*** Describe how you would investigate the gain of an inverting amplifier, for which the gain is about −5, for a range of +ve and −ve input voltages up to and including the supply rail voltages of the op-amp. Sketch the result you would expect by drawing an appropriate graph.

(b) Explain how closely you expect the experimental value you measure for the gain will agree with the theoretical value $-R_f/R_{in}$.

27.15 Explain how, using *only* inverting amplifiers, you would design an amplifying system with a gain of +20. Draw a full circuit diagram including component values where relevant.

27.16 For the circuit below, V_{in} is a sinusoidal signal of amplitude 12 mV. Calculate

(a) the voltage gain and

(b) the power gain of the circuit.

[Hint: take the power gain to be the mean power dissipated in the 1.0 kΩ load resistor divided by the mean power drawn at the input.]

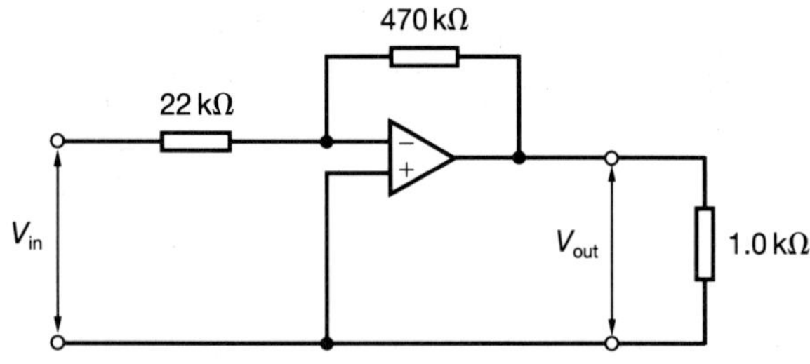

27.17 The following circuit shows a non-linear amplifier which behaves as a perfect half-wave rectifier for a sinusoidal input voltage (of less than 5 V peak).

By considering each half of the cycle separately explain how the circuit works.

27.18 Each resistor in the circuit shown has a resistance *R*.

(a) Copy the circuit and show that $V_{out} = V_B - V_A$. [Hint: start by writing down the potential at the non-inverting input.]

(b) Suggest a practical application for a circuit which subtracts two analogue input voltages which vary with time.

(c) Add components to your circuit so as to provide a warning lamp which comes on if $V_B - V_A$ rises above a preset value.

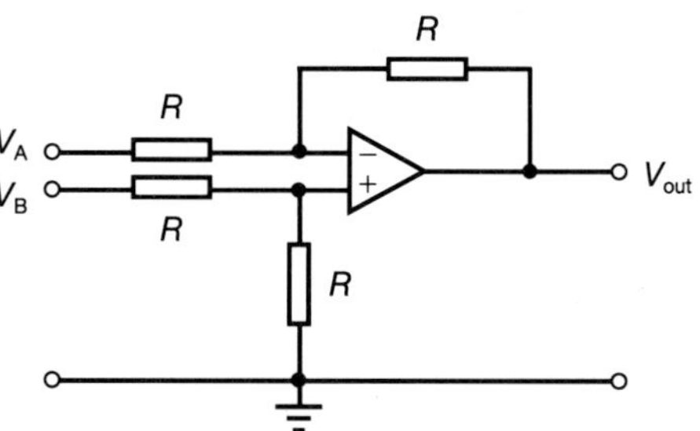

27.3 Non-inverting amplifiers

27.19 ***(a)*** Calculate, from first principles, V_{out} and thus find the gain of the circuit shown on the next page. Does the gain depend on the open loop gain of the op-amp chosen for the circuit? Explain.

(b) Draw a circuit for a non-inverting amplifier with the same numerical gain as the circuit shown. Give values for any components you use.

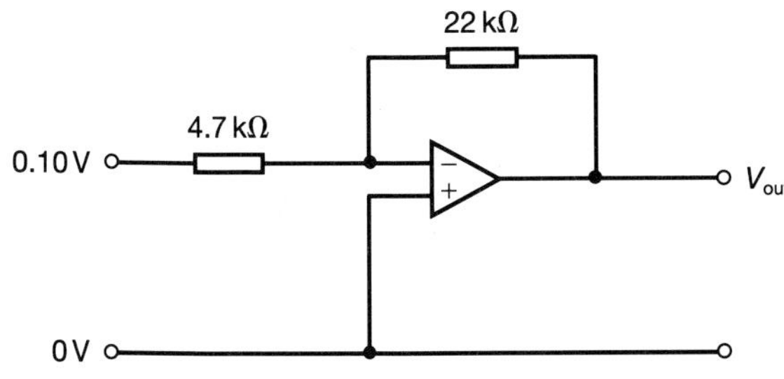

27.20 Calculate the output voltage in each of the circuits shown (a) (b) and (c).
(This question is really an exercise in topology, i.e. circuit layout.)

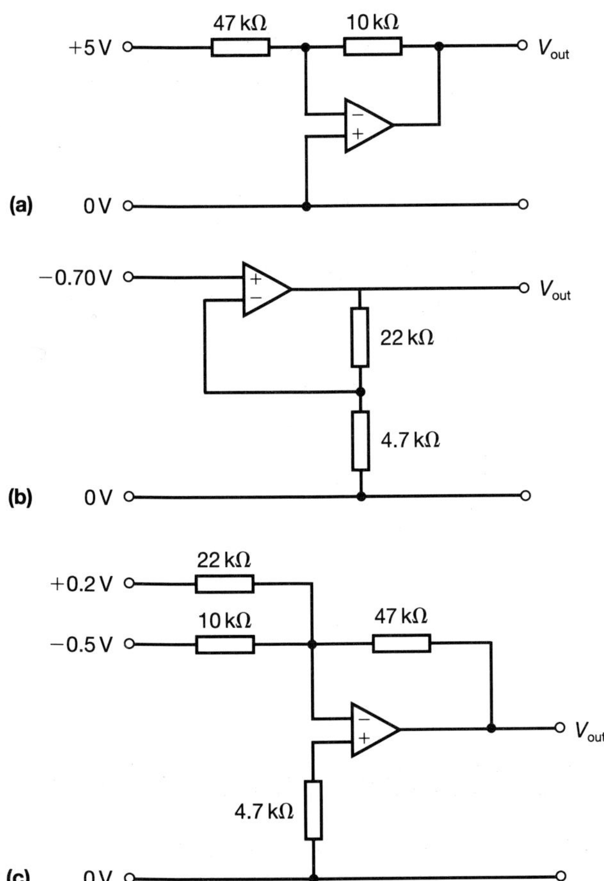

27.21 A non-inverting amplifier has a feedback resistor $R_f = 47\,k\Omega$ and a resistor to earth $R_g = 10\,k\Omega$. The output voltage is a steady 1.5 V.

Calculate from first principles the voltage, V_{in}, at the non-inverting input. State carefully, at the appropriate places in your calculations, any assumptions that you make.

27.22 A non-inverting amplifier using an op-amp with negative feedback has a voltage gain of +5.0 and saturates at ±4.5 V.

(a) Draw a sketch graph of its transfer characteristic.

(b) Describe how you would derive the transfer characteristic for d.c input voltages of up to ±5.0 V in the laboratory.
Be careful to explain the polarity of any meters you connect.

27.23 For an amplifier with negative feedback, the voltage gain is equal to $A/(1 + \beta A)$ where A is the open loop gain of the amplifier and β is the fraction of the output signal which is fed back.

Use this expression to explain why, for large values of βA, the amplification achieved becomes independent of the characteristics of the op-amp used.

27.24 If, in the previous question, the feedback is positive, β is a negative number. Discuss the result of the product βA approaching 1.

27.25 Explain the purpose of the voltage follower in the circuit shown. You may take the output impedance of the signal source, the potentiometer, to be 1 kΩ and the resistance of the LED to be negligible.

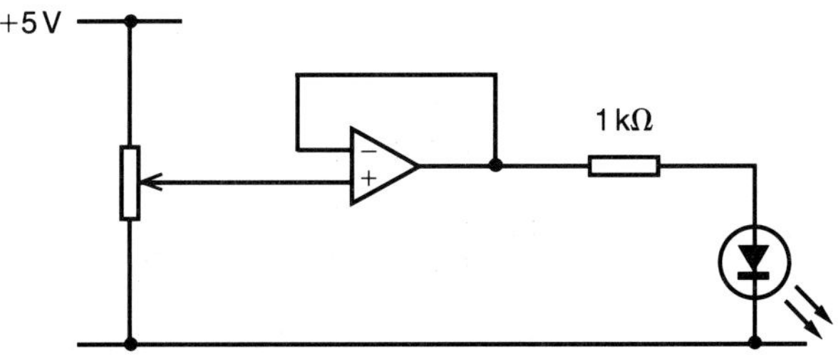

27.26 A coulombmeter has a 4.7 μF capacitor connected across its input terminals. It is required to check the calibration of the meter at 500 nC, 1000 nC and 1500 nC. Draw the circuit diagram which you would use and explain how you would perform the check.

27.27 *(a)* The circuit diagram shows a coulombmeter which measures the charge transferred to the input terminal P. Show, from first principles, that the charge Q will result in a voltage Q/C registered on the voltmeter, stating any assumptions you make at the appropriate point in the proof.

(b) a capacitor of capacitance 1.0 μF is charged to 30 V.

(i) What is the charge on the 1.0 μF capacitor? The charged capacitor is then connected to P and E. Calculate, for a coulombmeter in which C = 4.7 μF,

(ii) the common p.d. across the two capacitors

(iii) the resulting charge registered by the instrument.

(c) Use your results from part *(b)* to discuss the limitations implicit in using a coulombmeter of this kind.

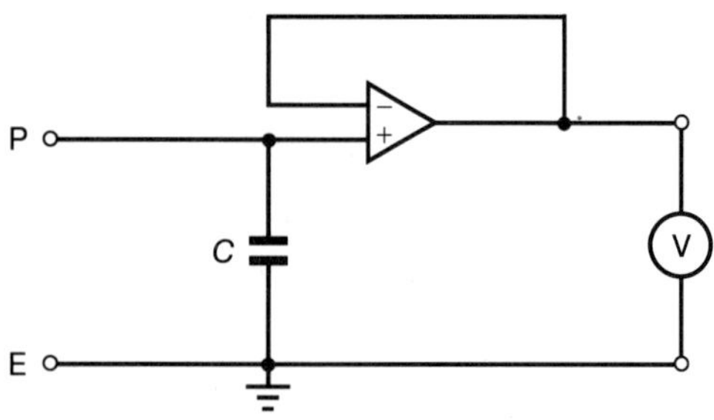

27.28 Measuring the potential difference produced across a capacitor is often used as the basis of a device for measuring charge. The diagram shows two circuits which achieve this.

Explain how the circuit involving the op-amps works and suggest why it may be more useful than the circuit using only a capacitor.

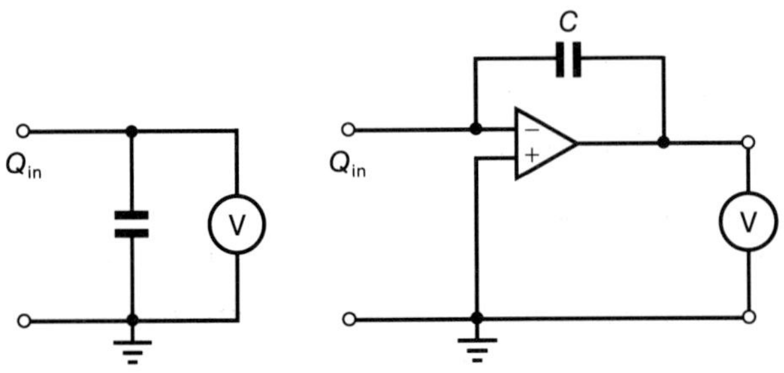

27.29 When using a non-inverting amplifier as an a.c amplifier, increased negative feedback leads to a smaller gain over a wider range of frequencies. Explain this statement by sketching appropriate graphs of gain against frequency.

27.30 You wish to investigate the frequency response of a non-inverting amplifier known to have a voltage gain of 150 at low frequencies. An uncalibrated sinusoidal oscillator gives a constant output voltage of 600 mV r.m.s. over a wide range of frequencies up to 1 MHz.

(a) Explain why the oscillator's voltage is too large for your experiment and draw a circuit to show how you would reduce it to a suitable magnitude. Give the values of components which you use and calculate the r.m.s. voltage you have chosen to use.

(b) Describe how you would use a calibrated oscilloscope to establish the frequency response of the oscillator over its range, i.e. investigate how the voltage gain varies (if at all) with frequency.

27.31 The graph shows the open loop voltage gain of a non-inverting amplifier against frequency *f* (the full line). The dashed line is for a closed loop gain of 10 000 for which the bandwidth of the amplifier is limited to a maximum frequency of about 100 Hz. Estimate the bandwidth for gains of 100 and 300.

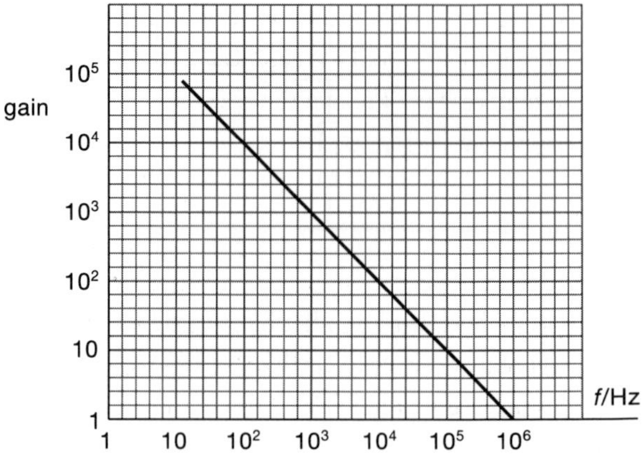

27.32 *(a)* What is the closed loop gain for each of the circuits shown.

(b) Referring to the graph of the previous question, what is the bandwidth for each circuit?

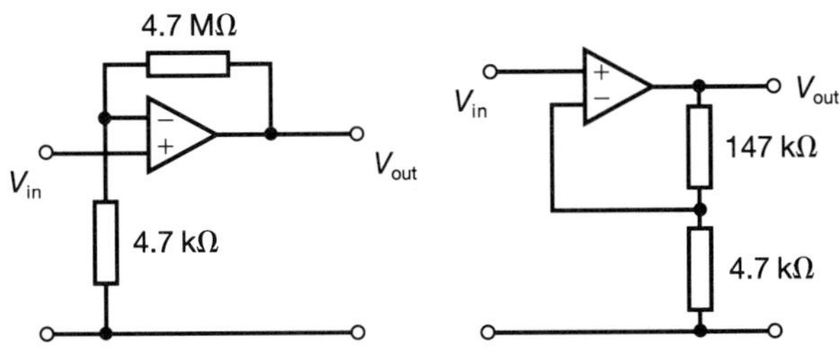

27.33 A voltage gain can be expressed in decibels: gain $= 20 \lg (V_{out}/V_{in})$ dB.
Explain why the constant slope of the graph of question *27.31* shows a reduction in bandwidth of a factor of 10 for reach 20 dB rise in gain.

27.4 Switching devices

27.34 Two potential dividers are connected between the supply rails of an op-amp. One contains three resistors 4.7 kΩ, 10 kΩ and 4.7 kΩ in series, the other a thermistor and a 10 kΩ variable resistor in series.

Using these two potential dividers, draw a circuit using the op-amp as a comparator to detect when the temperature of the thermistor is above or below a chosen value. Arrange for a red LED to come on if the remperature is too low and a green LED to come on when the temperature is above the chosen value. Explain how your circuit works.

27.35 An electrocardiograph (e.c.g.) uses a comparator as a differential amplifier. A signal proportional to the difference between the two chest electrodes, see the diagram, is required but there is a large noise signal present in both electrodes. Explain why the noise is not displayed and why small e.c.g. signals produce regular visible oscilloscope pulses.

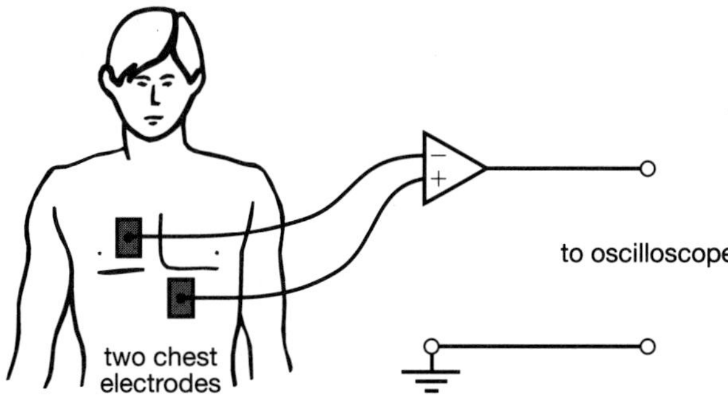

27.36 The potential at the inverting input to the op-amp in the figure is adjusted to be exactly 1.00 V.

(a) Draw a sketch graph of the output voltage as displayed on the oscilloscope if the non-inverting input V is a sinusoidally varying voltage of peak value 2.00 V and frequency 1.00 Hz.

(b) Explain how the output changes as the connection to the input is now moved from the top to the bottom of the 50 kΩ resistor.

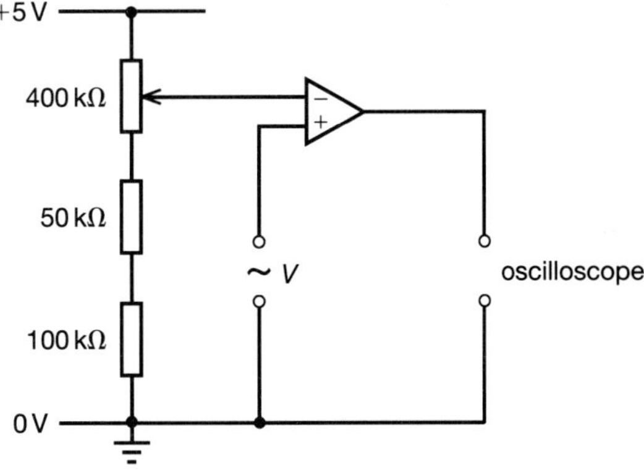

27.37 A strain gauge bridge, see question *8.1*, produces an output voltage of up to 5 μV. Draw a circuit diagram to show how you would arrange for this to register on a moving coil meter which has a resistance 10 kΩ and a full-scale deflection for 1.0 V.

27.38 Explain as fully as possible the working of the circuit overleaf for a range of light levels. Hence deduce its probable use. (Copy the circuit and label points to which you want to refer in your explanation.)

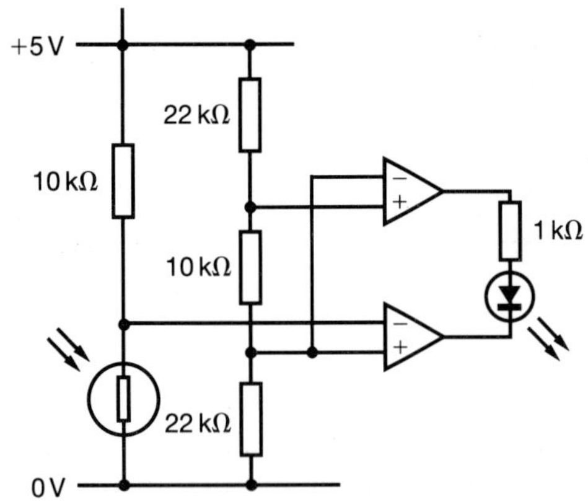

27.39 Two drivers can be used to 'square' a repetitive signal, i.e. to regenerate pulses which have picked up noise or have become degraded in some way.

Explain the principle involved and discuss the properties which an ideal driver should possess.

27.40 The switch at S in the circuit below is initially closed. Describe how the potential at X varies with time when S is opened and hence suggest a use for such a circuit. Be as quantitative as possible.

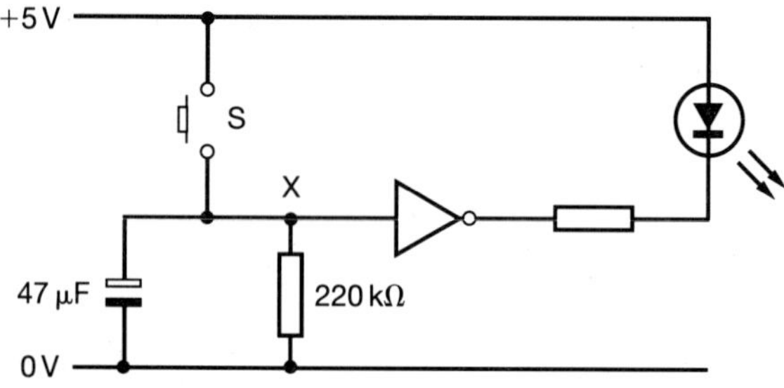

27.41 Draw a circuit diagram using a driver and relay which could be used to switch on a 240 V mains lamp when darkness falls. Explain how your circuit operates.

27.42 The diagram shows two circuits which act as current-to-voltage converters. In each case $V_{out} = RI_{in}$. Explain how this result is achieved for each circuit and suggest why the circuit including the op-amp is sometimes the better one to choose.

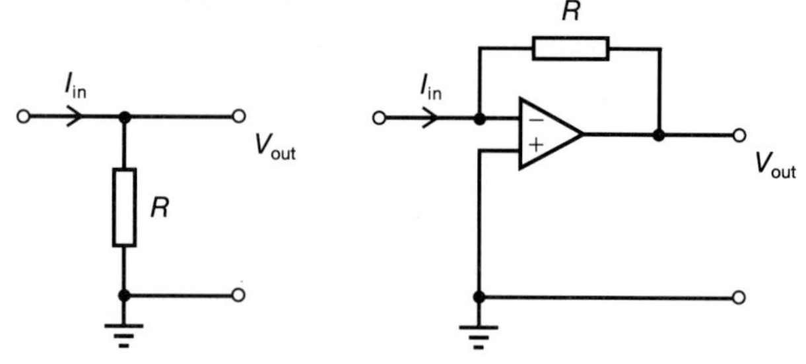

27.43 A source of e.m.f. $\mathscr{E}$ and resistance r is connected to load, an output transducer of some kind, of resistance R as shown in the figure below.

(a) If the current in the circuit is I write down (i) the power delivered to the load (ii) the power wasted in the source.

(b) Calculate the efficiency with which power is transferred to the load and sketch a graph of efficiency against R as R varies from zero to a high value. Mark the point on your sketch where $R = r$. What is the efficiency at this value for R?

(c) Discuss the implications of these results for the design of systems involving input and output transducers linked via, for example, an amplifier.

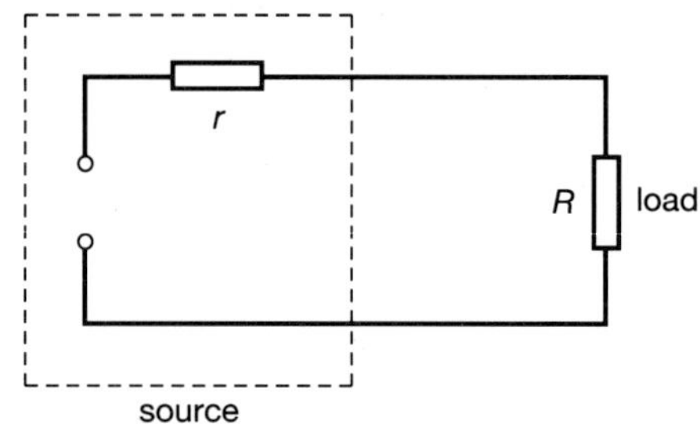

27.44 *(a)* What is the net gain of two amplifiers in series with individual voltage gains of 10 and 80?

(b) Express the individual and net gains in decibels (dB) and thus explain why the use of a decibel scale is useful when describing voltage amplification. (See question *27.33*.)

(c) What is the power gain of the pair of amplifiers?

27.45 One useful property of a capacitor is that it can 'block' d.c. signals but 'pass' a.c. signals. Explain from first principles how a capacitor passes a.c.

27.46 By considering the microphone-speaker system in the diagram, explain what is meant by positive feedback and discuss its effect.

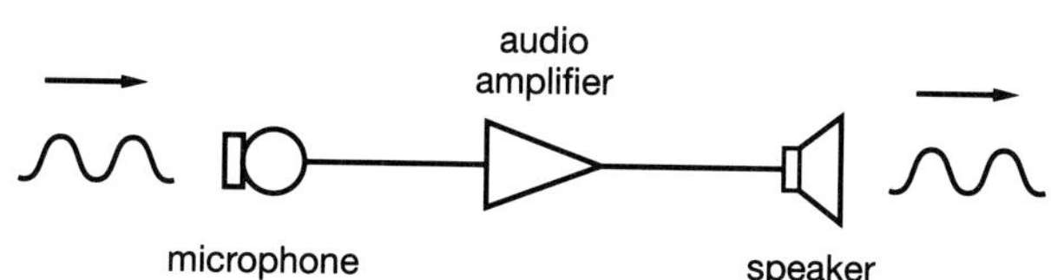

27.47 *(a)* Explain the logic function performed by the circuit shown below.

(b) Draw circuits using the same components which operate as (i) OR (ii) AND (iii) NAND circuits for turning on the lamp.

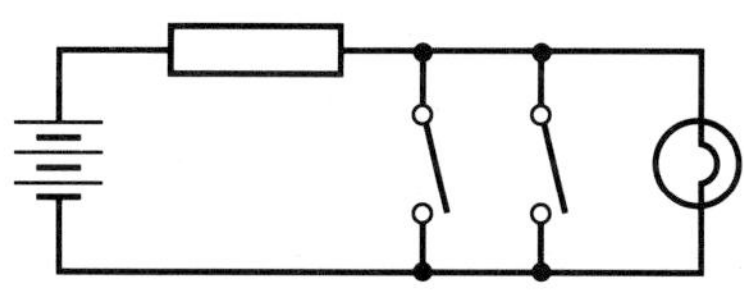

27.48 In each of the gates shown below, A_1 and A_2 may take either of the values 0 or +5 V depending on the states of other circuits connected to them. Explain the logic function of each where the output of the gate is 0 or +5 V at B.

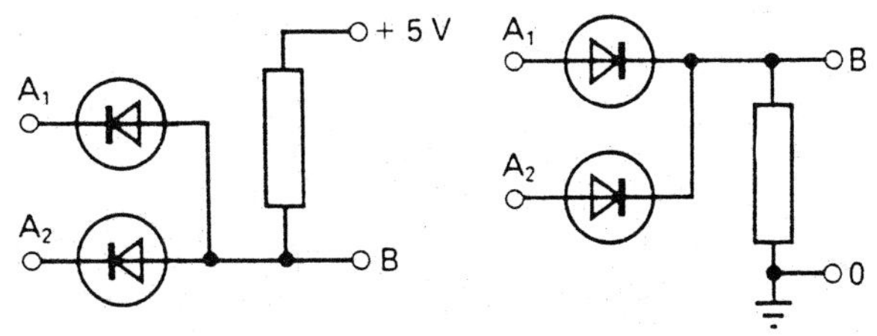

27.49 *(a)* Use truth tables to show that each of the gates shown in the figure at the top of the next column is acting as a NOT gate.

(b) Explain in words why the first and last gate is acting as a NOT gate.

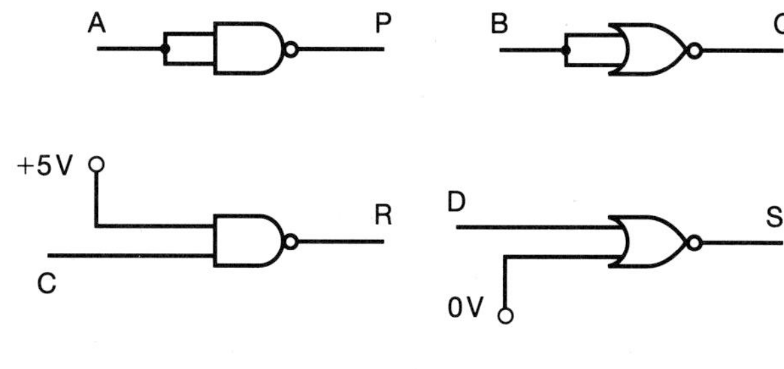

27.50 *(a)* The pair of pulses shown in figure (a) below are fed to the inputs of (i) an AND gate (ii) a NAND gate (iii) a NOR gate. Sketch the output pulses from each gate.

(b) Repeat each of (i) (ii) (iii) above for the pair of pulses shown in figure (b).

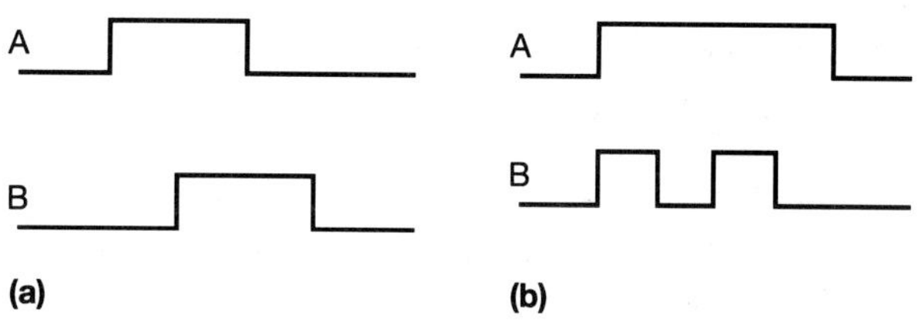

27.51 Show that the combination of logic gates shown in the diagram, one OR, two AND, and three NOT, operates as an exclusive OR gate.

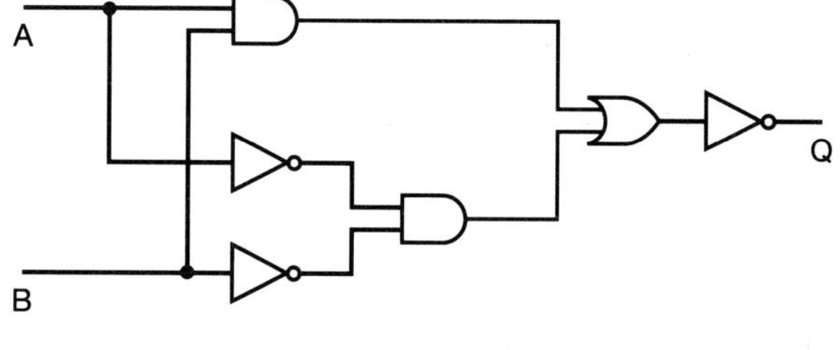

27.52 A parity or exclusive NOR gate is one for which the output is high when the inputs are the same, i.e. both low or both high.

(a) Show that such a gate can be made using only NOR gates. [Hint: four are needed.]

(b) Suggest a use for parity gate.

27.53 ***(a)*** By feeding two inputs A and B into both an EOR gate and an AND gate connected in parallel, show that the output of the EOR can be considered as the *sum* A + B and that the output of the AND gate can be considered as the *carry* for this half adder.

(b) How can a half adder be produced using only NAND gates?

27.54 Show that the combination of gates in the diagram produces a high output at Q when C plus either A or B are high.

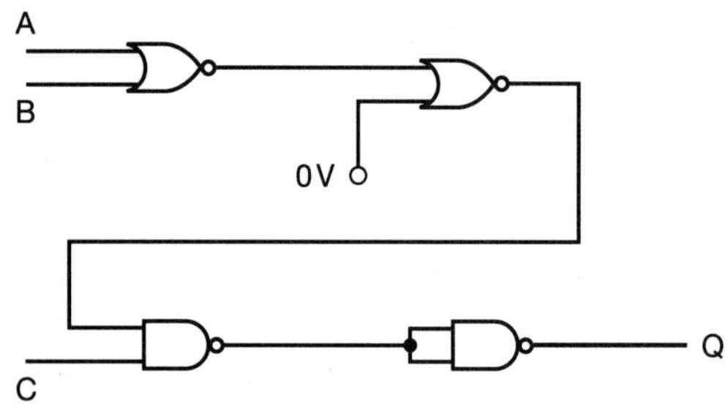

27.55 ***(a)*** Deduce which of the two combinations of NAND gates shown is equivalent to an OR gate and which is equivalent to a NOR gate.

(b) Using the result of *(a)* reduce the system shown in question *27.51* to one using a minimum number of NAND gates. How many NAND gates do you need?

(c) With one fewer NAND gates you could produce a parity gate. Explain which NAND gate you would remove.

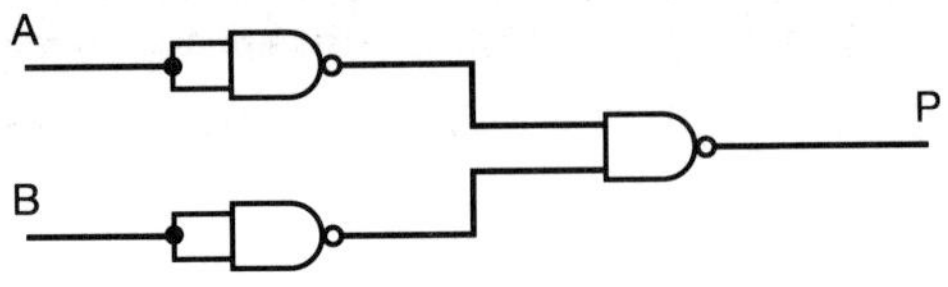

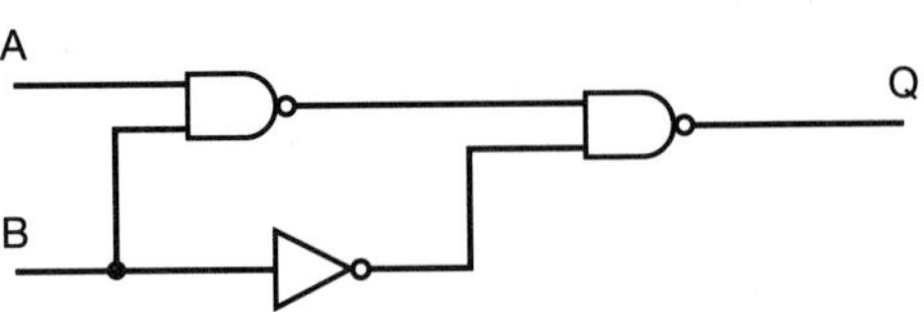

27.56 The figure shows a system with three inputs.

(a) Set up a truth table for A and B with P high.

(b) Set up a truth table for A and B with P low. Hence confirm that Q = A when P is high and that Q = B when P is low.

(c) Draw a timing diagram for a high frequency train of pulses entering B. Describe what emerges at Q as P is switched alternately high and low.

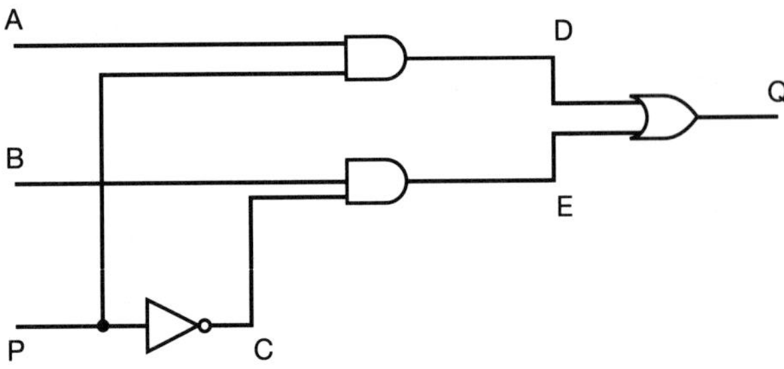

28 Communications

28.1 Analogue modulation

28.1 Draw diagrams showing an r.f. carrier signal modulated by a sinusoidal a.f. information signal when the depth of modulation is ***(a)*** about 0.25 ***(b)*** about 0.75. Explain why the modulated signal in *(b)* does not carry the information accurately.

28.2 'The minium acceptable value for the signal-to-noise ratio in the public switched telephone network in the U.K. is 40 dB.'

(a) Explain what this statement means.

(b) Calculate the minimum input power for a 20 km transmission line which collects noise of power 2.0×10^{-12} W.

(c) If the attenuation of the signal is 4 dB km^{-1}, what must the input power now be?

28.3 The attenuation in fog of infra-red waves of wavelength 1.6 μm is about 500 dB km^{-1}. What distance in fog would halve the power of a parallel beam of these waves?

28.4 The signal power loss between an Earth station and a geosynchronous satellite is 196 dB.

(a) If the power transmitted from the Earth station is 8.0 kW, what is the power collected by the satellite?

(b) What is the minimum noise power at the satellite if the signal-to-noise ratio is to be no less that 45 dB?

28.5 The system shown in the diagram produces a power output of 80 mW. Calculate the length of the transmission line. [Hint: power gains and losses expressed in dB simply add.]

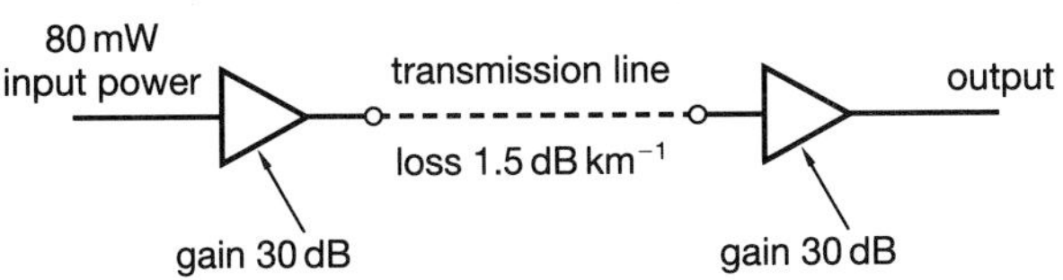

28.6 The minimum acceptable signal-to-noise ratio in a given commumications system is 22 dB.

(a) If the noise power is 2.0×10^{-20} W, what is the minimum power that the received signal may have?

(b) If the signal power at a distance of 1.4 km from the signal source is 1.5×10^{-17} W, calculate the maximum range for this system. Assume that the signal power decreases according to an inverse square law.

28.7 In the block diagram of a radio transmitter, A is an information transducer, C is a modulator, D an r.f. oscillator and G a transmitting antenna.

(a) What is needed at B, at E and at F? Suggest a possible circuit using an op-amp for component A.

(b) Give two examples of information transducers.

(c) Draw a sketch to show how the signal from the transmitting antenna can be made more directional.

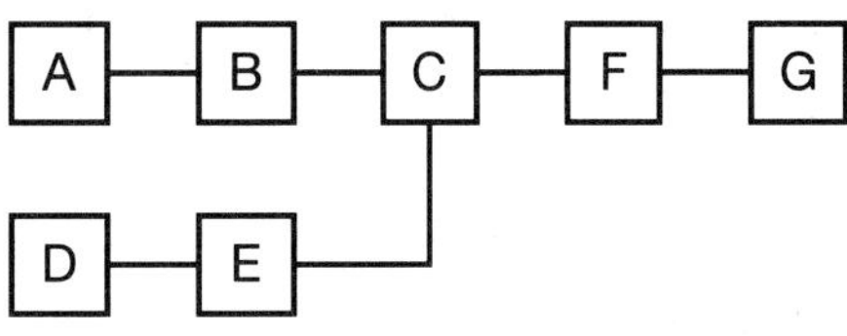

28.8 The aerial circuit of an a.f. radio receiver has a coil of inductance 2.4 mH. To what value should the capacitor be adjusted to receive waves of wavelength 1500 m? Take $c = 3.0 \times 10^{8}$ m s^{-1}.

28.9 Draw a frequency spectrum showing two AM channels with sidebands, the first for speech in the frequency range 300 Hz to 3.4 kHz using a carrier frequency of 600 kHz and the second for music in the range 50 Hz to 15 kHz using a carrier frequency of 650 kHz. Assume that the depth of modulatin is the same in each case and that the amplitude of the speech signal is half that of the music.

28.10 *(a)* How many frequency modulated signals each of signal bandwidth 180 kHz can be broadcast on VHF which has a channel bandwidth of 270 MHz?

(b) What disadvantage does VHF have compared with LF for broadcasting information?

28.11 The allowed range for MF broadcasts is 526 kHz to 1606 kHz.

(a) Explain why it is possible to broadcast high quality music, requiring a signal bandwidth of 30 kHz, on MF but not possible to broadcast television signals which need a signal bandwidth of 8 MHz.

(b) What is the maximum frequency of the music? Draw a frequency spectrum to illustrate how two different MF music channels could be broadcast simultaneously using carrier frequencies of 900 kHz and 950 kHz. Assume that amplitude modulation is used.

(c) In practice a bandwidth of 1.4 times the signal bandwidth is allowed for transmission. Is the above choice of carrier frequencies acceptable?

28.12 The attenuation in a transmission cable can be expressed as the loss of a fixed number of decibles per kilometre, n, or in terms of an attenuation coefficient, α, given by

$$P = P_o e^{-\alpha x}$$

where P is the power at a distance x (kilometres) along the cable.

(a) Show that these statements are equivalent, i.e. that $\alpha = kn$.

(b) Calculate a value for the constant k.

28.13 The r.m.s. thermal noise power P_n produced in a resistor by the random motion of conduction electrons depends on the temperature of the resistor. It can be shown that when a resistor is part of a system transmitting a signal of bandwidth B

$$P_n = 4kTB$$

where k is the Boltzmann constant ($k = 1.4 \times 10^{-23}\,JK^{-1}$) and T is the kelvin temperature.

For a bandwidth of 8.0 MHz, e.g. a TV channel, calculate the r.m.s. noise voltage across the terminals of a 4.7 kΩ resistor at *(a)* 27°C *(b)* −196°C.

28.2 Pulse modulation

28.14 Describe with the aid of diagrams how an audio signal can be encoded as a pulse amplitude modulated wave.

28.15 An audio signal is sampled at intervals of 125 μs. The samples are digitally encoded as a series of 3-bit numbers and the following sequence is obtained:

100 010 001 010 100 110 111 110 100

(a) Reconstruct the analogue signal as it would appear at the receiving end of a transmission line.

(b) Estimate the frequency of the audio signal.

28.16 Under what circumstances can noise so affect a train of digital pulses as to make it impossible for them to be regenerated faithfully. Support your answer with appropriate sketches.

28.17 A PCM system using seven bits per number allows a range from zero to 127, so each sampling is quantised to within 1⁄128th of the voltage range.

Explain why the signal-to-noise ratio for such a system must be greater than 42 dB.

28.18 A pulse code modulated system for transmitting speech signals of 4.5 kHz bandwidth is designed to operate with 32 quantised voltage levels.

(a) How many bits are required to transmit each quantised sample?

(b) What is the required bit rate?

(c) If an extra bit is introduced to each sample to indicate the start of each number, what is now the required bit rate?

28.19 Suppose that, in the previous question, the duration of each transmitted pulse is 0.5 μs.

(a) Calculate the total time required to send each sample, including the indicator bit.

(b) What is the time interval between the starts of successive samples?

(c) Deduce how many speech signals could be transmitted simultaneously with this system.

(d) How may the number be increased?

28.20 INTELSAT V uses communications satellites in

geosynchronous orbits above the Earth's equator. Speech and television signals are transmitted up to the satellites in the frequency range 5.925 GHz to 6.425 GHz and are retransmitted back to Earth in the band 3.700 GHz to 4.200 GHz.

(a) What are the channel bandwidths for the uplink and the downlink signals?

(b) The signal bandwidth allowed for each speech signal is 15 kHz and for each TV signal 12 MHz. If the satellite is operating with 10 TV channels calculate the maximum number of telephone calls it can handle.

28.21 The analogue signal shown in the diagram is to be transmitted using PCM with eight sampling levels and a sampling frequency of 10 kHz.

(a) Write down the quantised levels at each of the eight sampling points.

(b) What are the 3-bit binary numbers for these quantised levels?

(c) Draw the transmitted pulse train for the 0.7 ms period shown.

(d) What is the bit rate for this transmission?

(e) Reconstruct, on graph paper, the received signal. Is it a faithful representation of the original analogue signal?

(f) Repeat *(a)* – *(e)* using only four sampling levels over the same range as the eight in the diagram.

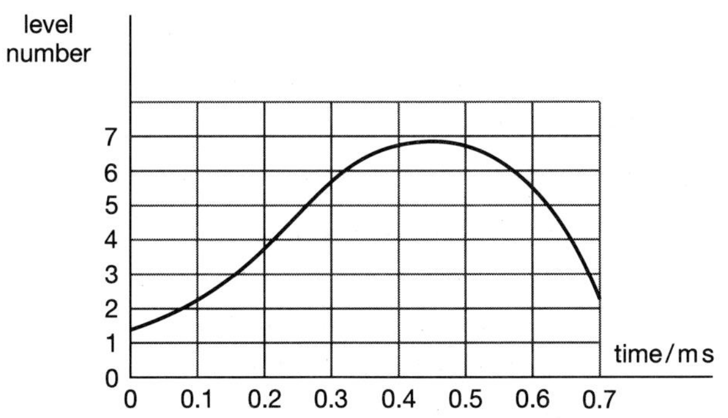

28.22 Write an explanation of the statement: 'In the UK the PSTN uses a TDM/PCM system with one-byte groups and employs regenerative repeaters'.

28.23 The circuit accompanying question *27.55* behaves as shown in the following truth table (drawn horizontally for convenience).

P	0 0 0 0 1 1 1 1
A	0 0 1 1 0 0 1 1
B	0 1 0 1 0 1 0 1
Q	0 1 0 1 0 0 1 1

You can see that Q = A when P is high and that Q = B when P is low.

(a) Draw two streams of high frequency pulses to represent PCM signals arriving at A and B.

(b) By considering the signal at P as a relatively slow on/off pulse explain how this circuit can be used for time division multiplexing the signals arriving at A and B.

28.3 Fibre links

28.24 Discuss the advantages of

(a) pulse as opposed to analogue modulation

(b) the use of fibre links as opposed to free space for the transmission of information signals.

28.25 The diagram shows a stream of data and a noise signal.

(a) Draw the received signal which results when these two signals are mixed.

(b) Suppose the amplitude of the noise signal was (i) twice (ii) three times that shown. What would the received signal now look like in each case?

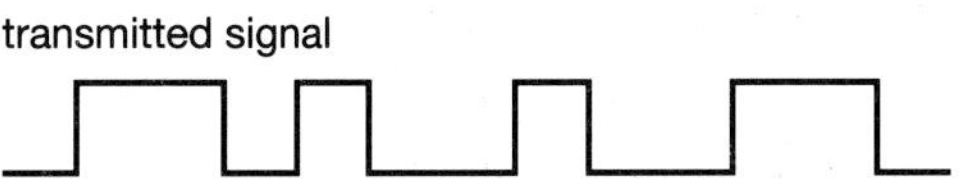

28.26 The output of an LED contains a lot of energy between wavelengths of 820 nm and 880 nm. The refractive indices of an optical fibre for these wavelengths are 1.479 and 1.482 respectively.

(a) Calculate the times taken by infra-red waves of these two wavelengths to travel 1000 m along a monomode optical fibre. What is the time difference? Take $c = 2.997 \times 10^8 \, \mathrm{m\,s^{-1}}$.

(b) Would this material dispersion enable regenerative repeaters spaced 1 km apart to resolve PCM signals with a bit rate of $140 \, \mathrm{Mbit\,s^{-1}}$? Explain your answer.

28.27 The diagram shows part of the shortest and longest paths that a laser beam can follow along a step-index multimode fibre (see also question *24.19*). The longest path is that of the most inclined ray which is just totally internally reflected at the core/cladding boundary.

(a) Calculate the difference between the greatest and the least times for a pulse from a monochromatic laser to travel 1000 m along the fibre. Take the refractive index of the core and cladding to be 1.480 and 1.460 respectively and $c = 2.997 \times 10^8 \, \mathrm{m\,s^{-1}}$.

(b) What is the maximum bit rate which such a step index multimode fibre could reliably transmit with regenerative repeaters every 1.0 km?

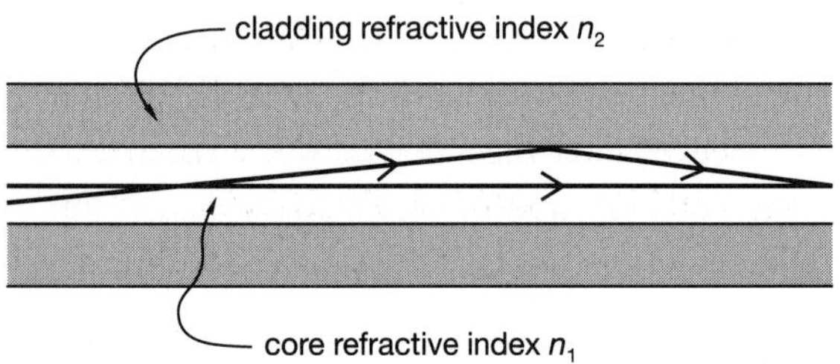

28.28 'Pulse broadening in optical fibre communication systems results from both material and modal dispersion.'

(a) Expand this statement in the light of the calculations of the two previous questions.

(b) Hence explain why a monomode fibre with a laser source can carry very high bit rates.

28.29 (a) In window glass the attenuation of infra-red waves of wavelength 1.6 μm is about $50\,000 \, \mathrm{dB\,km^{-1}}$. The power of a parallel infra-red beam is 200 mW as it enters one face of a plate glass window 10 mm thick. What power is absorbed from the beam in the window glass?

(b) In high quality optical fibre the attenuation of these waves is only about $0.5 \, \mathrm{dB\,km^{-1}}$. What length of optical fibre produces the same power loss as in *(a)*?

28.30 An optical fibre system operates at a wavelength of 1.3 μm and at a bit rate of $480 \, \mathrm{kbit\,s^{-1}}$.

(a) Where in the electromagnetic spectrum do such waves occur? Why are such wavelengths chosen for optical fibre links?

(b) Calculate the sampling frequency if there are 16 bits (2 bytes) required to encode each sample such as might be required for high-quality music.

(c) What is the maximum frequency in the transmitted music signal which this sampling frequency can successfully handle?

28.31 Some of the secondary advantages of optical fibre links for communication are: no externally radiated signals, the use of common natural materials, greater safety, small and lightweight cables.

(a) Explain these secondary advantages.

(b) Give a list of the primary advantages.

28.4 ADC and DAC

28.32 Draw a block diagram of an analogue-to-digital converter using a ramp generator. Explain the function of each block.

28.33 Give examples of physical measurements, inside or outside the laboratory, where it is ***(a)*** advantageous ***(b)*** disadvantageous to display the output digitally. Explain the reasons behind your choices.

28.34 The ramp voltage in simple digital voltmeters (DVMs) rises to a maximum of 199.9 mV and repeats precisely 3 times per second.

If it is generating an 8-bit output will a 1.0 kHz pulse generator be adequate for its operation?

28.35 The circuit for question *27.12* produces a steadily rising output voltage – a ramp voltage. The rate of rise of voltage after the switch is closed is given by V_{in}/RC, where V_{in} is the (negative) input voltage, R the value of the input resistor and C the value of the feedback capacitor.

(a) Calculate the rate of rise of voltage for the values given in question *27.12*.

(b) If a ramp voltage which rises at $1600\,\mathrm{V\,s^{-1}}$ is required, suggest suitable values for R and C. Take V_{in} to be $-200\,\mathrm{mV}$.

28.36 In the diagram each comparator switches on its LED when the voltage at the +input is greater than that at the −input.

By calculating the fixed voltages at the −inputs draw up a table to show which LEDs are glowing for a range of values of V_{in} from 0 V to 5 V. (This is used in the bargraph voltage level indicators on hi-fi equipment.)

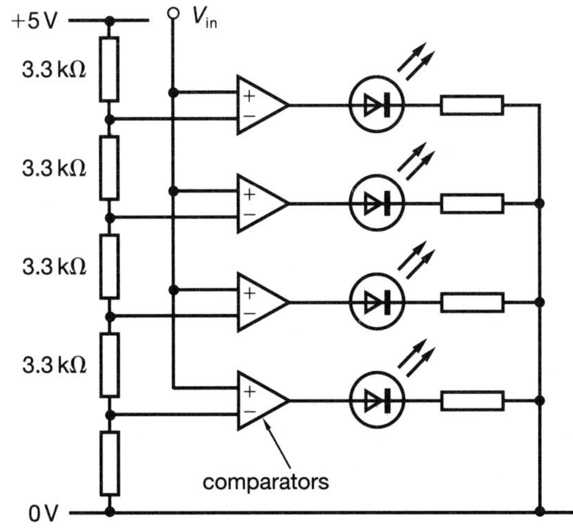

28.37 It is usual to use identical resitors, all formed on a single chip, to provide the input resistors for a summing amplifier used as a digital to analogue convertor. Draw a circuit diagram of a 3-bit DAC using only 22 kΩ resistors and explain how it works.

28.38 The circuit diagram shows a repeating network of resistors of value R and $2R$.

(a) Calculate the equivalent resistance of the section to the right of the dashed line (the last resistor is R).

(b) Show that the resistance of the network measured between A and B is R and that this is independent of the number of R–$2R$ sections.

(c) Suppose a current of 16 mA enters the network at A and leaves at B. What will be the current (i) in the $2R$ resistor nearest to AB (ii) in the next $2R$ resistor?

(d) [Hard] Design a digital-to-analogue converter using an R–$2R$ network of this kind as the inputs to a summing amplifier.

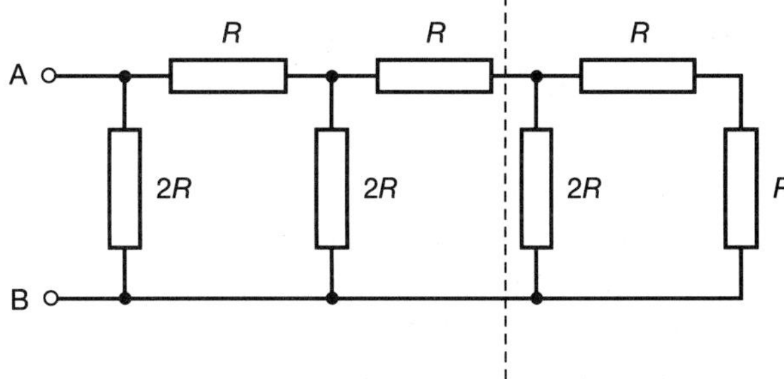

28.39 A fast type of ADC uses the idea of guessing the size of the analoge voltage, comparing it with a known voltage from a DAC and moving the guess down or up until it finds the right level.

The diagram shows the programmed output of the successive approximation register, SAR, for an 8-bit system. If, for example, after the third try 00001111 is found to be too low, then the next selected guesses become 00010111, 00010011, 00010001 etc. It then recycles again after finding that one of these is too low.

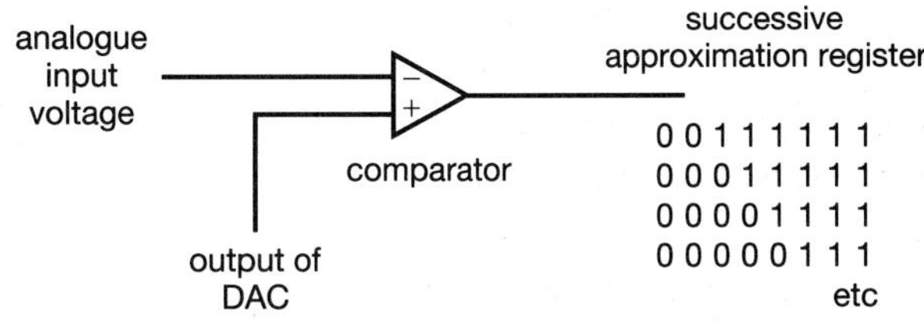

Why is the successive approximation converter fast compared to an ADC using a counter-ramp generator?

Answers

1 Describing motion

1.2 $8\,ms^{-1}$, 1.6%
1.3 (a) 35 ms (b) 2.8%
1.4 (a) (i) 1.57 mm (ii) 0.176 mm
(b) (iii) $7.9\,mm\,s^{-1}$
(iv) $0.88\,mm\,s^{-1}$
1.8 (a) $+9.0\,ms^{-1}$ (b) $-21\,ms^{-1}$
(c) $-12\,ms^{-1}$ (d) $20\,ms^{-1}$ west
1.9 (a) $3.0\,ms^{-1}$ (b) $10.6\,ms^{-1}$
1.11 (a) 50 s, 33 s, 20 s
(b) (i) $1.6\,ms^{-1}$ (ii) $0.27\,ms^{-1}$
(c) $1.6\,ms^{-1}$ at 10° to direction of walkway
1.12 (a) 495 N down, 408 N and 89 N up
(b) 209 N down, zero and 210 N up
1.13 (a) $10\,ms^{-1}$ (b) $10\,ms^{-1}$ (c) 0
(d) $6.4\,ms^{-1}$ south
(e) $9.0\,ms^{-1}$ SE
(f) $20\,ms^{-1}$ west
(g) $14\,ms^{-1}$ SW
1.14 (a) 8.4 m, N 17° W
(b) $2.9\,ms^{-1}$, S 79° W
1.15 (a) 3.0 m north
(b) 112 m, N 27° E
(c) 0 (d) 127 m north
1.16 (b) $1.8\,ms^{-1}$, $0.95\,ms^{-1}$, $0.61\,ms^{-1}$
(c) $0.62\,ms^{-1}$
1.17 $9.2\,ms^{-1}$ south
1.18 (a) $57\,ms^{-2}$ (b) $190\,ms^{-2}$
1.19 1.2 m
1.20 $-0.89\,ms^{-2}$
1.21 $12\,ms^{-2}$
1.22 1.8 km, 32 s
1.23

	t /m	b /m	s /m
$108\,km\,h^{-1}$ dry	15	56	71
$108\,km\,h^{-1}$ wet	15	112	127
$72\,km\,h^{-1}$ dry	10	25	35
$72\,km\,h^{-1}$ wet	10	50	60

1.24 $230\,ms^{-2}$
1.25 after 2.0 s
1.26 400 m
1.27 (a) (i) 0.15 km (ii) 0.49 km
(b) (iii) $0.96\,ms^{-2}$
(iv) $3.0\,ms^{-2}$
1.28 (a) $9.50\,ms^{-1}$, 21.3 m.p.h; 3.0 s
(b) (i) $8.0\,ms^{-2}$ (ii) $1.5\,ms^{-2}$
1.29 (b) 45 m, 20 m, 5 m
1.34 (a) (i) 0.45 s (ii) 0.64 s
1.35 (a) $10.1\,ms^{-2}$
1.36 (a) 1.2 m (b) 1.4° (c) greater
1.37 1.5 s
1.38 (a) $800\,ms^{-2}$
(b) (i) 0.07 s (ii) 0.03 m
1.39 (a) $12.5\,ms^{-1}$ (b) 1.3 s (c) 8.0 m
(d) 55 m
1.41 13.7 times; s/mm: 48, 130, 274, 431, 650, 917
1.42 $9.7\,ms^{-2}$
1.43 about 2 m
1.44 (a) 2.3 s (b) 0.44 s (c) $23\,ms^{-1}$
(d) about 9° to vertical

2 Momentum and force

2.1 (a) (i) $150\,kg\,ms^{-1}$ north
(ii) $150\,kg\,ms^{-1}$ south
(b) $2.0 \times 10^4\,kg\,ms^{-1}$ east
(c) $5.0 \times 10^9\,kg\,ms^{-1}$ west
2.2 (a) 0.28 kg (b) (i) yes (ii) yes
2.3 mass in trolley = 32 kg
2.4 (a) moves away from the bank at $3\,ms^{-1}$
(b) $0.52\,ms^{-1}$ south
2.5 2.0 kg
2.6 (a) $+0.7\,ms^{-1}$
2.8 1.3 feet per second
2.9 $3.40 \times 10^5\,ms^{-1}$
2.12 $24\,ms^{-1}$
2.16 (b) 6000 N, 2000 N
(c) both unchanged
2.17 (b) on pulley, zero; on leg, 0.21 kN
2.18 (a) 10 N (b) 17 N (c) 17 N
2.19 (i) 51 N (ii) 61 N
2.21 (a) yes (b) 5.6 N, 2.1 N
2.22 6.0°
2.23 1.5°
2.24 (a) 31 N (b) 60 N
2.25 740 N, N 22° E
2.27 (a) 140 N (b) 38 N
2.28 front 120 N, back 80 N
2.29 (a) 3.0 kg
2.31 (b) 0.27 kN
(c) X = 0.25 kN, Y = 0.10 kN
2.32 (a) 4.0 m from P
(b) X = 9.6 kN, Y = 12 kN
(c) 15 kN at 39° to vertical
2.33 (a) 7.36° (b) 151 N (c) 19.4 N
2.34 (a) 225 N (b) 590 N
2.35 40°
2.36 (a) $-3.0 \times 10^3\,ms^{-2}$
(b) 600 MN
2.37 (b) $15\,ms^{-2}$ (c) $4.5\,ms^{-1}$
2.38 (a) 12 kN (b) 12 kN
2.39 1.46
2.40 20 kN
2.41 (a) $0.55\,ms^{-2}$ (b) 1.2 kN
2.42 (a) $8.5\,ms^{-2}$ (b) 68 cm
2.44 (a) $4.6\,ms^{-2}$ (b) $0.81\,ms^{-2}$
2.45 $4.9\,ms^{-2}$
2.46 (b) (i) 2.8 kN (ii) 1.6 kN
2.48 (a) thread 4.7° to vertical
2.49 (b) 7.8 N (c) 3.9 kg
2.51 (a) $0.61\,ms^{-2}$ (b) 134 N, 86 N
2.52 (a) 3000 N s east
(b) 100 N s down
(c) 100 N s down
2.53 (a) $2.6\,kg\,ms^{-1}$ (b) 2.6 N s
2.54 (a) (i) 32 N (ii) 64 N
2.55 (a) $2.3\,kg\,ms^{-1}$, $39\,ms^{-1}$ (b) $1.5\,km\,s^{-2}$
2.56 (a) 7.4 kN, a small car
2.57 (a) $0.40\,ms^{-1}$ to left (c) ±24 kN
2.59 only *D* and *E*
2.62 (a) 6.0 kN (b) 5.2 kN
2.64 0.44 kN
2.65 (a) $4.8\,ms^{-2}$ (b) 0.29 kN
(c) 0.29 kN
2.66 (a) nothing (b) nothing
(c) acceleration $2.0\,ms^{-2}$
2.67 (a) 20 N (b) 13 N
2.68 about 5 kN
2.69 $-1.7\,ms^{-2}$
2.70 2.0 N
2.71 1.7 N
2.72 $1400\,ms^{-1}$, $1000\,kg\,s^{-1}$, 3.4×10^7 N
2.73 $67\,ms^{-1}$
2.74 170 kN, the air which is being accelerated

3 Energy and its conservation

3.1 (a) about 10 MJ (b) about 2 kW
3.2 (a) 43 MJ (b) 96p
3.3 (b) by about 2020
3.10 (a) $1.7 \times 10^7 \, m^2$ (b) 0.006% (c) 0.3%
3.11 about 250 MW
3.12 (a) 1.2 GW (b) (i) 9.0×10^{10} J (ii) 5.4×10^{12} J
3.13 about 10^{10} kg, i.e. a lake 10 m deep of area 1 km^2
3.14 8 kJ, −8 kJ
3.15 0, 0, 24 J, −16 J
3.16 (a) 2.3 kJ (b) −1.4 kJ; the barbell has 0.9 kJ of k.e.
3.17 0.59 N (a) by thread tension 0, by pull of Earth 12 mJ (b) 0, −12 mJ
3.18 (a) $2\pi r(F_1 - F_2)$ (b) 53 W
3.19 about 80 W
3.20 (a) (i) 0.80 J (ii) 2.4 J
3.21 (a) 2.6 J; 0.06 J
3.22 53 mJ
3.23 5.1×10^{10} J
3.24 (a) 44 s (b) 180 kJ
3.25 98 W
3.26 50 kN
3.27 about (a) 26 J (b) 450 J (c) 3.5 kJ (d) 20 MJ
3.28 (a) 1.6 kN (b) 800 m
3.29 (a) 9.0 kJ (b) −1.5 kJ
3.30 (a) 3.0×10^{10} J (b) -5.0×10^6 N
3.31 (a) 7.4 J (b) 7.0 $m s^{-1}$ (c) −0.42 J
3.32 g.p.e. −14 kJ, k.e. +14 kJ k.e. +14 kJ, g.p.e. −27 kJ +16 kJ, 4.1 kN
3.33 (a) 0.76 mJ (b) 45 mW
3.34 (a) 0.83 $m s^{-1}$ (b) no
3.35 (a) 110 J (b) ⁻75 J (c) 4.4 $m s^{-1}$ (d) −110 J (e) 22 N
3.36 0.30 kN
3.37 17 $m s^{-1}$, no
3.38 2.3 $m s^{-1}$
3.39 (a) 0.25 J (b) 0.049 J
3.40 (a) 1.2 kJ (b) (i) 1.4 kJ (ii) 0.26 kJ (c) 0.75 $m s^{-1}$
3.41 (a) (i) 0.27 kJ, 130 W (ii) 0.21 kJ, 56 W
3.42 (a) 0.20 J (b) 0.10 J
3.43 A ball bouncing on the ground
3.44 (a) (i) 3.0 N (ii) 0.12 J (b) 8.9 $m s^{-1}$
3.45 (a) −0.80 J (b) +0.40 J (c) +0.40 J (d) −1.6 J (e) +1.6 J, the lump has no k.e.
3.48 (a) 2.2 $m s^{-1}$ north (b) 1.5×10^5 J
3.49 no
3.50 (a) 0, + 0.30 $m s^{-1}$ (b) −0.10 $m s^{-1}$, 0.20 $m s^{-1}$
3.51 (a) 0.40 $km s^{-1}$ (b) 0.79 kJ
3.52 6.0 $m s^{-1}$, N 68° E; 2.8×10^4 J
3.53 (a) (i) electron $-u$, atom $2u \times 10^{-5}$; electron energy unchanged (ii) electron $2u$, atom u (b) (i) ≈ zero (ii) 4.0×10^{-5}
3.54 (a) 0.14c (b) 0.42c (c) 0.75c
3.55 9.10×10^{-31} kg, 1.67×10^{-27} kg
3.56 (a) 3.1×10^{-12} kg (b) 1.7×10^{-10}
3.57 the mass increases

4 Structure of matter

4.1 (a) about 2000 (b) about 300 000
4.2 The number of carbon atoms in the backbone chain of the fatty acid
4.3 (a) about 0.3 mm (b) about 3 m
4.4 (a) 2.1×10^{-4} (b) 2.4×10^{18} $kg m^{-3}$
4.5 (a) 12, 13, 14 (b) 2.32×10^{-26} kg
4.6 28.1
4.7 (a) $A_r = 39$ (b) $1.24 \times 10^4 \, m s^{-1}$, $1.21 \times 10^4 \, m s^{-1}$ (c) 48.3 μs, 49.5 μs
4.8 (a) 5.5×10^{-7} kg (b) 0.32 kg (c) 0.32 kg
4.9 (a) 6.0×10^{23}
4.10 256, 4.25×10^{-25} kg
4.11 (a) 3.27×10^{-25} kg (b) 5.90×10^{28} (c) $1.70 \times 10^{-29} \, m^3$ (d) 2.57×10^{-10} m; for aluminium: (a) 4.47×10^{-26} kg (b) 6.04×10^{28} (c) $1.65 \times 10^{-29} \, m^3$ (d) 2.55×10^{-10} m
4.12 (a) 0.13 mol (b) 17.8 mol (c) 1.71 mol (d) 1.71 mol
4.18 (a) 23.8×10^{-9} N, 6.9×10^{-9} N, 16.9×10^{-9} N repulsive (b) 1.3×10^{-9} N, 3.9×10^{-9} N, 2.6×10^{-9} N attractive
4.20 (c) about 0.15×10^{-10} m (d) no (e) 7.30×10^{-9} N, zero
4.28 0.1 $m s^{-1}$
4.30 499.95 $m s^{-1}$
4.31 nearly 6 days
4.32 (a) $300d^3$ (b) $7d$

5 Performance of materials

5.2 (a) 24 MPa (b) 160 MPa (c) 11 MPa
5.3 (a) 5.0×10^{-5} (b) 2.0
5.4 (a) 59 N (b) 59 N
5.5 (a) 59 N (b) 69 N (c) 64 N
5.6 (a) 50 N, 50 MPa (b) 50 N, 100 MPa
5.7 end-to-end: force side-by-side: extension, strain, stress
5.8 (a) 7.7 $m s^{-1}$ (b) 17 kN (c) 34 kN (d) 70 MPa
5.9 0.51 mm, 1.6 mm
5.10 (a) 37 kN (b) 120 MPa (c) 5.9×10^{-4}
5.11 (a) tungsten (b) copper
5.12 (a) 78.5 kN (b) 11.2 mm (d) 12.9 mm
5.13 aluminium
5.14 all true
5.15 (a) 100 MPa (b) 7.7×10^{-4} (c) 0.92 mm
5.20 (b) 30 GPa (c) 3.0 mm
5.27 (a) 1.05×10^{-25} kg (b) $1.18 \times 10^{-29} \, m^3$, 2.28×10^{-10} m (c) 1.93×10^{13} (d) 1.0×10^{-12} N (e) 20.0 MPa (f) 1.5×10^{-4} (g) 1.5×10^{-4} (h) 3.5×10^{-14} m (i) 30 $N m^{-1}$
5.29 (a) P/mnd^2 (b) $\Delta d/d$ (c) $E = P/mnd\Delta d$ (d) P/mn (e) $\Delta d = P/mnk$ (f) $k = Ed$ (g) 31 $N m^{-1}$

5.33 (a) $10 N m^{-1}$ (b) $60 N m^{-1}$ (c) $60 N m^{-1}$
5.34 39 mJ
5.35 (a) 50 mJ (b) 200 mJ (c) 450 mJ
5.36 (a) 65 mJ (b) 33 mJ, 32 mJ
5.37 (a) high tensile steel (b) 2.5 J, 8.1 J (c) mild steel
5.38 (a) upper (b) hysteresis
5.39 (b) 340 J, 190 J (i) 340 J (ii) 150 J
5.42 (a) 20 N (b)(i) 1.5 J (ii) 2.5 J

6 Fluid behaviour

6.1 1.1 kPA, 1.6 kPa, 3.3 kPa
6.3 about 7 kPa
6.4 8.0 km
6.5 (a) B (b) 103.0 kPa
6.6 (a) 16 kPa, 11 kPa (b) about 24 kPa
6.7 (a) (i) 0.0005% (ii) 0.005% (b) only 0.05% up
6.10 (a) 50 kPa (b) 500 N (c) no
6.13 (a) 1.75 MN (b) 0.119 MN, 0.238 MN (c) 1.63 MN, 1.51 MN
6.14 (a) 2.0 kN
6.15 (b) (i) 0.381 mN, 0.443 mN (ii) 2.43 g, 23.87 g (c) approx 1.6%, approx 0.2%
6.16 (a) 0.15 N (b) 0 (c) 0.024 N
6.19 (a) $0.80 m s^{-1}$ (b) both $8 \times 10^{-5} m^3 s^{-1}$
6.20 (a) $1.8 m s^{-1}$ (b) $2.7 m s^{-1}$ (c) 0.98 cm

7 Electric currents, energy and power

7.2 1.4×10^2 C, 9.0×10^{20}
7.4 (a) B, C (b) B 0.20 A, C 0.20 A, D 0.05 A
7.5 (b) total charge (c) 360 C (d) 6.3 kC
7.6 $3.4 \times 10^{15} s^{-1}$
7.7 $8.2 mm s^{-1}$
7.8 $0.75 mm s^{-1}$
7.9 1:4
7.10 about 15 h
7.12 540 J
7.13 (a) 36 kJ (b) 25 h
7.14 (a) 8.0×10^8 V (b) about 11 000
7.15 (a) 270 J (b) 250 J
7.16 (a) 1.1 kJ (b) 3.2 kJ (c) 1.1 kJ
7.17 (a) all zero (b) 0.79 V
7.18 (a) A 1.46 V, B 1.46 V, C 0.67 V, D 0.67 V, E 0.00 V (b) (i) in resistor (ii) in resistor (iii) in bulb
7.20 all 2.89 V
7.21 (a) 2.45 V (b) 3.41 V
7.22 (a) (i) 1.35 V (ii) 0.45 V (b) (i) 0.15 V, B (ii) 0.30 V, F
7.23 (a) (i) A −1.5 V, B +1.5 V, D 0 (ii) A −1.5 V, B −1.5 V, D −1.5 V (b) (i) no effect (ii) current from C to D
7.24 (a) 3.0 V, 2.0 V, 1.0 A (b) −1.0 V, −3.0 V, 1.0 A (c) 1.0 V, −2.0 V, 1.0 A (d) −3.0 V; zero in 1.0 Ω, 1.5 A in 2.0 Ω
7.25 (a) 5 cells (b) 3.6 V
7.27 144 kJ
7.28 54 kJ
7.29 0.42 A, 360 kJ
7.30 (a) 2.5 mC (b) 250 A (d) 60 kW
7.31 (a) 2.5 kW (b) 3.5 kW (c) 8.8 A
7.32 (a) 20 kA (b) 4.3×10^{13} W (c) 2.6×10^{13} W

8 Electrical resistance

8.2 8.6×10^{10} Ω
8.3 50 V
8.4 (b) metal (c) 91 kΩ (d) (i) 9.9 kΩ (ii) 83 kΩ
8.5 (a) 0.12 A (b) 40 Ω, 0.15 A, (c) 30 Ω, 0.20 A; 20 Ω, 0.30 A; 10 Ω, 0.60 A
8.6 (a) 0.20 Ω (b) 0.12 V (c) 0.14 W
8.7 0.42 A, 0.25 A
8.8 larger
8.9 90 W
8.10 R_1, 3.6 W
8.11 (a) second, 2.6 W (b) first, 11 W
8.12 (a) 2.4 Ω (b) 15 W (c) lower resistance, larger power
8.13 0.51 m
8.14 (a) (i) 960 Ω (ii) 2.4 Ω (b) 20 bulbs (c) both bulbs dim (d) first bulb bright, second dark
8.15 (a) 33 A (b) 6.0 kV, 5.9 kV, 0.10 kV (c) 5.8 kV (d) 6.7 kW (e) 3.3% (f) 30%
8.16 (a) 25 Ω (b) 6.0 Ω
8.17 (i) 2.50 Ω (ii) 5.00 Ω (iii) 8.33 Ω (iv) 6.67 Ω
8.18 (a) (i) 6.0 V (ii) 3.0 V (iii) 2.4 V (iv) 3.0 V (b) (ii) zero (iii) 3.6 V
8.19 0.042 Ω
8.20 (a) 5.0 Ω (b) 1.0 Ω
8.21 both less than 1 Ω
8.22 (a) 0.990 Ω (b) 0.989 Ω
8.23 (a) 4 (b) 5
8.24 R/Ω = 0.9, 1.6, 2.1, 2.4, 2.5, 2.4, 2.1, 1.6. 0.9
8.25 larger
8.26 0.20 A, 0.30 A, 0.60 A
8.27 (b) tungsten 60 W, carbon 0.11 kW (c) (i) 0.60 A (ii) 0.16 A (d) 380 V (e) 165 V
8.28 (b) (i) infinite (ii) 29 Ω (iii) 4 Ω (c) almost zero
8.30 1.5 Ω
8.31 0.34 Ω
8.32 (a) $13 mm^2$ (b) 2.5 Ω (c) $0.42 Ω km^{-1}$
8.33 2.8 m
8.34 (a) 8.0 MΩ (b) 8.0 MΩ
8.35 890°C
8.36 (a) 2.0 Ω (b) 12 times (c) no, T increases 8 times
8.37 (a) 350 Ω (b) 13
8.39 (a) 2.4 V (b) 10 Ω
8.40 (a) 2.7 V (b) 230 Ω
8.41 (a) 1.25 V (b) 4.7 V
8.42 (a) (i) 1.2 V (ii) 1.7 V (b) 55 mA (c) 17/12 (d) 187 mA
8.43 A goes out, B gets brighter
8.44 (a) 6.0 Ω (b) (i) 2.5 V (ii) 3.2 V (c) (i) 0.53 A (ii) 0.32 A (iii) 0.21 A
8.45 (a) 12.5 Ω (b) 48 mA (c) larger
8.46 (a) 6.0 V, 6.0 V (b) 2.4 V, 9.6 V (c) 7.1 V, 4.9 V, (d) 9.1 V, 2.9 V
8.47 (a) 6.0 V (b) 2.4 V (c) 7.1 V (d) 9.1 V
8.49 (b) 2.1 V (c) (i) 46 mA (ii) 86 mA (iii) 132 mA
8.51 (a) 0.23 MΩ (b) 1.9 kΩ
8.52 (a) 4 times greater than (b)
8.53 (a) 960 Ω, 48 Ω (b) 0.24 A; 55 W, 2.8 W (c) lamp slightly dimmer, heater cold

8.56 (d) smaller, the heater most
(a) 8.8V (b) 15.1V (c) 2.5V (d) 10V (e)(i) 0.36A (ii) 0.96A
8.57 (a) 20 (b) 1.2W (c) 0.1A
8.58 (b) 115Ω
8.59 choose (a)
8.60 10Ω; current from X to Y
8.62 (a) 3.3×10^{-4} mm^2 (d) from Y to X
8.63 1.31V, 1.44V, 1.43V, 1.45V
8.65 (c) 2.0kΩ

9 Cells and meters

9.1 (a) 7.5V (b) 4.5V (c) 1.5V
9.3 (a) (i) 4.0V, 0.40A (ii) 2.0V, 0.20A (b) (i) 3.2V, 0.29A (ii) 2.0V, 0.20A
9.5 (a) 0.10A (b) 1.42V (c) 0.08V
9.6 (a) 1.485V (b) 1.500V
9.7 0.50Ω, 1.50V
9.8 (a) 1.52V, 0.64Ω (b) 1.04V, 0.60Ω
9.9 (a) 3.00V, 1.0Ω (b) 1.50V, 0.25Ω
9.10 (a) 0.148V (b) 1.48V (c) 0.229W (d) 0.218W
9.11 (a) 8.3Ω (b) 11.7Ω (c) 1.7Ω
9.12 (a) chemical to electrical (b) electrical to internal (c) I^2r
9.13 P/W = 0.22, 0.28, 0.36, 0.50, 0.56, 0.56, 0.53. (a) both zero (b) 1.1Ω
9.14 (a) 1.0A (b) 5.7V, 4.2V, 1.5V (c) 6.0W, −4.0W (d) 0.3W, 0.2W, 1.5W
9.15 (a) 40μA (b) 120μA
9.16 (a) $V_{C2} = 1.5\text{V} - (1.0\Omega)b$, $V_R = (1.0\Omega)(a+b)$ (c) 1.5V (d) 1.5V (e) 3.0Ω (f) *b* reverses
9.17 28kJ, 43kJ, 86kJ; 0.36MJkg^{-1}, 0.43MJkg^{-1}, 0.78MJkg^{-1}
9.18 0.61MJkg^{-1}, 0.54MJkg^{-1}, 0.49MJkg^{-1}
9.19 19h
9.20 100mV
9.21 (a) 18.2Ω in parallel (b) 8.20kΩ in series
9.22 (a) 0.758Ω in parallel (b) 9.925kΩ in series
9.23 (a) 0.27m (b) longer
9.25 (a) 0.69V (b) 0.89V (c) 0.69V
9.26 (a) 60μA, 6.0V (b) 60μA, 6.0V (c) 40μA, 6.0V
9.28 (a) +1.0div (b) +1.0div (c) +2.0div (d) zero (e) +1.5div (f) +0.5div (g) −0.5div
9.29 (a) 25Hz (b) 42Hz (c) 50Hz
9.30 (a) 1.28×10^{-16}J (b) 1.7×10^7ms^{-1} (c) 1.6mA (d) 1.7×10^7ms^{-1} (e) 0.38W
9.31 (a) 1.0 div right, 1.5 div up (b) 2.0 div right, 1.5 div up (c) 3.0 div above centre
9.32 (a) straight line from (−2div, −3div) to (+2div, +3div) (b) circle of diameter 4.0 div (c) two loops one above the other, touching a square of side 4.0 div

10 Heating solids and liquids

10.5 (a) 19.4°C (b) 19.00°C
10.9 (a) heating; i.e. from man to room (b) working; c.e. from man, i.e. to wood (c) heating; i.e. from heater to room (d) working; g.p.e. from ball, i.e. to ball and surroundings (e) working; k.e. from coffee, i.e. to coffee (f) working; c.e. from girl, i.e. to pump

Note. Answers to questions *10.10* to *10.12* depend on the form chosen for the First law. Answers are given for the First law in the form $\Delta U = \Delta Q + \Delta W$. If the other form ($\Delta Q = \Delta U + \Delta W$) is used, reverse the signs for all values of ΔW.

10.10 (a) +0.20MJ (b) −0.080MJ (c) + 0.12MJ
10.11 (a) ΔU zero, ΔQ positive, ΔW negatve (b) ΔU positive, ΔQ zero, ΔW negative (c) ΔU negative, ΔQ zero, ΔW positive (d) ΔU positive, ΔQ negative, ΔW negative
10.12 ΔU positive, ΔQ negative, ΔW negative; ΔU zero, ΔQ negative, ΔW negative
10.13 (a) 8.4kJk^{-1} (b) 0.31kJK^{-1} (c) 38JK^{-1} (d) 7.0JK^{-1}
10.14 3.2GJ
10.15 78p
10.16 10s
10.17 (a) 7.0kW
10.18 1.3K
10.19 29Kmin^{-1}
10.20 about 5kJ lost
10.21 7.1Kmin^{-1}
10.22 about 5 minutes
10.23 130K
10.24 (a) 3.3K
10.26 0.12K
10.28 (a) 250kJ (b) 18kJ
10.29 90°C
10.30 0.38kJkg^{-1}K^{-1}
10.31 (a) 379Jkg^{-1}K^{-1} (b) 954JK^{-1} (c) 653Jkg^{-1}K^{-1}
10.32 (a) 4.0min (b) 0.54kW (c) 0.54kW (d) 56°C (e) 0.28kW (f) 67kJ
10.33 (a) 23.2°C (b) 0.99kJkg^{-1}K^{-1}
10.36 (a) 28W (b) 19W
10.37 113W
10.39 (a) 4.5MJ (b) 0.17MJ
10.40 (a) 38min (b) 74min
10.42 (a) 13g (b) final temperature 3.4°C
10.43 23g
10.44 15.4W
10.45 1.8Kmin^{-1}, 3.5Kmin^{-1} (a) 0.95kJkg^{-1}K^{-1} (b) 14W (c) 87kJkg^{-1}
10.51 (a) 0.19Kmin^{-1} (b) 0.12Kmin^{-1} (c) 13gmin^{-1} (d) 0.17Kmin^{-1}
10.52 (a) rate of loss of energy at 70°C = 20W (b) 0.24MJkg^{-1}
10.53 (a) 1.25×10^{-4}m^3 (b) 3.72×10^{-2}m^3 (c) 3.74kJ (d) 39.4kJ (f) 3.75×10^5Jkg^{-1}

11 Energy transfer

11.2 (a) 1.229kgm^{-3} (b) 12.06mN (c) 12.68mN (d) 0.50ms^{-2}
11.5 450W

11.6 (a) 9.7 kW (b) 0.025 K

11.7 (a) 36 kW (b) 64 s

11.10 (a) $0.0104\,\mathrm{kg\,s^{-1}}$ (b) 3.5 kW (c) $2.3\,\mathrm{W\,m^{-1}K^{-1}}$

11.11 (a) 54 W (b) 27 W (c) 13 W (d) 11 W

11.12 (a) 50°C (b) 40°C (c) 40°C (d) 32°C

11.13 (a) both 18 W
(b) (i) $5.5 \times 10^2\,\mathrm{K\,m^{-1}}$
(ii) $2.7 \times 10^2\,\mathrm{K\,m^{-1}}$

11.14 $395\,\mathrm{W\,m^{-1}K^{-1}}$

11.15 (a) 2.0 kW (b) 22.5°C, 100 W

11.17 (a) $\mathrm{W\,m^{-2}K^{-1}}$
(c) $U/\mathrm{W\,m^{-2}K^{-1}}$ = 8.3, 3.3, 0.63, 250, 10;
$R/\mathrm{m^2\,K\,W^{-1}}$ = 0.12, 0.30, 1.60, 0.0040, 0.10
(d) $R/\mathrm{m^2\,K\,W^{-1}}$ = 0.32, 2.04, 0.204
(e) $U/\mathrm{W\,m^{-2}K^{-1}}$ = 3.1, 0.49, 4.9
(f) (i) 0.84 kW (ii) 0.13 kW
(g) 0.18 kW

11.18 no; $U = 1.56\,\mathrm{W\,m^{-2}K^{-1}}$

11.19 0.51 kW

11.21 (a) $4 \times 10^{-3}\,\mathrm{m^2\,K\,W^{-1}}$

11.23 4.0×10^{26} W

11.25 (c) 80 K temperature rise

11.27 (a) 4 (b) 0.5

11.32 (a) 32 W (b) 4.0 kW (c) 0.40 W

12 The ideal gas

12.1 40°C

12.2 (a) $570\,\mathrm{cm^3}$ (b) $530\,\mathrm{cm^3}$

12.3 1.9×10^{21}

12.4 (a) 85 kPa (b) 0.16 MPa (c) 0.16 MPa (d) 0.19 MPa (e) 70 kPa

12.5 (a) 33 mmHg (b) 28 mmHg (c) 147 mm (d) 27 mm

12.6 5.7 MPa

12.7 (a) 17 mol (b) 1.0×10^{24}
(c) (i) 33 g (ii) 465 g

12.9 1.74×10^{-3} mol

12.10 greatest (a), least (b)

12.11 $1.7 \times 10^{-4}\,\mathrm{m^3}$

12.12 (a) hydrogen 1.0 mol, helium 2.0 mol
(b) 3.0 mol (c) 40 kPa

12.14 (a) 2.0 ms
(b) $5.0 \times 10^{-23}\,\mathrm{kg\,m\,s^{-1}}$
(c) $2.5 \times 10^{-20}\,\mathrm{kg\,m\,s^{-2}}$
(d) 1.25×10^4 N (e) 104 kPa

12.15 (a) 104 kPa (b) 167 kPa (c) 150 kPa

12.18 (a) $3nRT/2N$ (b) $3kT/2$ (c) Boltzmann constant

12.22 (a) $32.2\,\mathrm{m\,s^{-1}}$ (b) $32.4\,\mathrm{m\,s^{-1}}$

12.23 (a) $432\,\mathrm{m\,s^{-1}}$ (b) $432\,\mathrm{m\,s^{-1}}$

12.24 (a) 10 ms (b) 2.0 ms (c) 5 (d) $405\,\mathrm{m\,s^{-1}}$

12.27 (a) 273 K (b) 599 K

12.28 all; 6.00×10^{-21} J

12.29 (a) $1.9\,\mathrm{km\,s^{-1}}$ (b) $0.51\,\mathrm{km\,s^{-1}}$ (c) $0.21\,\mathrm{km\,s^{-1}}$

12.30 (a) lower graph; 600 K
(b) (i) 600 (ii) 1200
(c) yes, number of molecules
(d) (i) about 150 000
(ii) about 65 000
(e) (i) $400\,\mathrm{m\,s^{-1}}$ (ii) $560\,\mathrm{m\,s^{-1}}$
(iii) 1.4
(f) (i) $483\,\mathrm{m\,s^{-1}}$ (ii) $683\,\mathrm{m\,s^{-1}}$
(iii) $\sqrt{2} = 1.41$

12.31 (b) A (c) $362\,\mathrm{m\,s^{-1}}$ (d) $226\,\mathrm{rev\,s^{-1}}$

12.32 both 36 kJ

12.33 (a) 19 kJ (b) 37 kJ

12.34 1200 K

12.35 (a) 28.3 kJ (b) 40 K

12.36 $20.52\,\mathrm{J\,mol^{-1}K^{-1}}$, $20.87\,\mathrm{J\,mol^{-1}K^{-1}}$

12.37 (a) 0.50 kN (b) 2.5 J

12.39 (a) 2.4 mol (b) 133 kPa (c) $8.0 \times 10^{-2}\,\mathrm{m^3}$

Note. Some of the answers to questions *12.40* to *12.43*, and *12.48* to *12.53*, depend on the form chosen for First law. Answers are given for the First law in the form
$\Delta U = \Delta Q + \Delta W$.
If the other form
($\Delta Q = \Delta U + \Delta W$)
is used, reverse the signs for all values of ΔW.

12.40 (a) +2.0 kJ (b) −3.0 kJ (c) −5.0 kJ

12.41 (b) $\Delta U = +0.77$ kJ; $\Delta Q = +0.77$ kJ; $\Delta W = 0$
(c) $\Delta U = +0.77$ kJ; $\Delta Q = +1.28$ kJ; $\Delta W = -0.51$ kJ

12.42 (a) p/MPa = 0.20, 0.17, 0.14, 0.12, 0.11; $\Delta W = -5.9$ kJ
(b) $\Delta U = 0$, $\Delta Q = +5.9$ kJ

12.43 (b) $\Delta W = -5.3$ kJ (c) smaller
(d) $\Delta Q = 0$, $\Delta U = -5.3$ kJ

12.44 (a) adiabatic (b) isothermal (c) constant volume

12.45 $12.5\,\mathrm{J\,mol^{-1}K^{-1}}$

12.46 (a) yes (b) yes (c) no

12.47 (b) 2.0 (c) 95 kJ (d) 70 kJ
(e) (i) 45 kJ (ii) 25 kJ (f) −85 kJ
(g) work done by gas in *abcda* (= 20 kJ) (h) 30 kJ (i) 2.1

12.48 (a) *b*: 200 kPa, $1.0\,\mathrm{m^3}$; *c*: 200 kPa, $2.0\,\mathrm{m^3}$; *d*: 100 kPa, $2.0\,\mathrm{m^3}$
(c) to (f)

paths	ΔQ/kJ	ΔW/kJ	ΔU/kJ
ab	+150	0	+150
bc	+500	−200	+300
cd	−300	0	−300
da	−250	+100	−150
abcda	+100	−100	0

12.49 (a) 900 K
(b)

	ΔU/kJ	ΔW/kJ	ΔQ/kJ
(i)	−0.75	+0.50	−1.25
(ii)	+1.50	0	+1.50
(iii)	+2.25	−1.50	+3.75
(iv)	−3.00	0	−3.00

(c) −1.00 kJ
(d) +5.25 kJ (e) 0.19 kJ

12.50

	ΔW	ΔU	ΔQ	ΔT
(a) (i)	−	0	+	0
(a) (ii)	+	−	−	−
(a) (iii)	0	+	+	+
(b)	−	0	+	0

12.51

	ΔW	ΔU	ΔQ	ΔT
(a)(i)	+	+	0	+
(a) (ii)	−	0	+	0
(a) (iii)	0	−	−	−
(b)	−	0	+	0

12.52

	ΔW	ΔU	ΔQ	ΔT
(c) (i)	+	0	−	0
(c) (ii)	+	+	0	+
(c) (iii)	−	0	+	0
(c) (iv)	−	−	0	−
(d)	−	0	+	0

12.53 (c) to (e)

	ΔW/kJ	ΔU/kJ	ΔQ/kJ
ab	+7.3	0	−7.3
bc	+15	+15	0
cd	−13.4	0	+13.4
da	−15	−15	0

(f) 6.1 kJ, 13.4 kJ (g) 0.45
(j) 0.54

12.54 (a) 0.45 (b) 0.54 (c) 0.60
12.55 (a) 3.5 times

13 Circular motion

13.1 (a) 1.05 rad (b) 2.62 m
13.2 (a) (i) 57°, 45°, 38°
(ii) 1.6 rad, 0.087 rad, 2.1 rad
(b) (i) 5% (ii) 2%
13.3 0.660 m
13.4 17.5 rad = 1000° = 2.8 rev
13.5 (a) 1.3×10^2 rad s^{-1} (b) 75 rad
(c) 12
13.6 (a) 523.6 rad s^{-1}
(b) 1.74532×10^{-3} rad s^{-1}
(c) $7.272205216 \times 10^{-5}$ rad s^{-1}
13.7 (a) 1.7×10^6 m (b) 9.4×10^5 m
13.8 (a) 7.3×10^{-5} rad s^{-1}
(b) 3.1 km s^{-1}
13.9 (a) 3.5 rad s^{-1} (b) 0.52 m s^{-1}
(c) 0.26 m s^{-1}
13.10 (a) 100 rev s^{-1} (b) 630 rad s^{-1}
13.11 40 m s^{-2}; this is > g
13.13 (a) $r\theta$ (b) $r\theta/v$
(c) $(2v^2\sin\frac{1}{2}\theta)/r\theta$; 0.9549, 0.9798, 0.9949, 0.9987, 0.9996; v^2/r
13.14 (a) 12 m s^{-1} (b) 7.1 m
13.16 (a) 1.0 m s^{-2} (b) 4.0 m s^{-2}
13.18 (a) 0.46 km s^{-1}
(b) 3.4×10^{-2} m s^{-2} towards Earth's centre
13.19 (a) 733.5 N (b) 731.0 N
13.20 (a) 0.83 m s^{-1} (b) 0.57 m s^{-2}
13.21 (b)(i) 11 m s^{-2} (ii) 0.63 kN
13.22 (a) 3.1 m s^{-2} (b) 0.28 kN
13.23 (b) 3.0 kN (c) 22 m s^{-1}
13.24 (a) 0.25 kN up the shaft
(b) 0.25 kN towards clubhead
13.25 3.2 kN
13.26 (b) 38 m s^{-1} (b) opposite
13.29 1.6 N m, smaller torque
13.30 (a) +0.06 N m, −0.20 N m, +0.80 N m, −1.20 N m; sum = 0, yes
(b) (i) 0.60 N m (ii) −0.60 N m, sum = 0 (c) yes
13.31 (b) one author obtained 0.07 N m
13.32 (b)(i) 88 N (ii) 9.2 N m
13.33 (a) 9.4 N m (b) 54 N
13.34 (a) 57 kW (b) 140 N m
13.35 (a) 35 N m (b) 11 kW
13.36 (a) 13 N m (b) 71 N
13.37 17 N m

14 Gravitational fields

14.1 3.3×10^{-8} N, -3.3×10^{-8} N
14.2 (a) (i) 2.0×10^{20} N
(ii) 2.8×10^{-3} ms^{-2}
(b) (i) 23 N (ii) 0.23 m s^{-2}
(c) (i) 0.50 N (ii) 6.2 m s^{-2}
14.4 (a) (i) 2.2×10^{-7} N
(ii) 3.5×10^{-6} N
(b) 6.77×10^{-6} N
14.5 0.11 kN
14.6 (a) 1.9×10^{-44} N (b) 1.2×10^{36}
14.7 1/81 = 0.012
14.8 (a) 49.1 N
(b) 5.97×10^{24} kg
(c) 5.51×10^3 kg m^{-3}
14.9 (a) 2.2 (c) Moon and the Sun in line with the Earth
14.10 (b) 380 000 km (c) 8.6×10^{25} kg
14.11 (a) 47 J (b) 16 J kg^{-1}
14.12 5.3×10^7 m
14.15 (a) 10 m (b) both 19.6 N
(c) (i) 5.88 J (ii) 196 J (d) 392 J
(e) (i) 20 m s^{-1} (ii) 24 m s^{-1}
14.18 (a) 2.64×10^6 m
(b) 6.37×10^6 m
14.19 (a) (i) -4.0×10^7 J kg^{-1}
(ii) -2.0×10^7 J kg^{-1}
(b) $+3.0 \times 10^{10}$ J (c) 7.5 km s^{-1}
14.20 5.51×10^3 kg m^{-3}
14.21 (a) 10.58 km s^{-1}
(c) 1.90×10^{27} kg
14.22 1.5×10^8 J
14.23 (b) (i) 0.44 N kg^{-1}
(ii) 0.11 N kg^{-1}
14.24 (a) -6.25×10^9 J
(b) 6.25×10^9 J
(c) 11.2 km s^{-1} (d) no
14.25 5.9×10^{13} N kg^{-1}
14.26 (b) 64 km
14.27 2.44 m s^{-1}
14.28 (c) 4.2×10^{17} s or 13×10^9 years
14.29 84 minutes
14.30 (a) 42.2×10^6 m ≈ 6.6 Earth radii (b) 38°
14.31 1.87×10^{27} kg
14.32 (a) 158 km (b) 1.73 km s^{-1}
14.33 (a) 9.25 N kg^{-1}
(b) 9.25 m s^{-2} (c) 0.65 kN
(d) 9.25 m s^{-2} (e) 0.65 kN
(f) no (g) 0

15 Storing electric charge

15.6 $\pm 1.2 \times 10^{-4}$ C
15.7 250 V
15.8 26 μC, 2.0 V, 7.1 μC, 0.30 mV
10 pF, 467 μF
15.9 (a) ±20 mC (b) 5.0 mA, greater
15.10 2.2 μA
15.11 200 μF
15.14 (a) 0.70 s (b) 18 V (c) 26 V s^{-1}
(d) constant at 12 μA
15.15 (a) (i) 0 (ii) 12 V (iii) 12 μA
(iv) 0
(b) (i) 12 V (ii) 0 (iii) 0
(iv) ±0.26 mC
(c) 22 s
15.16 (a) 9.5 V, 2.5 V
(c) ±55 μC
15.17 0.54 μA
15.18 (b) 4.0 μF
15.20 (a) 60 μC flows from x to y, total charge stays constant
(b) 2.0 V and 1.0 V (c) 3.0 V
(d) 20 μF
15.22 (a) 11 μF (b) 1.0 μF
15.23 A 18 μC, 6 V; B 4.5 μC, 3 V; C 13.5 μC, 3 V
15.24 (a) 1.8 J (b) 1.8×10^5 W
15.25 36 V
15.26 (a) ±2.4 mC, 0.18 J
(b) (i) 100 V (ii) 0.12 J
15.27 (a) 4.0 mC (b) 2.0 J (c) 1.0 J

15.29 (a) 1.9 mC (b) 0.56 J
15.30 (a) 0.40 mC, 0.80 mC (b) 100 V (c) 0.40 mC (d) 30 mJ
15.31 (a) 0.40 μF (b) 80 μC (c) 40 V and 160 V (d) 1.6 mJ and 6.4 mJ
15.32 (a) 1.9 μF (b) 2.1 μF (c) 0.29 nJ
15.33 (a) 7.9 K
15.34 3.0 μF in series with 6.0 μF, and 8 μF in parallel with both
15.35 9 capacitors, 3 groups in parallel, each of 3 in series
15.36 25 mC
15.37 (a) $1.0 \times 10^{11}\,\Omega$ across input (b) 0.40 μF across input
15.39 0.047 μF and 0.47 μF
15.40 (a) (i) 2.5 nC (ii) 83 pF (b) 21 pF (c) 0.83%
15.41 (a) 5.0 pA (b) $1.5 \times 10^{14}\,\Omega$
15.42 (a) (i) 850 V (ii) 560 V (b) 8×10^{-14} A (c) $9 \times 10^{15}\,\Omega$
15.43 (a) yes, from about 400 V to 900 V (b) no (c) (i) about 50 V (ii) about 400 V (d) 70°
15.44 5 s
15.45 (a) (i) 20 V (ii) 100 μA (b) (iii) 1000 μC (iv) 9000 μC (c) (i) 18 V (ii) 90 μA (iii) 900 μC (iv) 8100 μC etc.
15.46 (a) 0.67 μA (b) 21 mV s^{-1} (c) 32 μF (d) 48 s (e) 32 μF
15.47 (a) 15.0 V (b) 35 s (e) 1.8 mC (f) 7.5 V (g) 240 μF
15.49 (a) 433 s (b) 4.33 MΩ
15.50 (b) 10 V (c) 10 mA (d) 0.50 mA
15.52 (a) 0.67 mA (b) 67 W (c) 0.80 K s^{-1} (d) 315 K
15.53 (a) 280 μC (b) 6.0 μA, 47 s (c) 47 s

16 Electric fields

16.2 (a) 2.5 mN horizontally (b) 2.9 mN vertically (c) 40°
16.4 −1.4 nC
16.5 1.05×10^{-7} m
16.6 $+2.8 \times 10^{-5}$ J
16.7 (a) 9.6×10^{-18} J (b) 4.6×10^{6} m s^{-1}
16.8 (a) 50 kV m^{-1} (b) both 1.0 μN
16.9 (a) 20 kV m^{-1} (b) 3.2×10^{-15} N (c) 2.1×10^{-9} s.
16.10 (b) 6.0 kV m^{-1} B to A, 12 kV m^{-1} C to B, 18 kV m^{-1} C to D, zero inside the metal
16.11 (a) (i) 1.00×10^{-8} J (ii) 0 (iii) 1.00×10^{-8} J (b) B 600 V, C 200 V, D 600 V; lines of force BA, DC equipotentials AC, BD (c) earthed plate 10 mm from AC, other plate 20 mm from BD
16.13 6.4×10^{-19} C
16.14 490 V, top
16.15 (a) $+1.57 \times 10^{-16}$ J (b) -1.54×10^{-16} J (c) -3.4×10^{-18} J
16.16 (a) -2.7×10^{-9} C m^{-2} (b) −800 C
16.17 1.8 MV m^{-1}
16.18 (a) 3.3×10^{5} V m^{-1} (b) ±2.9 μC m^{-2} (c) 0.12 μC (d) 0.29 μC
16.19 0.50 μF, 62 mJ
16.20 1.7 nF
16.21 (a) 2.5×10^{-5} m (b) 0.94 m^{2} (c) 48 kJ m^{-3}
16.22 (a) 35 pF (b) 0.18 μC (c) 0.44 mJ (d) 10 kV (e) 0.88 mJ
16.23 22 pF
16.24 (a) ±0.96 nC (b) 1.15×10^{-7} J (c) ±3.2 nC (d) 6.4 nC, charging (e) $+1.54 \times 10^{-7}$ J (f) -0.77×10^{-7} J (g) 0.77×10^{-7} J (h) 2.6×10^{-5} N
16.25 (a) 53 s (b) 32 V
16.26 (c) 9.2×10^{-12} F m^{-1}
16.27 27 μC m^{-2}
16.31 1.8×10^{-9} N attraction, 3.2 kV m^{-1} towards B
16.32 9.7 nC, yes
16.33 (a) (i) 3×10^{20} V m^{-1} (ii) 7 MV (b) (i) 0.1 kN (ii) 2×10^{-12} J
16.34 (a) 4.0×10^{-7} J (b) 1.0×10^{-5} N
16.35 (a) 150 kV (b) 2.5 μC (c) 1.0 MV m^{-1}
16.36 1.1 μC s^{-1}, 1.1 μA

17 Magnetic fields and forces

17.2 (b) zero at some point (c) increases towards top
17.9 (b) $F = BIl$ (c) (i) N A^{-1} m^{-1} (ii) kg s^{-2} A^{-1}
17.10 (a) 75 mN, vertical
17.11 OA, OB, OC 75 mN upwards; OD zero
17.12 (b) 3.2 mN (c) 0.32 g
17.14 (b) 1.2 N (c) 48 mN m (d) (i) 24 mN m (ii) 0
17.15 (e) 1.2 μN m (f) 34°
17.17 (b) 0.56 mN (c) 0.53 mN
17.18 (a) up out of paper (c) 7.8 N
17.20 (a) 4.8×10^{-14} N
17.22 (a) 1.9×10^{-15} N up (b) 1.2×10^{-15} N up (c) 0
17.23 (a) 18 μT, 43 μT (b) horizontal
17.24 (a) to the left (east) (b) 3.2×10^{7} m s^{-1} (c) 2.2×10^{-16} N, 2.5×10^{14} m s^{-2} (d) 7.7 ns (e) 7.3 mm
17.25 (a) it moves up (b) it moves right (c) it turns clockwise
17.26 (b) 9.6×10^{-15} N (d) 60 kV m^{-1} (e) $E = Bv$
17.27 (a) 6.00×10^{5} m s^{-1} (b) ^{24}Mg: 0.299 m, ^{25}Mg: 0.311 m, ^{26}Mg: 0.324 m
17.28 (a) 9.4×10^{-5} m s^{-1} (b) 2.3×10^{-23} N (e) 1.4×10^{-4} V m^{-1} (f) 1.4 μV
17.29 both 1.7×10^{8}
17.30 (a) both towards AB (b) (i) positive (ii) negative
17.31 (a) 8.0×10^{-14} N to right (c) 4.6×10^{-5} m (d) 1.4×10^{-10} s (e) 9.1×10^{-5} m (f) 1.4×10^{-10} s
17.32 (a) $r = mv/BQ$ (b) $T = 2\pi m/BQ$
17.33 (a) 9.4×10^{6} m s^{-1} (b) 0.59 mT
17.34 (a) uniform, and perpendicular to plane of circle (b) smaller radius in both cases
17.35 (b) 5.3×10^{6} m s^{-1} (c) 2.1×10^{-8} s (d) same (e) 24 MHz
17.37 (a) 6.9×10^{-16} kg m s^{-1} (b) 7.6×10^{14} m s^{-1}

(c) more than speed of light; 2.3×10^{-24} kg

17.38 (b) 4.59×10^6 m s^{-1} (f) 1.15 A (g) 14.6 MHz

17.39 (a) 3.2×10^{-19} C (b) 9.6×10^{-12} N (c) 1.5×10^{15} m s^{-2} (g) 0.15 m

17.40 (a) (i) straight line (ii) circle above Oy (b) (i) 6.9×10^5 m s^{-1} (ii) 4.0×10^5 m s^{-1} (d) 1.25 μs (e) 8.9×10^{-10} s

17.42 (a) into paper (b) decreasing (c) decreasing (d) momentum = BQr

17.43 9.0 mT

17.46 (a) (i) 6.0 mT away (ii) 3.0 mT away (b) (i) 0 (ii) 3.0 mT away

17.49 4.7 mT

17.50 (a) 1.01 mT (b) 1.26 mT

17.51 (a) 0.90 mT (b) they enter it, S

17.52 (b) B/mT = 0.43, 0.53, 0.66, 0.81, 1.01, 1.24, 1.50, 1.78, 2.04, 2.23, 2.30, 2.23 etc., repeating these values in reverse (c) B/mT = 0.56, 0.68, 0.83, 1.02, 1.25, 1.53, 1.86, 2.21, 2.57, 2.89, 3.11, 3.24, 3.28, 3.28, 3.28, 3.28, 3.24, etc., repeating these values in reverse (d) constant to within 1% over 70% of axis between coils

17.53 5.6 kA

17.56 (a) 50 μT (b) similar

17.58 (a) 0.33 mT (b) 0.06 mT

17.60 0.20 m

17.61 (a) one cable could give 59 μT

17.62 0.1 N

17.63 attract

17.64 (a) $I^2 = 2\pi dmg/\mu_0 l$

17.66 a circle under tension

17.70 (b) (i) B (ii) A

17.71 0.38 T

17.72 (a) 2.2 T (c) nearly 25

18 Electromagnetic induction

18.2 opposed to motion

18.4 (a) 4.5 mV

18.5 (a) 0.70 V

18.6 (a) 3.6 mV

18.8 (a) 1.08 m^2 s^{-1} (b) 0.54 V

18.9 (a) 27 m^2 s^{-1} (b) 1.7 V

18.10 (a) 0.50 m s^{-2} (b) 15.1 mV (c) (i) +15.1 mV (ii) +3.8 mV (iii) +15.1 mV (d) no (e) still 15.1 mV

18.11 (a) 51 μV (b) 0 (c) 0

18.12 (a) COC' (b) 3.5 V

18.14 (a) $\mathscr{E} = BAn\omega \sin\theta$ (b) $BAn\omega$ (c) 90°, 270° (d) $(BAn\omega)^2/R$ (e) $(Ban)^2R$

18.16 (a) $2\pi rvB$ (b) $2\pi rvB/R$ (d) $mgR/4\pi^2B^2r^2$

18.22 longest, copper; shortest, plastic

18.25 15 MWb

18.26 1.6 T

18.27 (a) 15 mWb (b) (i) 0 (ii) −7.5 mWb (iii) 0 (iv) −15 mWb (v) − 30 mWb (vi) 0

18.28 ϕ/μWb = 15, 4.5, 1.0

18.29 (a) 19 μWb (b) 44 μWb (c) 45 μWb

18.30 (a) both 3.8 mT (b) (i) 6.0 μWb (ii) 3.4 μWb

18.32 (a) (i) 5.3 μV (ii) 2.7 μV

18.33 (a) +2.5 μV (b) −10.0 μV (c) −2.5 μV

18.35 (a) (i) anticlockwise (ii) clockwise (iii) clockwise (iv) anticlockwise (b) (i) ×0.50 (ii) ×1.0 (iii) × 2.0 (c) (i) ×0.25 (ii) ×0.50 (iii) × 2.0

18.36 (a) 63 μV (b) 6.3 mA

18.40 (a) 80 mm (b) 20 mm (c) 20 mm (d) 20 mm (e) 20 mm

18.41 (a) when field is zero (b) 2.2 V

18.43 (a) $\phi = \mu_0 ANnI_0 \sin 2\pi ft$ (b) $d\phi/dt = 2\pi f\mu_0 ANnI_0 \cos 2\pi ft$ (c) $2\pi f\mu_0 ANnI_0$

18.44 (a) 3.3 mH (b) opposite (c) 2.0 s

18.45 (b) 8.0 V (c) 0.80 H

18.46 (b) 100

18.47 1 H = 1 kg m^2 s^{-2} A^{-2}

18.49 (a) 4.3 A (c) 6.0 V

18.50 40 mV

18.51 (a) 3.0 A s^{-1} (b) 0.60 A (c) 2.5 A s^{-1}

18.52 (a) (i) 2.0 A s^{-1} (ii) 3.0 A s^{-1} (b) (i) 3.0 A (ii) 2.0 A

18.53 (a) $\mathscr{E} = IR + L(dI/dt)$

18.55 (a) 300 V

18.58 (a) BIl (b) BIl (c) $P_m = BIlv$ (d) $P_e = \mathscr{E}I$ (f) $\mathscr{E} = Blv$

18.59 0.637 Nm

18.60 (a) 21.8 V (b) 0.40 Ω

18.61 (b) 11.5 V (c) (i) 6.0 W (ii) 0.25 W (iii) 5.75 W (d) 10.0 V (e) 2.0 A (f) (i) 24 W (ii) 4 W (iii) 20 W

18.62 (b) 0.80 T (c) 31 V (d) 32 V

18.63 (a) 60.0 A (c) 11.31 W (d) 11.76 W (e) 0.962 (f) 0.192 W (g) 0.258 W (h) 11.8 V

18.64 (a) (i) falls (ii) rises (b) 11.3 V

18.67 (a) $\mathscr{E} = I(R+r)$ (c) 113 Nm (d) 530 W (e) 477 W (f) 6.4 A, 74 V

19 Alternating currents

19.1 (b) and (c)

19.2 (a) 2.8 V (b) 42 V

19.3 (a) r.m.s. p.d. = 12 V

19.4 (a) 10 V (b) 7.1 V (c) 71 mA

19.5 (d) 15 W

19.6 (b) V_0 (c) 500 Hz

19.7 (a) 5.0 A (b) 3.5 A (c) (i) 5.0 A (ii) 4.8 A (d) 2.0 ms, 8.0 ms etc.

19.8 (a) I_0 = 0.884 A, f = 50 Hz (b) 300 W

19.9 (a) 18 V (b) 1.7 A

19.14 (a) 100 Hz (b) 4.5 mC (c) 29 mA (d) 0.29 mC (e) 9.0 V

19.17 (a) doubled (b) doubled (c) halved

19.18 (d) 0

19.19 (a) 68 Ω (b) 34 Ω (c) infinite

19.20 18 mA

19.21 1.4 mA peak value, 0.98 mA r.m.s.

19.25 (a) 3.1 Ω (b) 6.3 Ω (c) 0

19.26 (a) 6.4 mA (b) 6.0 A

19.28 (a) 4.7 kΩ (b) 0.66 kΩ (c) 0.47 kΩ

19.29 (a) 0.47 kΩ (b) 0.67 kΩ (c) 4.7 kΩ

19.30 (a) 240 Ω (b) 440 Ω (c) 390 Ω, 8.1 μF (d) > 300 V

19.31 (b) and (c)

19.32 (a) (i) 470 Ω (ii) 4.7 Ω (b) (i) 2.1 Ω (ii) 210 Ω

19.34 (c) (i) and (ii)

19.35 (c) 1.5 mH
19.36 73 Hz
19.37 (a) 390 kHz (b) lowest (c) 24 pF
19.39 (a) 240 V (b) 0.15 A (c) 36 W
19.40 (a) 3.6 W (b) 7.2 W
19.41 (a) 10:1 (b) 10.4 A (c) 2 A
19.42 (b) 0.040 A
19.43 (a) 10 A (b) 2.0 A
19.44 (a) 113 (b) 5.4 A (c) 45 mA
19.45 0, 10, 20 ... 60 turns
19.46 (a) 20:1, 10:1, 5:1
(c) diameters in ratio 1: $\sqrt{20}$
(d) 5.0 mA
19.50 (a) 3.0 Ω (b) 7.2 V (c) 17 W
(d) 20 V (e) 32 W (f) 0.20 A
(g) 240.4 V (h) 12.02 V
(i) 0.080 W
19.51 (a) 40 kA (b) 240 V (c) 2.5 kA
(d) (i) 15 V (ii) 3000 V

20 Oscillatory motion

20.6 (a) (i) 4.5×10^4 s
(ii) 2.2×10^{-5} Hz
(b) (i) 0.83 s (ii) 1.2 Hz
(c) (i) 0.020 s (ii) 50 Hz
(d) (i) 3.82×10^{-3} s (ii) 262 Hz
20.7 0.42 m s^{-1}
20.8 170 m s^{-1}
20.9 0.16 m s^{-1}
20.10 s^{-2}, $f_A = \sqrt{10} f_B$
20.11 (a) 1.6 m (b) 0.67 s (c) 1.6 m
(d) 0 (e) −140 m s^{-2}
20.12 (a) 0.13 m s^{-1} (b) 29 m s^{-2}
20.13 2.05 p.m.
20.14 (a) 2 (b) 4*m*
20.15 8.8 kN m^{-1}
20.16 0.72 kN m^{-1}, 3.1 Hz
20.17 (a) 0.38 kN m^{-1} (b) 0.94 s
(c) 0.53 m s^{-1}
20.18 (a) 3.2 m s^{-2}
(b) 1.6 s (i.e. π/2 s)
(c) 0.080 m s^{-1}
20.19 0.79 s
20.20 accelerating upwards
at 0.87 m s^{-2}
20.24 (c) 4.0 m s^{-1}, 3.5 m s^{-1}
20.26 (a) 230 N m^{-1}
20.28 13 m s^{-1}
20.29 (a) 0.74 m (b) 200 N m^{-1}

21 Mechanical waves

21.6 (a) (i) 2.0×10^{-6} W m^{-2}
(ii) 5.5×10^{-8} W m^{-2}
(b) amplitude ∝ 1/*r*
21.7 25 W, for uniform radiation in a hemisphere
21.8 (a) (i) 4:1 (ii) 2:1
(b) (i) 8.0×10^8 W m^{-2}
(ii) 1.0×10^{19} J
21.10 42 g
21.11 2.1×10^{11} N m^{-2}
21.12 (b) 8.9 m s^{-1} at top, 3.1 m s^{-1} at 1 m from end
21.13 (b) 6.3 m s^{-1}
21.14 5.2 km s^{-1}
21.15 0.71 s
21.16 47 ms, 53 ms
21.17 $c \propto \sqrt{(p/\rho)}$, independent of λ
21.18 (a) $c = k\sqrt{(E/\rho)}$
(b) $k = 0.99$ (≈ 1)
21.19 620 km
21.20 (a) (i) 2.5 s and 4.7 s
(ii) 3.3 s and 3.8 s
21.24 6 mm to 15 mm
21.26 (a) (i) 0.25 m (ii) 1.50 m
(b) (i) 0.63 m s^{-1} (ii) 0.42 Hz
(iii) 2.4 s
21.27 (a) 0.63 m (b) 40 Hz
(c) 5.0 m s^{-1}
21.30 (a) 40 mm
21.32 (a) 80 mm (b) (i) max (ii) min
21.33 (a) e.g. 0.80 m, 0.88 m, 0.96 m
(b) e.g. 0.84 m, 0.92, 1.00 m
21.35 510 Hz
21.37 (b) (i) 10 mm (ii) 14 mm
21.38 at first 250 Hz heard

22 Electromagnetic waves

22.2 (a) 10^{-18} s (b) 15 ns (c) 1.2 s
22.7 ± 0.25 μs
22.87 6.6×10^6 m s^{-1}
22.9 134 Hz; no
22.11 (b) 1.6×10^{-26} N
22.13 (a) (i) 0.25 GHz (ii) 2.8 μV m^{-1}
(b) 1.7 μV
22.14 1.5×10^6
22.17 (a) 20λ and 24λ
(b) antiphase
22.18 ghost signal went an extra 1.5 km
22.20 (a) 1.869×10^8 m s^{-1} and
1.861×10^8 m s^{-1}
(b) 109.0 and 109.5 (c) π rad
22.21 (a) 85 W m^{-2} (b) 0.21 W m^{-2}
22.22 (a) 3.9×10^{26} W
(b) 4.3×10^9 kg s^{-1}
22.25 (a) 0.80 m (b) 0.74 m
22.26 60 W
22.30 (a) about 2×10^{-13} W m^{-2}
(b) about 3×10^{-3} rad

23 Interference patterns

23.1 $f = 2.3$ Hz; also $2f$, $3f$ $4f$ etc.
23.2 (a) (i) 333 Hz (ii) 500 Hz
(iii) 667 Hz
(b) 333*n* Hz, for *n* = 2, 3, 4 etc.
23.4 5.11 km s^{-1}
23.5 (b) (ii) $1/4l^2\mu$ (iv) $2\sqrt{(\mu/T)}$
23.6 53 g
23.7 (b) 52 N (c) 5.8 N (d) 3.8 m s^{-1}
23.9 98.2 N
23.10 peaks of *I* at *d* of about 9 cm and 37 cm
23.11 maxima heard every 2.0 s
23.12 (b) 343 m s^{-1}
(c) end correction = +20 mm
23.13 (a) 32 mm
23.14 (b) 28 mm
23.15 (a) 104 m (b) fading every 3.5 s
23.16 (a) $v\lambda/4c$ (b) 0.10 μm
23.18 48 μm
23.21 minima at 24° and 53°
23.22 560 nm
23.23 no, beam diameter is 0.32 m at the flag
23.24 yes, just
23.25 (b) 4.0°
23.27 (a) 800.0064 mm, 800.0049 mm,
1.5 μm
(b) minimum
23.28 40 mm (±2 mm); yes
23.29 *d/D* = 0.034
23.31 0.50 m
23.32 (a) min at 875 m and 2625 m;
max at 1750 m
(b) minima are more widely spread
23.33 (a) 0.28 mm (b) 0.080 mm
23.34 (a) 1.57 μm,
6.36×10^5 lines m^{-1}
(b) 647 nm
23.35 the zero order plus seven on each side
23.38 (a) 10.5° (b) 37 mm
23.40 about 6×10^{-7} m
23.41 1040 nm

24 Optics

24.3 (a) (i) 140° (ii) 10° (b) (iii) 2*x*

24.4 for $\theta_a = 0$ to about 45°

24.5 (a) 59° (b) ray is at 36° to vertical

24.6 (a) 27° (b) 27 mm

24.8 (a) 48.5° (b) 32.5°, 75°; symmetrical diagrams

24.11 (a) (i) 3.87° (ii) 4.03° (b) 0.17° (c) (i) 6.70° (ii) 6.86°; 0.17°

24.13 (a) 0.10 $\mathrm{m\,s^{-1}}$ (b) 29°

24.14 46 ns

24.16 0.49°

24.17 (a) yes (b) 14°

24.19 (a) ln_1/c (b) $1/\sin\theta$

24.20 (b) 53°

24.21 (b) 0.15 mm (c) yes, 0.74 mm

24.23 (b) 1.5 (c) 1.5

24.24 (a) 2.26 m

24.25 (a) 0.40 m and 0.50 m (b) 0.66 m and 1.00 m

24.26 (a) 1.32 m by 0.825 m (b) 130 mm

24.27 (a) 300 mm (b) at infinity

24.28 (a) R, 0.25 m, 1.25 mm, I (b) R, 0.40 m, 5.0 mm, I (c) R, 2.2 m, 50 mm, I (d) V, 0.60 m, 20 mm, U

24.30 (a) 0.24 m (b) 2.5 mm

24.31 (a) 240 mm (b) 2.5 mm

24.32 (a) 1.30 m (b) 1.06 m

24.33 (a) red circle at S_b, diameter 11 mm (b) blue circle at S_r, diameter 14 mm

24.34 0.25 mm, 1.0 mm, 5.0 mm, 20 mm

24.35 (a) 0.19 mm (b) (i) unchanged (ii) 9 times brighter

24.37 (a) 4.0 mrad (b) 3 times (c) probably about 6 m

24.38 (a) $m = 0.50$ (b) (i) 80 mrad (ii) 35 mrad (iii) M = 2.3

24.39 yes – just

24.40 (a) $f/14$, $f/3.2$, (b) 19

24.41 (b) 10 ms, 20 ms, 40 ms

24.42 5.6 mm

24.43 (a) 7.8 mm (b) 0.039 rad (c) 0.30

24.44 6.6 mm

24.45 (a) 12

24.46 20 m from the lens, at least 0.19 m across

24.47 550

25 Probing the nucleus

25.4 0.19 MeV

25.5 (a) 3.90×10^{-13} J, 3.98×10^{-13} J (b) 0.990 (c) 2.5×10^{-11} m

25.8 11 mm, assuming exponential decrease

25.9 1.4 m; measurable deflection of 3.5 mm

25.10 (b) $-1.76 \times 10^{11}\,\mathrm{C\,kg^{-1}}$

25.11 (a) 1.1 mT (b) 4.2 T

25.13 (a) about 13% (c) (i) 5% (ii) 40%

25.17 (a) 74 (b) 3

25.18 (a) 2.2×10^5 pairs (b) 8.7 nA

25.21 (b) (i) from A towards B (ii) negative

25.23 (a) 1.6×10^5 pairs (b) 5.1 MeV (c) 14 mm

25.26 1.4×10^{-15} m

25.27 3.4 keV

25.29 63.6

25.30 23.0 g

25.32 neodymium–143

25.33 (a) 19 p, 21 n, 19 e (b) $^{40}_{18}\mathrm{Ar}$

25.34 (a) $^{140}_{57}\mathrm{La} \rightarrow {}^{136}_{55}\mathrm{Cs} + {}^{4}_{2}\mathrm{He}$

25.35 (a) 3.56×10^{-25} kg (b) 6.64×10^{-27} kg (c) 132, 84, 3.59×10^{-25} kg (d) $1.7 \times 10^7\,\mathrm{m\,s^{-1}}$, 1.2×10^{-19} N s (e) $3.2 \times 10^5\,\mathrm{m\,s^{-1}}$ (f) 0.12 MeV

25.36 (a) 38, 87 (b) (i) 4×10^{-14} J (ii) 0.3 MeV

25.37 31.9739 u

25.38 (a) 1.02 MeV (b) 1.21×10^{-12} m (c) 0.512 MeV

25.40 (a) 1:2 (b) $\sqrt{2}$:1

25.41 942.7 MeV

25.42 7.6 MeV, 1.6×10^{-13} m

25.43 0.19

25.44 (b) 30 kBq, 12 kBq (c) about 50 s

25.45 (b) 170 $\mathrm{min^{-1}}$ (c) 180 $\mathrm{min^{-1}}$

25.46 (c) 40 minutes

25.47 $^{99}_{43}\mathrm{Tc}$, $^{99}_{44}\mathrm{Ru}$ (a) 6.0×10^{23} (b) $2.2 \times 10^{-13}\,\mathrm{s^{-1}}$ (c) 9.9×10^4 y

25.48 $6.6 \times 10^6\,\mathrm{s^{-1}}$

25.49 6.2×10^{-11} kg

25.50 (a) (i) 1.3 × × $10^{-2}\,\mathrm{s^{-1}}$ (ii) 53 s

25.52 (a) 1.5×10^{24} (b) 3.1 kBq

25.53 (a) $3.84 \times 10^{-12}\,\mathrm{s^{-1}}$, 3.91×10^{13} atoms (b) 0.62 kg

25.54 200 litres

25.55 (a) 1.25×10^{11} (b) $3.84 \times 10^{-12}\,\mathrm{s^{-1}}$ (c) 389 (d) 2750 y

25.56 (a) 1.7×10^{-6} mol (b) 1.0×10^{18} (c) 31.7 Bq (d) $3.1 \times 10^{-17}\,\mathrm{s^{-1}}$ (e) 7.1×10^8 y

25.57 (a) U, $^{239}_{93}\mathrm{Np}$, $^{239}_{94}\mathrm{Pu}$, $^{235}_{92}\mathrm{U}$ (b) 235.044

25.58 (a) 0.1181 u, 110 MeV; 0.1282 u, 120 MeV; 0.1250 u, 117 MeV (b) $^{15}_{7}\mathrm{N}$; $^{15}_{7}\mathrm{C}$ by β^-–emission, $^{15}_{8}\mathrm{O}$ by β^+–emission

25.59 8.84 MeV, 7.62 MeV

25.60 (a) (i) 6.5 MeV (ii) 4.9 MeV

25.61 (a) 2.8×10^{20} (b) 4.7×10^{-4} mol (c) 0.11 g

25.62 (a) 2.79×10^{-11} J (b) 7.14×10^{10} J

25.63 (b) (i) 2.3×10^{20} (ii) 90 mg

25.64 (a) 1.64×10^{-13} J (b) $4.2 \times 10^7\,\mathrm{m\,s^{-1}}$

25.65 (a) $^{2}_{1}\mathrm{H} + {}^{2}_{1}\mathrm{H} \rightarrow {}^{3}_{2}\mathrm{He} + {}^{1}_{0}n$ (b) 3.0150 u (c) 3.82×10^{20}; 1.28 $\mathrm{mg\,s^{-1}}$

25.66 (a) 26.7 MeV = 4.27×10^{-12} J (b) (i) 8.1×10^{26} atoms (ii) 1.35 kg

26 Photons and electrons

26.1 (a) 4.0×10^{26} W (b) $4.4 \times 10^9\,\mathrm{kg\,s^{-1}}$

26.2 (a) 1.33×10^{-19} J (b) 3.64×10^{-19} J (c) 5.45×10^{-19} J (d) 1.29×10^{-15} J

26.3 (a) 3.14×10^{-19} J (b) $2.2 \times 10^{15}\,\mathrm{s^{-1}}$

26.4 (a) about 0.10 $\mathrm{W\,m^{-2}}$ (b) about $1.8 \times 10^{16}\,\mathrm{s^{-1}}$

26.5 (a) 3.37×10^{-19} J (b) $4.4 \times 10^{20}\,\mathrm{s^{-1}}$ (c) $1.4 \times 10^{11}\,\mathrm{s^{-1}}$ d) 2.2 mm

26.6 (a) 1.2×10^{-27} N s (b) $3.9 \times 10^{21}\,\mathrm{m^{-2}}$ (c) 4.7 $\mu\mathrm{N\,m^{-2}}$

26.11 (a) 2.3 eV (b) 0.41 eV (c) $3.8 \times 10^5\,\mathrm{m\,s^{-1}}$

26.12 (a) 1.00×10^{15} Hz, ultraviolet

	(b) 0.81 eV
26.14	(a) 6.6×10^{-34} J s (b) 2.0 eV (c) 4.85×10^{14} Hz
26.15	0.20 μA
26.16	(a) 1.31 eV (b) −1.31 V
26.20	(a) 2.19×10^{6} m s^{-1} (b) 91.4 nm
26.21	(a) 1.03×10^{-7} m, ultraviolet (b) 1.22×10^{-7} m, ultraviolet (c) 6.5×10^{-7} m, red
26.22	−13.6 eV, −3.40 eV, −1.15 eV, −0.85 eV, −0.54 eV
26.23	(a) 2.5×10^{-7} m, ultraviolet
26.24	(a) 50.0 eV (b) 58.9 nm, 53.6 nm, 51.8 nm
26.25	(a) Balmer (b) Paschen (d) 31.967×10^{14} Hz, 32.208×10^{14} Hz (e) 7 (f) 122 nm
26.27	6
26.28	ultraviolet
26.29	(b) $f_2 - f_1$
26.30	(c) (i) penetrating power increased (ii) intensity increased
26.33	(b) 1.9×10^{16} s^{-1} (c) 150 W
26.34	(a) 1.6×10^{-14} J (b) 2.4×10^{19} Hz (c) 1.2×10^{-11} m
26.35	(a) (i) light (ii) X–rays in TV tube (iii) infra-red, fire (iv) microwave oven (v) radio waves (b) (i) 2.5 eV (ii) 4.1 keV (iii) 0.62 eV (iv) 1.0×10^{-5} eV (v) 8.3×10^{-10} eV
26.36	(a) 4.8×10^{18} Hz (b) 62 pm upwards
26.37	(a) (i) 8.3×10^{-10} eV (ii) 0.025 eV (iii) 6.2×10^{5} eV
26.38	(b) 1.6×10^{-18} J, 1.7×10^{-24} N s, 3.9×10^{-10} m (c) 1.6×10^{-17} J, 5.4×10^{-24} N s, 1.2×10^{-10} m
26.39	(a) 5.4×10^{-23} N s, 1.2×10^{-11} m (b) 2.3×10^{-21} N s, 2.8×10^{-13} m (c) 4.7×10^{-21} N s, 1.4×10^{-13} m
26.40	(a) 4.4×10^{-24} N s (b) 1.1×10^{-17} J (c) 67 V
26.41	(b) 11 kV
26.42	(b) 2.2×10^{-19} N s (c) 3.0×10^{-15} m (d) radius ≈ 2.4×10^{-15} m (e) 6.8×10^{-15} m

27 Electronics

27.3	(a) (i) 2.1 V (ii) 2.6 V (iii) 3.0 V (b) −0.08 V K^{-1}
27.4	(a) 9, 55, 22, 7, 35 (b) 1100, 100011011, 1001010, 10100100
27.6	(a) 2.5 V (b) 4.5 V (c) 1.6 V
27.7	(a) 2.0 V (b) 0.50 V (c) 0.91 V
27.8	(a) 2.0 V (b) 11.0 V (c) 1.5 V
27.9	(a) 1.0 kHz (b) 17 (c) 106 mV; inverting
27.10	(a) inputs: A 3.0 μA; B 20 μA; $V_{out} = -2.3$ V
27.12	(a) −0.91 μA (b) 0.91 μC s^{-1} (c) 9.1 μV s^{-1}
27.13	(a) 1.0 MΩ (b) bright, −2.5 mV; dark, −5.0 V (c) bright, − 1.7 mV; dark, −5.0 mV
27.16	(a) −21 (b) 1.0×10^{4}
27.19	(a) −4.7
27.20	(a) −1.06 V (b) −4.0 V (c) 1.9 V
27.21	0.26 V
27.27	(b) (i) 30 μC (ii) 5.3 V (iii) 25 μC
27.31	10 kHz, 3 kHz
27.32	(a) 2, 32 (b) 500 kHz, 50 kHz
27.40	RC = 10 s
27.43	(a) (i) I^2R (ii) I^2r (b) 50%
27.44	(a) 800 (b) 20 dB, 38 dB; net gain 58 dB (c) 58 dB
27.47	(a) NOR
27.48	AND, OR
27.55	(b) 6

28 Communications

28.2	(b) 2.0×10^{-8} W (c) 2.0 W
28.3	6 m
28.4	(a) 2.0×10^{-16} W (b) 6.3×10^{-21} W
28.5	40 km
28.6	(a) 3.2×10^{-18} W (b) 3.0 km
28.8	260 pF
28.10	(a) 1500
28.11	(b) 15 kHz (c) Yes
28.12	0.23
28.13	(a) 25 μV (b) 13 μV
28.15	(b) 1.0 kHz
28.18	(a) 5 (b) 45 kbits^{-1} (c) 54 kbits^{-1}
28.19	(a) 3.0 μs (b) 110 μs (c) 36
28.20	(a) 500 MHz (b) 25000
28.21	(d) 30 kbits^{-1}
28.26	(a) 4.935 μs, 4.945 μs; 10 ns (b) no
28.27	(a) 68 ns (b) 15 Mbits^{-1}
28.29	(a) 22 mW (b) 1.0 km
28.30	(b) 30 kHz (c) 15 kHz
28.35	(a) 9.1 mV s^{-1} (b) e.g. 5 kΩ, 25 nf
28.38	(a) R (c) (i) 8 mA (ii) 4 mA